MW00837528

# Electric Power System Protection and Coordination

# Electric Power System Protection and Coordination

## A Design Handbook for Overcurrent Protection

### Michael A. Anthony
*University of Michigan*

## McGraw-Hill, Inc.

New York   San Francisco   Washington, D.C.   Auckland   Bogotá
Caracas   Lisbon   London   Madrid   Mexico City   Milan
Montreal   New Delhi   San Juan   Singapore
Sydney   Tokyo   Toronto

**Library of Congress Cataloging-in-Publication Data**

Anthony, Michael A.
Electric power system protection and coordination / Mike Anthony.
    p.   cm.
   Includes index.
   ISBN 0-07-002671-8
   1. Electric power systems—Protection—Data processing.
  2. Computer-aided engineering.  I. Title.
   TK1005.A7385   1994
   621.31'7—dc20                   94-31276
                                             CIP

Copyright © 1995 by McGraw-Hill, Inc. All rights reserved. Printed in the United States of America. Except as permitted under the United States Copyright Act of 1976, no part of this publication may be reproduced or distributed in any form or by any means, or stored in a data base or retrieval system, without the prior written permission of the publisher.

1 2 3 4 5 6 7 8 9 0  DOC/DOC  9 9 8 7 6 5 4 3

ISBN 0-07-002671-8

*The sponsoring editor for this book was Harold Crawford and the production supervisor was Donald F. Schmidt. This book was set in Century Schoolbook by North Market Street Graphics.*

*Printed and bound by R. R. Donnelley & Sons Company.*

Information contained in this work has been obtained by McGraw-Hill, Inc. from sources believed to be reliable. However, neither McGraw-Hill nor its authors guarantee the accuracy or completeness of any information published herein and neither McGraw-Hill nor its authors shall be responsible for any errors, omissions, or damages arising out of use of this information. This work is published with the understanding that McGraw-Hill and its authors are supplying information but are not attempting to render engineering or other professional services. If such services are required, the assistance of an appropriate professional should be sought.

This book is printed on acid-free paper.

*McGraw-Hill books are available at special quantity discounts to use as premiums and sales promotions, or for use in corporate training programs. For more information, please write to the Director of Special Sales, McGraw-Hill, Inc., 11 West 19th Street, New York, NY 10011. Or contact your local bookstore.*

# Contents

Preface    xi
Acknowledgments    xvii

## Part 1    Introduction                                                    1

### Chapter 1.  Introduction to the Coordination Problem                     3

   1.1  Foreword                                              3
   1.2  Time-Current Characteristics of Loads                 4
      1.2.1  Motors                            5
      1.2.2  Transformers                      8
      1.2.3  Combination Loads                 8
   1.3  Origin of Power System Faults                         10
   1.4  Overview of Fault-Time Frame                          12
   1.5  Protection Points on Low- and Medium-Voltage Circuits 15
      1.5.1  Protection Zones                  16
      1.5.2  Preview of Zone Selective Interlocking (ZSI)  20
   1.6  Core NEC Requirements for Overcurrent Coordination    21
   1.7  Manufacturer Time-Current Characteristic Curves       21
   1.8  Solving Problems in Time-Current Characteristic Scaling Arithmetic  25
  Bibliography                                                     36

## Part 2    General Considerations                                          37

### Chapter 2.  Basic Short-Circuit Calculations                            39

   2.1  Foreword                                              39
   2.2  Basic Longhand Calculations                           39
   2.3  Beyond the Infinite Bus Calculation                   42
      2.3.1  Line-to-Line Short-Circuit Current  47
      2.3.2  Voltages and Currents Under Unbalanced Fault Conditions  47
   2.4  Fault Current Sources                                 48
      2.4.1  Utility Contribution              48
      2.4.2  Generator Contribution            52
      2.4.3  Motor Contribution                53
   2.5  The Fault Power Method of Short-Circuit Calculation   56
   2.6  Very Low Level Fault Currents                         63
   2.7  Single-Phase Short-Circuit Calculations               64

2.8   Computer Modeling of Fault Dynamics                        64
      2.8.1   Input Data                                          85
      2.8.2   Output                                              65
2.9   Overview of Methodologies                                  67
2.10  Solved Problems                                            69
Bibliography                                                     79

**Chapter 3.  Design and Application Principles                  81**

3.1   Foreword                                                   81
3.2   Device Selection Considerations                            82
      3.2.1   Nominal Voltage and Continuous Current Ratings     82
      3.2.2   Protective Device Withstand Ratings                84
      3.2.3   Protective Device Interrupting Ratings             84
3.3   Asymmetry in Protective Device Ratings                     86
3.4   Fuse Application Principles                                88
      3.4.1   Low-Voltage Fuses                                  88
      3.4.2   Single-Element Low-Voltage Fuses                   90
      3.4.3   Dual-Element Low-Voltage Fuses                     90
      3.4.4   Low-Voltage Current-Limiting Fuses                 92
      3.4.5   Medium-Voltage Fuses                               93
3.5   Low- and Medium-Voltage Breaker Application Principles     95
      3.5.1   Low-Voltage Breakers                               95
      3.5.2   Medium-Voltage Breakers                            96
3.6   Sensing Elements                                          98
      3.6.1   Essential Facts About Instrument Transformers      98
      3.6.2   Voltage Transformers                               99
      3.6.3   Current Transformers                              100
3.7   Transformer Through-Fault Protection                     105
      3.7.1   Analysis of Transformer Under Short-Circuit Conditions  106
      3.7.2   Category I Transformers                           106
      3.7.3   Category II Transformers                          107
      3.7.4   Category III Transformers                         107
      3.7.5   Special Consideration for Transformer Connections 108
3.8   Applications of the Differential Principle               109
3.9   Time and Current Margins Between Overcurrent Devices     113
      3.9.1   Relays over Relays                                115
      3.9.2   Relays over Trip Devices or Fuses                 116
      3.9.3   Fuses over Relays                                 116
      3.9.4   Fuses over Fuses                                  116
      3.9.5   Trip Devices over Fuses                           119
      3.9.6   Trip Device over Trip Device                      119
      3.9.7   Instantaneous Device over Instantaneous Device    120
      3.9.8   Time-Delay Relay over Time-Delay Relay            121
3.10  Overcurrent Devices                                      122
3.11  Principal Applications for Relays                         122
Bibliography                                                   126

**Chapter 4.  Ground-Fault Protection                          129**

4.1   Foreword                                                 129
4.2   Relevant Theory                                          130
      4.2.1   Separately Derived Systems                        132
      4.2.2   Stray Neutral Currents                            132

4.3   Models of Faulted Circuits                                      135
      4.3.1   Low-Voltage Circuit                                     135
      4.3.2   Arcing Faults                                           137
      4.3.3   Medium-Voltage Current                                  140
4.4   Controlling Ground-Fault Current                               140
      4.4.1   Ungrounded (Free Neutral) Systems                      140
      4.4.2   High-Impedance Grounding                                143
      4.4.3   Low-Impedance Grounding                                 146
      4.4.4   Solidly (Zero Impedance) Grounded Systems               147
4.5   Methods of Sensing Ground-Fault Current                        150
      4.5.1   Low-Voltage Distribution Systems                        151
      4.5.2   Medium-Voltage Distribution Systems                     154
      4.5.3   Zero Sequence Relay                                     158
4.6   Typical Ground-Fault Protection Schemes                        159
      4.6.1   Phase Overcurrent Ground-Fault Protection               160
      4.6.2   Systems with an Alternate Power Source                  164
4.7   Solved Problem                                                 166
Bibliography                                                         168


Chapter 5.  Protection and Coordination in Power Panels             171

5.1   Foreword                                                       171
5.2   Low-Voltage Distribution Circuits                              172
5.3   Application of Low-Voltage Fuses                               176
      5.3.1   Common Plug Fuse                                        176
      5.3.2   Non-Current-Limiting Fuses (Class H)                    176
      5.3.3   Current-Limiting Fuses                                  176
      5.3.4   Dual-Element or Time-Delay Fuses                        176
      5.3.5   Cartridge Fuses                                         177
      5.3.6   Fuse Selectivity Ratio Tables                           177
5.4   Application of Low-Voltage Circuit Breakers                    180
      5.4.1   Comparison of Molded Case and Power Circuit Breakers    181
      5.4.2   Electromechanical (Thermal-Magnetic) Breakers           182
      5.4.3   Classical Solid-State Trip Unit                         186
5.5   Conductor Protection                                           189
      5.5.1   Short-Circuit Protection of Cables                      190
5.6   Transformer Protection                                         195
      5.6.1   Transformer Inrush and Instantaneous Trips              197
      5.6.2   Ferroresonance                                          197
      5.6.3   Transformers for Fire Pumps                             198
5.7   Solved Problems                                                200
Bibliography                                                         201


Chapter 6.  Protection and Coordination for Motors and Motor
Control Centers                                                      203

6.1   Foreword                                                       203
6.2   Relevant Theory of Induction Motors                            203
6.3   Overcurrent Protection Strategies                              206
      6.3.1   Summary of 1993 NEC Requirements                        207
      6.3.2   Example Motor Circuit                                   208
      6.3.3   Thermal-Magnetic Breakers                               213
      6.3.4   Fused Combination Starters                              214

6.3.5  Simple Motor Circuit Protection with Thermal Elements
(Heaters)                                                              214
6.3.6  Arcing Faults in Small Induction Motor Circuits              216
6.4  Protection for Groups of Induction Motors                      216
6.4.1  Withstand and Interrupting Ratings                           217
6.4.2  Coordinating Interrupting Capacities of Motor Control Center
Components                                                     219
6.5  Protecting Larger Motors                                       222
6.5.1  Special Problems Associated with the Protection of Large
nduction Motors                                               222
Bibliography                                                        227


Chapter 7.  Protection and Coordination in Unit Substations        229

7.1  Foreword                                                       229
7.2  Transformer Protection                                         230
7.3  Medium-Voltage Power Fuses                                     231
7.3.1  Expulsion Fuse                                               233
7.3.2  Current Limiting                                             234
7.4  Transformer Primary Circuit Breakers                           238
7.4.1  Instantaneous Relays                                         240
7.4.2  Coordination of Primary Fuses with Main Breakers            241
7.5  Secondary Main Breakers                                        242
7.6  Secondary Feeder Breakers                                      245
7.6.1  Cable Protection                                             246
7.6.2  Small Transformer Protection                                 247
7.6.3  Motor Feeder Protection                                      247
7.7  Unit Substation Overcurrent Coordination                      249
7.7.1  Classical Ground-Fault Coordination                         252
7.7.2  ZSI of Ground-Fault Coordination in a Unit Substation       253
7.8  Double-Ended Substation Coordination                          253
7.8.1  Main-Tie-Main Phase Protection                              255
7.8.2  Coordinating Ground-Fault Protection                        256
7.8.3  Tie Circuit Protection                                      259
7.9  Flowchart for Selection of Substation Breaker Trip Functions  265
Bibliography                                                        266


Chapter 8.  Protection and Coordination for Bulk Distribution
Switching Stations                                                 267

8.1  Foreword                                                       267
8.2  Medium-Voltage Breakers                                        268
8.3  Instrument Transformers                                        269
8.4  Generalized Overcurrent Relays                                275
8.4.1  Overview of Application Principles                          276
8.4.2  Coordinating Inverseness                                    277
8.4.3  Voltage Drop Considerations                                 277
8.4.4  Instantaneous Elements                                      278
8.4.5  Directional Overcurrent Relay—Devices 67 and 87G          280
8.4.6  Ground Overcurrent Relays                                   284
8.4.7  Directional Overcurrent Ground Relays                       284

8.5  Special Application Considerations Regarding Microprocessor-
     Based Relays                                                      286
     8.5.1  Power to the Intelligence and Output Contacts              286
     8.5.2  Reset, Power Down, and Return to Normal                    287
     8.5.3  Equations for Inverse Curves                               288
     8.5.4  Effect of Harmonics                                        288
     8.5.5  The Human Effect                                           290
8.6  Cable and Feeder Overcurrent Protection                          291
     8.6.1  Ampacities of Medium-Voltage Cable                         291
     8.6.2  Medium-Voltage Cable Shielding Considerations              292
     8.6.3  Medium-Voltage Distribution Cable Phase Protection         294
     8.6.4  Multiple Sources                                           300
8.7  Bus Differential Protection                                       301
8.8  Transformer Differential Protection                               302
     8.8.1  Application Principles                                     303
8.9  Solved Problems                                                   306
Bibliography                                                           310


Chapter 9.  Protection and Coordination at the Utility Interconnect    313

9.1  Foreword                                                          313
9.2  Generalized Consumer-Utility Interconnect Protection
     Scheme                                                            314
     9.2.1  Utility Supply: Group A                                    315
     9.2.2  Service Entrance: Group B                                  316
     9.2.3  Supply Transformer Primary Protection: Group C             317
     9.2.4  Supply Transformer Secondary Protection: Group D           318
9.3  Single-Feed Service                                               319
     9.3.1  Single Service with Primary Fuse                           319
     9.3.2  Single Service with Relayed Secondary Breaker              321
9.4  Dual-Feed Service                                                 325
     9.4.1  Dual-Feed Service with Single Transformer                  325
     9.4.2  Dual Service *without* Transformation                      327
     9.4.3  Dual Service *with* Transformation                         327
9.5  Typical Service Configurations with Local Generation             337
     9.5.1  Synchronizing Relays                                       340
9.6  Coordinating Consumer Switchgear with Utility Circuit
     Reclosers                                                         342
Bibliography                                                           346


Appendix   349
Index   389

# Preface

The increasing prevalence of microprocessor-based devices in electrical power protection systems allows us to use the word *program* with some confidence now. We could not use such a word when the better part of our protective devices was thermal-magnetic, electromechanical, or chemical in nature. Although a large part of the installed base of protective devices still operates—and operates very well—on nonelectronic principles, there are few who doubt that we are migrating toward an environment in which microprocessor-based protective devices are the rule rather than the exception.

We can say with some confidence, also, that the methods by which we engineer the operating parameters for our protection systems are substantially changed. Microcomputer software computes short-circuit currents, maintains time-current characteristic curve libraries for overcurrent devices, and instantly redrafts them to reduce the drudgery in handling data among equipment classes and among jobs. With the drudgery mastered, we have time to educate our intuitions regarding the transient behavior of large-scale networks under fault conditions and to hasten our sense of the "rightness" of an answer.

But computer software for protection design has risks associated with its application that are as old as computers themselves: the use by electrical people who are long on experience with computers and short on mastery of longhand calculation methods and basic protective device application principles. These microcomputer tools arrived at a time when the electrical utility industry was undergoing a period of disinvestment in engineering. In some utilities, this disinvestment is still ongoing; in others, engineering is itself is being "reengineered." For some protection specialists who were on top of the situation all along, the era of the affordable microcomputer was a second wind. For many small and large engineering staffs, it has been a giant step between the way it used to be and the way it is now.

There are at least three noteworthy trends in the current electrical engineering environment that have bearing on the subject matter of this book:

First, microprocessor-based equipment (such as overcurrent relays) may be manufactured without the enormous investment in the precision machinery that was required to build electromechanical relays. Polarizing coils, induction disks, and precision balance beams have been replaced with printed circuit boards which do not require sequence inputs. The reduced initial cost has advantages, of course, but it creates opportunities for ignoring the richness of symmetrical component theory and application that has got us this far.

Second, a period of deregulation of the industry in which bulk power may be purchased in an "open" market is being followed by disinvestment in engineering. Utilities used to have the resources to provide engineering support for its customers. Competitive pressures have caused many utilities to downsize their engineering staffs precisely when the technical challenges of an open market create the greatest need for engineering talent.

Finally, a legal/liability environment has emerged in which many consulting architectural/engineering firms feel the need to push outward the responsibility of short-circuit calculations and system protection to electrical contractors and/or equipment testing specialists. This strikes the author as peculiar because the expertise for performing complex calculations ought to lie in the professional engineering staff of the A/E firm that has been retained to design a facility that meets the needs of the client.

Protection engineering has always been regarded as something of an art. Not only do you have to be comfortable with symmetrical components, and be comfortable with looking through the standards and catalogs for protective device performance ratings, but you also have to reconcile the requirements of protection and coordination that are sometimes at odds with one another. Electrical people who are not primarily protection engineers nearly always opt to err on the side of safety. Safety can mean something other than freedom from catastrophe, however. Particularly in hospitals and industrial process power systems, continuity of service is synonymous with safety. As electrical power systems and user loads have become more sensitive to power quality, electricians, contractors, and design professionals have discovered that it is no longer appropriate to regard the coordination problem as subordinate to the protection problem.

The subject of electrical system protection engineering is very broad. We cannot discuss everything in electrical power circuit protection engineering in this book, but what we do discuss will be useful to a sizeable number of people who are responsible for providing safe and economical electricity to our nation's factories, schools, hospitals, and commercial centers. By selecting the word *coordination* in the title of this book, we mean to suggest that our primary focus will be upon protective devices in which current and time are the discriminating quantities. We will discuss similarities and differences between the operating characteristics of contemporary microprocessor-based protective devices and the devices which preceded them. We will solve the overcurrent coordination problem in detailed, step-by-step fashion on the computer screen as well as with pencil and light table. If you are considering an investment in commercial coordination software, this book will guide you toward the appropriate product while still being useful as an independent, practical companion to solving the problem should you decide to remain with longhand methods.

While our strategy in mastering the skills necessary to produce coordination studies will be to break it into manageable pieces (avoiding as much as possible the graphic clutter that is characteristic in other treatments of the subject), you will find that solving the coordination problem will require you to put everything you know together. Until engineers have the economic opportunity to become extremely specialized in their work, users of overcurrent coordination software are likely to lament that the use of coordination software involves learning new skills as complex as solving the coordination problem in longhand. Setting up is more difficult since we have to deal with computer hardware configurations, peripherals, and software updates. Experienced users complain that they have traded one problem for another. Should you decide to make a commitment to computer solutions to the coordination problem, there may be some comfort in knowing that your new problems will be state of the art.

## Remarks on the Organization of this Book

The traditional treatments of this subject were to discuss protection from a zone standpoint: i.e., generators, transformers, lines, buses, and motors were treated separately no matter what the voltage—low, medium, or high. There was some repetition in the manner in which different protection configurations were treated with respect to voltage levels. For example, small induction motors were treated in the same chapter as large induction motors and a reader looking for information on small induction motors would have to look through the more complex information pertaining to medium-voltage motors.

In this book, we have treated the subject from load to source, at progressively higher voltages. This permits an electrician who merely wants to know about protection at the building level to avoid looking through the chapter on the consumer-utility interconnect, or vice versa. There is still some repetition and crossover but we have tried to keep this to a minimum without sacrificing the independence with which each chapter may be used. We have attempted to organize the book in dual fashion: chapters that progress from first principles to complex material, as well as provide self-contained application "snapshots" (boxed text) that can be used independently of the progressive development of the rest of the book. We believe that this will be the most useful to the greatest number of people who care about electrical power circuit protection. Protection technology and its related disciplines has advanced to the point where traditional treatments of the subject are too broad to obtain much depth of understanding. This book covers the overcurrent coordination problem at a level of detail that has long been necessary.

Comments to the publisher will be appreciated and answered personally by the author. Protection specialists do not always agree even when they are all technically correct. First editions of any textbook—almost by definition—have errors in them and this fact alone will hasten a second edition into print. Future editions of this book will at least feature user recommendations and will follow significant changes in low- and medium-voltage protection that appear in the *National Electrical Code*\* and elsewhere within the industry. The author regrets that more space could not have been given to consideration of IEC electrical standards. There will be no slowing down of the internationalization of the electrical industry by the time we are ready with another edition. The author regrets that more space could not have been given to more one-of-a-kind coordination problems and even more commonly occurring design situations in which coordination and protection are at odds. For the moment, the author hopes that this book will have at least pulled together enough up-to-the-minute but widely scattered information to save another colleague time. I hope that the reader will, in turn, use the time saved to advance someone else's understanding.

### Remarks upon the Choice of Manufacturers Cited in This Book

Efforts have been made to represent as many manufacturers of electrical protection equipment in this book as possible. The author decided early in the writing of this textbook that the risk in citing manufacturers in a textbook would be worth it if application principles could be illuminated in a context that would be most similar to actual practice.

---

\* National Electrical Code ® and NEC ® are registered trademarks of the National Fire Protection Association, Inc., Quincy, MA 02269.

The downside of this risk, however, is that it is impossible to include all manufacturers and we risk dating some of the material in this book because of the restructuring and internationalization of the industry. Any perceived biases are more than likely the result of the availability of information; though, admittedly, the information available to the author may be highly personal in itself. There is very little in this book that has not appeared elsewhere in the technical literature of the industry, as the Appendix should indicate. If the reader perceives any biases, the author would be grateful to be informed of them before publication of the next edition of this book.

The author hopes that this book has served the purpose of expanding upon and unifying the treatment to the coordination problem that will lead to the development of practical skills in people who might have considered the problem too difficult. The author hopes that this book will, however, create a context of its own from which others will advance the practice and principles of protection engineering at the electrical customer level.

*Mike Anthony*
*Utilities Department*
*University of Michigan*
*Ann Arbor, Michigan*
*1 May 1994*

# Acknowledgments

I would like to acknowledge the following colleagues for their contributions and their tips: Bob Appledorn, Bill Battle, Steve Beckman, Redjem Bouhenguel, James Bright, Hal Bunge, Jack Chandler, Lee Curts, Cary Cook, William Edwards, Walt Elmore, Ron Fesl, Bob Gustin, Jim Harvey, Brian Harrington, Joe Iott, Lawrence Jackson, Jack Janveja, George Johnson, Russ Johnson, Glenn Keats, John LaDronka, Don Leiter, Lon Lindell, Jim Lindsay, Richard McEnhill, Ali Nasle, Jim North, Frank Orlandi, Dennis Panoff, Clair Sparling, Mike Stump, Jim Santilli, Mike Shaw, Gary Walls, Dave Wheeler, Jeff White, and Richard Zientar.

Thanks to Harold Crawford for his encouragement and direction. Thanks also to Margaret Cummins, Mary Ellen Haramis, Don Schmidt, Geraldine Fahey, and especially Ginny Carroll and the folks down at North Market Street Graphics for their guidance through the production process.

**Disclaimer**

The information and data contained in this textbook is presented solely for the purpose of following the examples and solving the problems. Every attempt has been made to have the data reflect current standards in industry, the manufacturers of the equipment types discussed within this text should be contacted for confirmation of all data and ratings before using any equipment type in actual design specifications. The author and McGraw-Hill Book Company, Inc., can assume no responsibility for damages that might result from the use of the information presented in this textbook.

Part

1

# Introduction

# 1

# Introduction to the Coordination Problem

## 1.1 Foreword

The overcurrent coordination problem cannot be regarded independently of the protection problem any more than electrical circuit protection can be regarded independently of good circuit design. We will attempt to do so only long enough to see how a narrow class of protection problem can enrich our understanding of electric power system protection systems in general. The manner in which protective devices work together shall be the organizing principle of our study. This restriction will illuminate the essentials of how protective devices work independently.

It is worth noting that the word *coordination* appears in the vocabulary of electrical people working in other concentrations. Insulation specialists refer to the task of managing the effects of traveling waves through the materials that comprise electric circuits as insulation coordination. They model surge voltage phenomena along a chain of insulation systems. When designers specify basic impulse ratings for cables and surge arresters according to ANSI or IEEE standards, they are actually undertaking a coordination problem. The objective is to minimize the damage to electrical materials as a transient wavefront travels (and is reflected) from one electrical component into the next.

The word coordination appears in the vocabulary of telecommunication specialists. When power and communication circuits are operated in proximity, the power circuit may produce certain conductive or inductive effects that may interfere with the normal operation of the communication circuit. These electrical interference effects that appear as a result of extraneous voltages and currents in the communication circuit may be minimized by measures that are applicable to either circuit alone, or both. Such measures provide the basis for the coordination of power and communication circuits to avoid interference.

In this book we shall use the term *coordination* to mean the quality of selectivity among protective devices, overcurrent devices in particular. Overcurrent devices (and their variants) represent the largest installed base of protective equipment on any power system and may be considered the backbone of any protection strategy. Protective devices that operate on the differential principle run a close second as far as versatility is concerned, but such devices are generally regarded as self-selective or definite-time and simply trip when required without regard to any upstream or downstream devices.

By themselves, the curves on a sheet of log-log paper that represent the tripping characteristics of overcurrent devices do not take very long to draw longhand or plot by computer. You can practically draw or plot a few curves at random in about a minute, and the result might look like a coordination study. Well-reasoned studies require considerably more time, of course, and, in the interest of giving you a realistic idea of the time involved, we want to advance the notion that a rigorous coordination study requires about one hour's worth of work for the first curve that needs to be plotted (with additional curves requiring decreasing portions of an hour). You may require, for example, 60 + 50 + 40 + 30 = 180 min to plot four curves. Be patient if it takes you 1 h per curve for a long time, especially if you only do coordination studies intermittently or you have not developed a mature time-current characteristic curve library.

This proposal may well be one of the most important items of this book. Included in this 1-h-per-curve rule of thumb is the time you will need to gather, find, or file system and device information as you begin and as you finish, the time you will need to perform a few calculations to orient the curves within the appropriate constraints, and the time you will need to discuss your approaches or results with the people who will be handling the devices or will be affected by the way they work. The 1-h-per-curve principle is advanced to encourage you to relax when you are doing coordination studies, to put other priorities aside, and to find enjoyment in how all this stuff hangs together.

## 1.2   Time-Current Characteristics of Loads

Protective devices must not trip circuits that are operating normally; however, normally operating circuits sometimes exhibit the behavior of circuits that are not. Our first coordination problem is to coordinate the fuse or circuit breaker with the normal time-current characteristic of the load. Cables, transformers, lights, and motors are loads, and they all respond differently when potential is applied. Cables are capacitive when lightly loaded and inductive when heavily loaded. In the case of highly inductive loads such as transformers and motors, we can plot this response on a current-versus-time plot, more commonly known as a time-current characteristic (TCC) plot. We could just as well provide this information in the form of a table of numbers (there will be situations in the chapters ahead in which we need to deal only with a pair of numbers) but a graphic plot is a more efficient method of organizing the information.

### 1.2.1 Motors

Most of the electrical load in the world involves rotating machinery such as motors, fans, compressors, pumps, and the like. The proportion is something on the order of 50 to 80 percent, and it varies among systems from country to country. A motor has an intrinsic magnetic requirement that lies mostly in the starting. Because the magnetic requirements of motors are directly related to current we must give special consideration to motors in overcurrent coordination studies. Figure 1.1 is a representation of the starting current requirements for a 10-hp induction motor. Note that the current required in the first

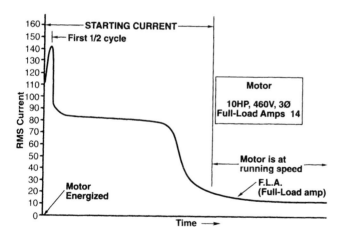

**Typical Motor Starting Current Characteristics.**

**Figure 1.1**  Actual time-current characteristic starting curve for typical induction motor. Note that this is a plot of current versus time. Classical motor protection involves a combination of a motor overload (for overload protection) and a dual-element fuse (for short-circuit protection). For a 10-hp motor, a NEMA Size 1 Starter would be selected. The dual-element fuse would limit the short-circuit current to a value less than the starter 5000-amp withstand rating while clearing the short current in less than one-half cycle. More discussion on this and related issues in Chaps. 3 and 6. (*Diagram courtesy of Cooper-Bussman*)

half-cycle after energization is about 10 times the starting current required at full running speed and that during the transition to full running speed the current drawn is about six times the steady state current. The magnetic requirement of the motor can be modified somewhat by any of several different starting methods.

Figure 1.2 is an idealized starting time-current characteristic of a classical induction motor that is quick to construct and very handy. It

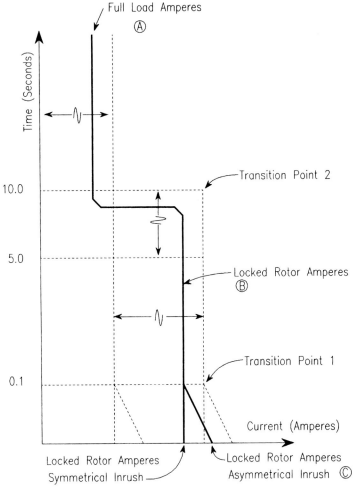

**Figure 1.2** Idealized time-current characteristic curve for induction motors applied in longhand coordination studies. This simple step-down representation of an induction motor starting characteristic is adequate for many coordination studies. Typically, you will need to specify a motor starter fuse to clear the current trace in the 5- to 10-second range at locked rotor current. See box in Chap. 6 for other motor starting time-current characteristics.

is constructed in three segments representing current levels and two transition points involving time (in seconds).

**Full load amperes: segment A.**   This number is stamped on the motor nameplate by law. If the nameplate cannot be read, you may find the nominal full-load current from Table 430-150 of the *National Electric Code* (NEC). If you do not have a copy of the NEC handy you can approximate the full-load current by using 1.0 kVA/hp for induction motors under 100 hp, 0.95 kVA/hp for motors from 101 to 1000 hp, and 0.90 kVA/hp for motors over 1000 hp. You might also want to adjust this estimate to take into consideration power factor and voltage levels.

**Locked rotor amperes: segment B.**   The National Electrical Manufacturers Association (NEMA) code letter should also be stamped on the nameplate. When you find it you can refer to NEC Table 430-7(b) to get a kVA/hp estimate. The manufacturer's technical data on the motor is the number you should use if you can find it.

**Inrush amperes: segment C.**   You can estimate this number by multiplying the locked rotor amperes times 1.6. The 60 percent is an empirical constant that takes the system X/R ratio into consideration. When you connect the three terminals of a motor to any source, there is a characteristic impedance at the source terminals that contributes to the symmetry (or asymmetry) of the inrush current.

So far, we've dealt only with the current benchmarks. Figure 1.2 is drafted to indicate that the current levels can shift around a little depending upon the kind of motor (size, winding configuration, starting method, and so on). To construct a complete curve from the current level segments A, B, and C, we need to deal with the two (time) transition points.

**0.1 s: Transition point 1.**   It is general practice to assume that the transition from asymmetrical inrush current to locked rotor current occurs at about 0.1 s. This is at about the 6.0 cycle point, and experience has shown that circuits that are operating normally have their asymmetries dampened by this time.

**5.0 to 10.0 s: Transition point 2.**   This is not actually a point but a time *range*. You can connect the locked rotor ampere level to the full-load current level at any time within this range. You can draw this transition as a step, a curve, or anything in between.

Refinements of this ideal motor starting curve may reasonably include acceleration and allowable stall time segments, even the magnetic requirements of newer, energy efficient motors. We shall defer a detailed discussion of these aspects of motor protection to Chap. 5.

### 1.2.2 Transformers

Transformers represent a significant magnetic and resistive load, but the impedance that a transformer adds to a circuit is usually a friend to the protection specialist. Transformer inrush current ranges from 6 to 12 times full secondary load and is rich in second harmonics. This occurs even in the absence of actual load. It lasts for about 0.1 s. We will want to make sure that devices protecting transformers will not open when we apply potential to the primary. The transformer inrush coordination problem is more common than you may think. When you have a bus shutdown and, upon reenergization, all of the substations connected to that bus open primary fuses, you know you have a transformer inrush coordination problem.

When faults originate in windings or when transformers pass fault current, they are subjected to mechanical and thermal stresses. To estimate the amount of fault current that a transformer will pass, we will have to attend to the arithmetic of winding connections. We will shift our curves left and/or right by multiples of $1/\sqrt{3}$ and/or $2/\sqrt{3}$ based on the kind of connection change between the transformer primary and secondary. Based on currents in terms of per unit three phase current, a $\Delta$-Y transformer connection requires a 15 percent shift to the right of the line-to-line thermal damage curve. A line-to-line secondary fault condition will cause 1.0 per unit to flow through one primary phase, and 0.866 per unit though the two faulted secondary phases. Refer also to Fig. 3.5.

### 1.2.3 Combination loads

The majority of switchgear at the bulk distribution level is devoted to distribution feeders that are protected by overcurrent devices. These distribution feeders contain mixtures of resistive, inductive, and capacitive elements. Typically, no single load element dominates the overall behavior. When power is lost and restored again, certain loads (such as motors) drop out and remain disabled as a matter of safety, but, in general, electricity users tend to leave more than normal load connected during an extended outage. The high transient current inrush associated with this tendency is called *cold load pickup*.

Finding a suitable pickup point on a time-overcurrent relay can be difficult because the trip points cannot be programmed above this transient without severely compromising the protection. Programming the relay below the transient will cause it to begin to operate on the cold load with the added complication that the current may well decrease below the pickup value before the relay has time to operate.

A time-current curve for the cold load inrush on an ideal distribution feeder is shown in Fig. 1.3. You will not find this time-current characteristic curve in any catalog: it has to be made from your own experience. It can be constructed from meter data, oscillographic traces, or your sense of feeder load profiles over time. Note that the impact of the cold load is at about 460 percent of normal load current and that the current level asymptotically approaches 100 percent of normal load current.

*Hot load pickup* refers to the restoration of power after only a short power outage. Its voltage and current requirements have a different

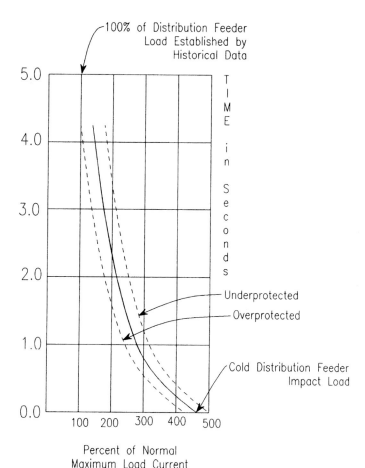

**Figure 1.3**  Cold load pickup time-current characteristic of a distribution feeder. Note how time changes as inrush current drops from, say, 300 to 200 percent of normal maximum load current (2.3 s − 0.8 s = 1.5 s). If fault current were to drop in the same ratio, you could use this number to set relays in series with the same time delays and still maintain time margins between devices. See also Fig. 8.4.

signature than a cold load pickup (as we shall see in Chap. 9). When automatic reclosing protective devices are applied in conjunction with fuses, the problem of obtaining the desired coordination is complicated somewhat by the fact that some of the heat stored in the fuse during the flow of fault current will be lost during the time that the automatic device is open. The amount of cooling that will take place in a fuse during the open time of the reclosing device will depend upon such factors as the temperature of the fuse link at the instant the circuit is opened, the length of time that the circuit remains open (four shots is common), and the magnitude of the fault current.

These variables, and others, make it impossible to predict the amount of fuse cooling accurately enough to be of any practical value. In cases in which a fuse is coordinated with a reclosing circuit breaker, it can be assumed that the fuse has returned to the normal operating temperature if the reclosing time at the circuit breaker is in the order of 5 s or longer (Westinghouse, 1964).

## 1.3   Origin of Power System Faults

A fault on a power system happens when current flows outside the path for which it was intended. Sometimes this happens when someone attempts to make an incorrect connection, a situation that is instantly annunciated and remembered by those who have had the misfortune to attempt such a connection and live to tell about it. The instant that it happens a new impedance (the fault impedance) is placed in parallel with the load impedance. The normal path of current from source to load has been bypassed, or short circuited. When the fault has a great deal of impedance compared to the load, very little short-circuit current may flow. When the fault has very little impedance compared to the load, a great deal of current may flow. In either case, the voltage profile of the entire circuit changes instantaneously.

Most electrical people do not attempt incorrect corrections, however, and it is fair to say that faults occur for other reasons. We can say with confidence that the higher the voltage, the more reliable the circuit. The reason for this is that there is greater investment in primary and backup protection systems at higher voltages because of the loss of revenue associated with large-scale outages.

Natural events that cause short circuits are lightning, either by induced voltage or direct strikes, wind, ice, earthquake, fire, explosions, falling trees, flying objects, physical contacts by animals, and chemical or atmospheric contamination. Human causes include faults resulting from vehicles hitting poles or contacting live equipment, people contacting live equipment, digging into underground cables, switchgear construction, and bolts on breakers insufficiently torqued.

---

### The Human Factor

. . . With rising costs and manpower shortages, the area of testing, particularly main-tenance testing, is being studied by many utilities. A number of users indicate that *less frequent* testing [emphasis added] has resulted in an improvement in the oper-ating record. The reasons are the reduction in errors caused by employee careless-ness which is inherently reduced by less frequent maintenance. The studies show that the two prime causes of troubles, equipment defects and employee carelessness, are both decreasing, and in such a manner that employee carelessness is now show-ing up as the cause of a much larger percentage of troubles . . .

—A Survey of Relay Test Methods Project Committee on Relay Test Methods, AIEE Relay Committee, AIEE Transactions, Vol. 75, 1956m, pages 254–260 (June 1956, No. 24 Power Apparatus and Systems)

---

A large majority of faults in an electrical utility, and thereby its cus-tomers, are the single line to ground faults resulting from lightning-induced transient high voltage. In many cases, the flashover caused by such events does not result in permanent damage. The strategy is to open the faulted circuit, permit the arc to extinguish itself naturally, then reclose the circuit.

A significant proportion of faults occur because of insulation failure unrelated to its manufacture. Insulation failure is caused by the fol-lowing:

- physical damage by personnel or machinery
- accelerated aging from sustained overtemperatures
- unsuitable environment
- overvoltage
- water damage
- improper construction of splicing or terminations
- bending radii that are too short or excessive stress in cable pulling
- normal end of life

Although we may perceive a fault to be a fast, finite event in real time, it is a very dynamic event in terms one part for every 60th of a second. By stretching the fault period time frame we would find the fol-lowing:

- Not all faults are persistent in nature. The action of circuit reclosers on galloping conductors upstream from the plant service entrance clear intermittent faults in 2 to 20 cycles.

- Faults are seldom solid and therefore involve varying amounts of impedance depending upon voltage, the materials involved, location on a circuit, path to ground, and so on. At high voltages, it is commonly assumed that faults have negligible impedance. At distribution voltages, very large impedances exist and must be figured into protection strategies.

- Not all faults draw the maximum available energy.

- Not all faults shut down equipment immediately. Low-level arcing faults, associated with insulation failure and peculiar to 480-V circuits—and usually the most destructive to equipment—can go undetected for relatively long periods of time before protective devices clear the fault.

- All voltages slant downward in the direction of the fault in proportion to the magnitude of the current. In the rare case of a solid, symmetrical, bolted, three-phase fault, the voltage will vanish.

## 1.4   Overview of Fault-Time Frame

The dynamic nature of faults might be better understood if we investigate the pathology of the 30 or so cycles in which a fault typically occurs and is cleared. Figure 1.4 is a very highly simplified schematic representation of the basic time-current relationships during what we shall henceforth refer to as *fault time*. It shows only one phase and does not show the full extent of asymmetry that is possible (depending on at what point in a cycle the fault strikes), but it should give you a feeling for the richness of events that appears only as an instant to human beings.

**–0.016 s: One cycle before.**   On a power frequency base of 60 Hz, power flows at prefault level *from* the source at some power angle (the difference between two voltage angles at the source terminals) *to* the load at some power factor (the angular difference between voltage and current at the load terminal).

**0.000 s: Fault occurs.**   All coordination studies plotted on log-log paper begin at $t = 0.0$, a precipitous drop in voltage at the point of fault. The source-load system enters a transition period from (relatively) high- to low-power factor. Begin subtransient reactance interval for rotating machines. Fault current will be at its least asymmetric if the fault hits the inflection point of the ac waveform.

**+0.004 s: One-fourth cycle after.**   Fault current increasing. Most current limiting fuses have already opened. Low-voltage circuit breakers have

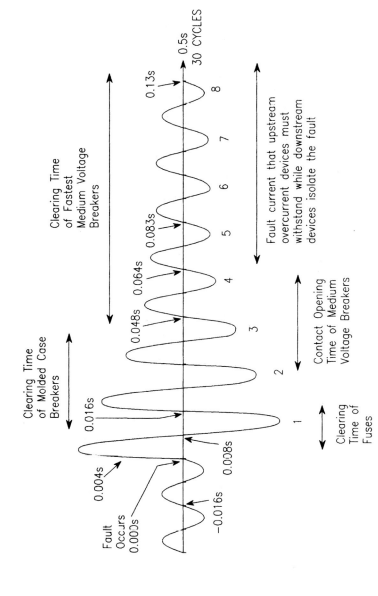

**Figure 1.4** Overview of fault clearing period. This is the real time frame of the dynamic behavior of electric power circuits under fault conditions. A great deal can, and does, happen in one-half second.

unlatched. Induction disks in electromechanical relays are turning. Microprocessors are digitizing the fault current waveform.

**+0.008 s: One-half cycle after.**  Fault current at its highest level. The current that flows is called momentary fault current. Magnetic and solid-state instantaneous devices are designed to respond to this level of fault current. Figure 1.4 shows zero crossing.

**+0.016 s: First cycle after.**  Fault currents decay with a time constant determined by the X/R ratio. End of subtransient reactance period. Most expulsion fuses have already opened.

**+0.048 s: Third cycle after.**  Fault current continues to decay. If all of the contributions are utility (or remote) type contributions, the asymmetrical fault current decays to a steady-state value commonly referred to as the three-phase fault current value. The contacts of five cycle medium voltage breakers begin to part.

**+0.064 s: Fourth cycle after.**  The contacts of eight cycle medium voltage breakers begin to open.

**+0.083 s: Fifth cycle after.**  Fault current continues to decay. Moderately fast breakers begin to open circuit. Fuses have long since opened.

**+0.133 s: Eighth cycle after.**  Fault current continues to decay. The slowest breakers begin to open circuit.

**+0.50 s: Thirty cycles after.**  The end of the short-time interval indicated in circuit breakers with a short-time rating. The short-time current rating specifies the maximum capability of a circuit breaker to withstand the effects of short-circuit current flow for a stated period, (typically 30 cycles or less) without opening. The short-time interval provides time for downstream protective devices closer to the fault to operate and isolate the circuit.

**+1.000 s: One cycle after = 1 s.**  Protective devices have long since opened or broken circuit. Successful clearing will have avoided synchronous machines falling out of step. End of direct axis transient reactance.

Thesc fractions of a cycle are the real-time behaviors of faults, and this is the time frame within which we shall work throughout this book. It is noteworthy that all of our protection design considerations would have to be adjusted with a different power frequency base. Although a great many protective devices will operate at 50 Hz as well as at 60 Hz, the radically different power frequency of 400 Hz—which is common in marine and aviation power systems—offers a different set of advantages (and disadvantages) for conductor sizing, grounding regimes, and the conditions under which associated protective devices must operate.

## 1.5   Protection Points on Low- and Medium-Voltage Circuits

The reason for applying a protective device at a given point on an electrical circuit is usually taken for granted by the electrical veteran. Someone new to the practice has every right to ask, "Do we need a fuse here?" or "Why do we put a circuit breaker there?" We shall answer this question by listing a few off-line considerations, based a little on science, common sense, and folklore.

- *Sectionability.*  It is not possible to have one continuous piece of wire from the power plant generator to, for example, the 120-V receptacles to our computers at home. There must be branches along the way for others to tap into the flow of electricity. Therefore a tap point becomes a reasonable place on a large network to also place a protective device.

- *Voltage change.*  Transformers are very common nodal points on a circuit so that placing a protective device either on the low or on the high side (or both) of a transformer not only provides sectionability but it also makes sense as far as economy of space is concerned.

- *Fault magnitude.*  We choose to put protective devices at the root of nodal branches because that is usually where fault current is greatest.

- *Convenience.*  When an overcurrent and the on/off switch are the same piece of equipment, it is not a bad idea to be able to shut off the electricity within sight of the load. Electrical people like to lump their circuit elements together, not just for analytic purposes but for maintenance and operation.

- *Trial and error.*  The people who have to look at the consequences of poor protection (firemen, building inspectors, insurance adjusters, and others) have codified the best of what we have learned about the safe use of electricity in over a hundred years of the electrical power industry into the NEC.

Perhaps the easiest way to answer the question posed by our hypothetical newcomer is to say that some combination of reading circuit diagrams, watching others around you, investigating actual circuits in operation or under construction, and continual self-study of the NEC will result in your comfort with the way protective devices are applied. In other words, you'll get used to it. You are likely to find circuits that do have enough protection, and you are likely to find circuits that have too much protection (which is not the same thing as having too many devices).

### 1.5.1  Protection zones

There are a few terms that have been used commonly among transmission-level protection engineering that have been adopted by electrical people involved in customer-level switchgear: primary and backup protection, protected and protecting devices, and protection zone. The concepts involved are fairly intuitive.

Primary and backup protection refers to your first and second line of defense against a large-scale outage. Your primary protection is designed to trip circuits closest to all faults possible, and if primary protection fails, backup protection is there to trip circuits even farther upstream from the (uncleared) fault, for example, the way a building substation main breaker is there to trip all power to the substation bus if a feeder breaker cannot clear a downstream fault. The distinction between primary and backup protection needs to be keener for transmission-level protection specialists, however, because primary and backup protection systems may need to operate *independently* of one another. By independence we mean that primary and backup protection may use completely different input quantities to enable the tripping of the protective devices involved. More on this is in Chap. 9.

Protected and protecting refer to the manner in which we not only want to protect motors, lights, cables, transformers, and the like, we also want to protect the protecting devices by interrupting the flow of power into them if they fail to open. If three protective devices A, B, and C are operating in series (with the direction of fault current flow from A to C), then device B is said to be protected for a fault downstream from the protecting device C. In other words, device C is protecting device B by its location between the fault and device B. Likewise, for a fault immediately downstream from B, device B is protecting the protected device A. In order to ensure that the protected device will operate prior to the protected device, the total-clearing time-current characteristic of the protecting fuse must lie below (down and to the left) of the protected device over the range of fault currents that will flow to a fault beyond the protecting device (Blackburn and Kresser, 1982).

The concept of a zone is virtually the same notion that is used in team athletic defensive strategies. Instrument transformers define the boundaries of the zones. In Fig. 1.5 the closed dashed lines indicate several zones of protection on a typical industrial or commercial power system.

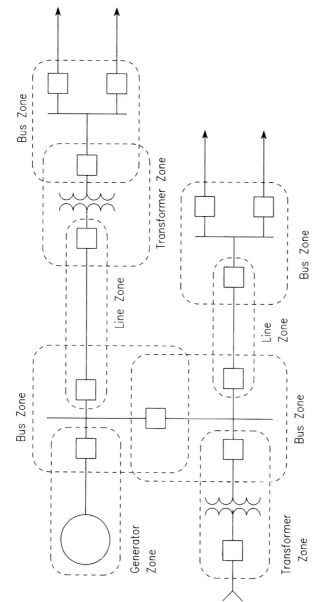

**Figure 1.5** Zones of protection. The problem of providing a protection system which is selective for all fault conditions while also providing minimum clearing times becomes increasingly difficult as components are added to a power system. Overcurrent protection, the slowest of all protection methodologies, must be supplemented with differential and distance protection. Each of the foregoing requires an input from some kind of instrument transformer, which also defines the boundary of the protective zone.

The boundary of each zone defines a portion of the power system so that for a fault anywhere within that zone the protection system responsible for that zone takes action to isolate everything within that zone from the rest of the system. Another important aspect of zones of protection is that adjacent zones overlap. Without this overlap, a small part of the system that falls between neighboring zones would be left without protection. In later chapters we will discuss a few common cases in which, for certain *kinds* of faults, protective zones do *not* overlap as a matter of choice.

In Fig. 1.6 consider a simple distribution circuit involving switching stations A and B with line AB between them. For now, let us ignore the direction of the source. Assume power can flow from either the left or right. (When we study looped or dual source distribution circuits, we will not have this luxury.) Assume that there is negligible impedance within the buswork of the switchgear buswork but that there is significant impedance in line AB. The symmetry of the situation will make the notion of primary and backup protection clear.

**Fault at $F_{AB}$.** Let's say that a fault occurs halfway down line AB and that the impedance in the line reduces the fault current but not to such an extent that this fault current cannot be seen by our relays. All the relays in all the breakers 1 through 4 will see the fault. Breakers 2 and 3 should be programmed to deenergize the line AB so that the other loads connected to switchgear A and B may continue to be energized. We refer to the middle zone of protection (according to Fig. 1.6) as the primary protection zone.

**Fault at either $F_A$ or $F_B$.** These faults are internal to switchgear A and B. If $F_A$ happens, breakers 1 and 2 will see it. If $F_B$ happens, breakers 3 and 4 will see it. It is possible for breakers 1 and 2 to see $F_B$ and for breakers 3 and 4 to see $F_A$, but because of the impedance in line AB, it is unlikely (or even undesirable) that they should. For the breakers to see faults on the opposite side of the line AB, the trip points would have to be set very low—so low, in fact, that we might trip the breakers with only a small variation in normal load current. We will want to shut down either busses entirely and source, load, and interconnect; this is usually done with bus differential relaying that is much faster than overcurrent relaying.

**Fault at either $F_{AL}$ or $F_{BL}$.** We deliberately avoid numbering the load breakers because there may be many, and we are deliberately ambiguous about how much impedance there may be in the conducting path between the bus and the fault. If $F_{AL}$ or $F_{BL}$ occurs near the switchgear, there may not be enough impedance to discriminate this external fault

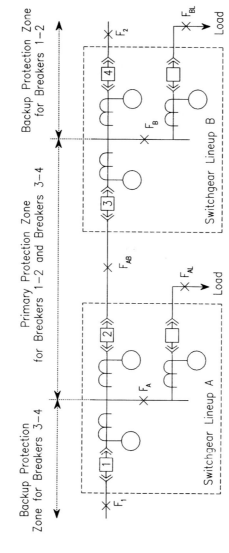

**Figure 1.6** Protection problem for protective relays at station A for line AB.

from an internal bus fault. Both faults $F_{AL}$ and $F_{BL}$ fall outside the zone of protection that is normally set up around buswork with bus differential relaying. If $F_{BL}$ occurs and breakers 3 or 4 fail to open and breaker 2 fails to open, then breaker 1 is said to provide backup protection for breakers 3 and 4. You can probably see already that it is important to keep in mind the direction that the power flows (left or right) in order to make this distinction because you need to know how many relays you have in series along the fault current path. Real distribution circuits frequently have localized rat's nests of series and parallel paths, thus giving you multiple sources of power into a fault.

**Fault at either $F_1$ or $F_2$.** The more relays you have in series along the fault current path the more opportunities you have for isolating the fault. You do this by successively raising the time and current trip points as you move away from the point of fault. The backup protection zone for breakers 3 and 4 occurs on the opposite side of line AB. The same applies to the backup protection zone for breakers 1 and 2.

### 1.5.2   Preview of zone selective interlocking (ZSI)

While we are on the subject of zones, this is a good place in our discussion to look ahead to the subject of zone selective interlocking. ZSI is a protection scheme that, by use of communication between at least two protective devices in the series path of fault current, enables us to reduce or eliminate coordination time delays. Refer to Fig. 1.6.

Suppose breakers 1, 2, 3, and 4 were able to communicate with each other and were able to make logical comparisons among them. Let's say a fault occurs at $F_2$. Since power is flowing from station A to station B, we know that all four breakers will see the fault. The usual practice is to stack time delays upon one another so that the breaker closest to the fault (breaker 4) will trip first. All four breakers have seen the fault, they have all communicated with one another, and they all have agreed to let breaker 4 trip first.

Now suppose the fault occurs at $F_{AB}$. Breakers 1 and 2 see the fault, and breakers 3 and 4 do not. If the speed of communication between the breakers is fast enough (and it usually is), and if the logical comparison and decision making can be made fast enough (which it is), then we have a chance to trip breakers 1 and 2 with *no time delay whatsoever*. We can simply program our breakers that if only breakers 1 and 2 see the fault, then the fault is somewhere in between breakers 2 and 3. Forget the time delay. The zones are thus said to be interlocked zones selectively. We want to do this to reduce the time that fault current flows through our equipment. If we can reduce the time that fault current flows through our equipment by only a few fractions of a second, our $I^2t$ fault energy level would be reduced and would likely extend the life of our switchgear.

ZSI is commonly applied in electrical consumer unit substations and resembles the pilot wire differential protective schemes that transmission line specialists have applied for many years, at least in the sense that information about the flow of current is communicated between local and remote devices. We used the distribution line of Fig. 1.6 for illustrative purposes, but ZSI is almost always used to discriminate between bus and feeder faults that involve ground and short-time delays. The ZSI scheme varies a little in function, flexibility, and terminology among different manufacturers. The point is that solid-state technology, making such logical comparisons possible with instantaneous communication, has given options to electrical people that were previously not economical. The disadvantage of the zone selective blocking arrangement is that the main provides no backup ground-fault protection for the second-level device. More on this subject is in Chap. 7.

## 1.6 Core NEC Requirements for Overcurrent Coordination

A large part of the NEC deals with construction requirements for electrical circuits—architectural spaces, grounding, special occupancies, etc. While all this is important, the protection specialist will only need to deal with part of it. Figure 1.7 is a pictorial summary of the parts of the NEC and the ANSI standards to which we shall refer with considerable regularity.

It is fair to say that knowledge of the NEC is a career-long enterprise. This text is no substitute for careful study of the NEC and its auxiliary publications. Figure 1.8 is provided to give you some feeling for the distinction between overcurrent and short-circuit protection in terms of a log-log scale. The NEC has a very specific meaning for overcurrent, and the region on a time-current log-log plot associated with it is fairly well defined. The region that can neither be called exclusively the overcurrent nor the short-circuit region will be of particular interest to us. A great deal of our adjustments to the settings of protective devices occur in this region.

## 1.7 Manufacturer Time-Current Characteristic Curves

Although the electrical equipment standards organizations have established some basic minimums regarding the manner in which the

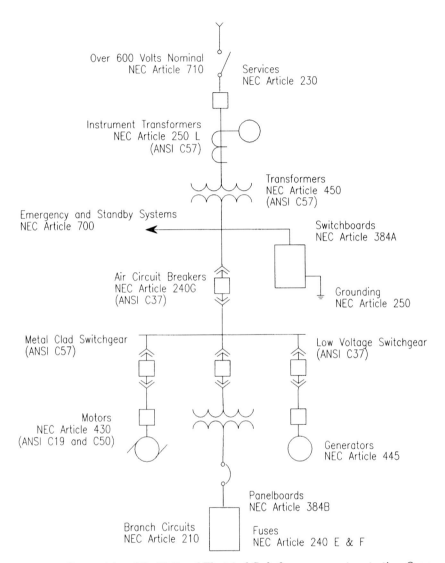

**Figure 1.7**   Core articles of the National Electrical Code for overcurrent protection. Over-current and short-circuit protection is a topic common to almost all articles of the National Electric Code. Among the other articles of the National Electric Code which contain requirements for overcurrent protection are 310, 364, 384, 424, 550, 551, 605, 630, and 645. The index of the *National Electric Code Handbook* (Ref. NFPA) is the best cross-reference to overcurrent and short-circuit requirements.

tripping characteristics of protective devices are reported, there are considerable differences among the manufacturers. These differences are usually to the designer's benefit, although these benefits increase the amount of time necessary for the designer to become familiar with the manufacturer's product line. Setting aside a full day's work for reading each manufacturer's product catalog and becoming familiar

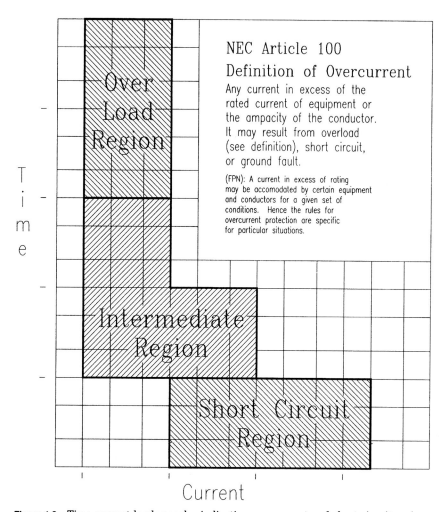

**Figure 1.8** Time-current log-log scales indicating overcurrent and short-circuit regions. The NEC defines overcurrent explicitly in Article 100. You will not find a definition for short-circuit, however. Most of the action and/or competition for daylight in phase and ground overcurrent coordination problems occur in the intermediate region shown. Breakers with (optional) instantaneous ratings may gobble up daylight from breakers with (optional) short time ratings or vice versa. Transformer damage curves may lie on the wrong side of primary fuses while coordinating well with downstream secondary breakers. Secondary main breaker ground fault relays may trip long before the fastest downstream time delay motor fuses open. It is fair to say that in this region, no two coordination studies (that occur naturally in practice) are alike.

with application literature is time well spent. The following are some things to watch out for when sorting through time-current characteristic curves of low- and medium-voltage protective devices:

- Do the trip unit and circuit breaker match? In the interest of interchangeability, many manufacturers have constructed trip units that

may be installed on more than one of their circuit breakers. Molded
case circuit breaker trip curves with thermal-magnetic time-current
characteristic curve may not be interchangeable but power circuit
breakers of the encased and open type may be interchangeable.
Other manufacturers—quite justifiably—have different curves for
RMS (root-mean-square) sensing trip units. In any case, this kind of
flexibility requires that the designer compare nameplate data with
trip curve labeling.

- Does the trip unit plug (or sensor) match the settings on the time-
current characteristic curve? Most manufacturers allow you to
adjust the sensor (in some cases on the order of 20 to 120 percent). If
there is a discrepancy, however, you should immediately proceed to a
visual confirmation of the sensor rating itself. Sensor + trip unit +
curves *must* match. No kidding.

- Do the trip curves match the circuit breaker nameplate information?
It is desirable, although not always absolutely necessary, that the
nameplate and the trip curves match. For example, if your breaker
has model nameplate ABCD-II, the trip curve labeled ABCD may be
the appropriate curve to use even though it lacks the II suffix. Sometimes the discrepancy is simply a matter of breaker-mounting style.
To be absolutely certain, you should contact a manufacturer's representative.

- Do all the trip functions on your trip unit match the trip functions on
the time-current characteristic curves? Some manufacturers have
ground-fault tripping characteristics on different sheets of paper
than phase-tripping characteristics such as long, short, and instantaneous trip functions. Some even have long and short tripping functions on different sheets of paper. You may need as many as three
different time-current characteristic curves for each of the breakers
you need to coordinate. This is where a computerized graphic
database of the curves you need can save a lot of time.

- Do the breaker frame and breaker trip ratings match the time-current characteristic curve? For example, the curves that apply to
breakers from 400- to 1200-A frames may be different than the
curves for breakers with 2000- to 4000-A frames. Frequently, the
time-current characteristic curves for the main breaker of a unit
substation will be different than the time-current characteristic
curves for the feeder breakers.

- Are the time delays indicated explicitly as bands or do you need to
determine these bands from multiples of the sensor setting? Some
manufacturers, in the interest of reducing the clutter on a time-current characteristic curve, will simply indicate the time delays as one

(rather wide) band and leave it up to you to determine the time-delay band. Other manufacturers indicate the time-delay bands explicitly, but it may take a while to understand how the time-delay bands are laid out.

- Do the trip unit dials match the time-current characteristic curves? Some manufacturers print the dials on the time-current characteristic curve, and others do not. Even if they do not, you can confirm or deny that you have the correct time-current characteristic by comparing the settings available on the trip unit with the time-current characteristic. For example, to check long time delay, you might draw a vertical line through the long time-delay tripping band (say, 6 times the continuous ampere value set at the sensor) and confirm or deny that the times available within this band on the time-current characteristic are available on the dials on the trip unit. You can do this with all the other trip functions such as ground-fault delay and $I^2t$ functions.

- Does the trip unit interrupting rating match the voltage at which the breaker shall be applied? The interrupting ratings of breakers decrease as voltage increases.

- Are there restrictions on the instantaneous setting based on the maximum trip unit rating? You will want the circuit breaker's interrupting capability to match the trip unit's instantaneous trip rating. Some manufacturers have a self-protecting instantaneous override function on their trip units.

- Do the NEC requirements for ground-fault protection explicitly appear on the time-current characteristic curve? Some manufacturers pack as much information as they can onto a single sheet of log-log paper by printing their curves with more than one horizontal and vertical scale to show the ground-fault tripping bands. Make sure you read the labeling on each axis.

- Do not assume that if a manufacturer gives you a complete set of time-current characteristic curves that you have all of them. In advance of a study that must be done in haste, you should try to find the curve you really need in the complete set you have been given. This will save you a great deal of anxiety when there is no time to search for the right curve.

## 1.8 Solving Problems in Time-Current Characteristic Scaling Arithmetic

Since the existence of transformers on our study systems will be more the rule than the exception, we will almost always have to adjust the alignment of source curves to the voltage scale on our target plots.

Aligning the current axes on a current base that makes sense for both voltages on a transformer requires some simple arithmetic. It is a good idea to be able to do this longhand, if for no other reason than to develop an eye for plots that make sense.

In order to work through these examples, you will need to assemble some materials. You will need to obtain the 11 × 17 manufacturer time-current characteristic curves and some blank 11 × 17 log-log paper of your own. For the reader's convenience, the time-current characteristic curves used in this chapter have been reproduced in the Appendix. In advance of getting these curves, it would not be time wasted if you were to reproduce these curves from scratch, taking a few points from the book page curves and plotting them on a blank sheet of 11 × 17 paper. You will have to do this to build up a computer library of time-current characteristic curves anyway.

An easy way of approaching the normalization aspect of the coordination problem is to remember that, for a *fixed load,* the higher the voltage the lower the current. You should always be asking yourself: 1 amp at 208 V equals how many amperes at 480 V? 1 A at 480 V equals how many amps at 13,200 V? and so on. Use your intuition. The fixed load does not have to be 1 A; it can be 100 A, a transformer full-load amp rating, or even a completely arbitrary (but conveniently chosen) number such as 87 or 1.21 (IEEE Buff Book, 1986).

Here are a few general principles that we shall apply throughout this text:

- We shall use the term *plot* and *curve* more or less interchangeably.

- We shall refer to the manufacturer's preprinted log-log time-current characteristic curve of a protective device as the *source* plot. Source plots are not easy to forget because you are likely to spend a great deal of time trying to find the one you need.

- We shall refer to the log-log plot that we intend to make one or more source plots as the *target* plot. If you use Keuffel & Esser (K&E) log-log paper, the target plot would be the plot on the green sheet of paper and would contain all the source plots normalized on a common current base.

- A scale corresponding to the current expected at the lowest voltage level is one criterion for selection of a base voltage; selection of a scale that will minimize multiplications and manipulations on devices where a range of settings is available is another criterion for selection of a base voltage.

- Be mindful of the vertical time scale. Some curves begin at 0.001 and others at 0.01 s. Low-voltage devices are quite fast and will have a long vertical scale (an extra logarithmic decade). Medium-voltage devices will be much slower.

- Plot devices that represent fixed constraints first. A fixed constraint might be a power fuse or medium-voltage relay with a setting that you would prefer not to change.

- In the absence of a fixed constraint, plot curves from left to right starting with the device closest to the load or fault location. You will be able to see whether the proposed time-current characteristic of each device coordinates with one on its load side.

- In general, the curves we plot must not touch each other. You will want to keep the gap between them on the vertical axis trimmed finely so that trip times do not accumulate above the setting of the source protective device. This is easier said than done, however, as you shall see. There are about a half-dozen rules that govern the daylight between plots that we shall discuss at length in later chapters.

- Time-current curves fuses, direct-acting breakers, and time-delay thermal devices are given as bands. These bands (or tolerances) represent the allowances for variations in performance variations. The device will operate somewhere between the boundaries of this band.

- Time characteristics of relays, on the other hand, are represented by families of one-line curves to which tolerances (such as ±10 percent) must be added when setpoints are determined. Most relay curves begin at 1.5 times their minimum pickup value because their performance below that value cannot be predicted very accurately. You can usually obtain curves showing expected time-current performance down to 1.1 times pickup value.

- When plots give you no hope of coordination, such as secondary devices landing to the right of a primary devices, it is likely that you have misread the scale (for example, some TCCs are drafted in terms of multiples of sensor rating; others in terms of actual amperes), or there is a scaling error present. Some scaling errors make themselves obvious. Others that have to do with current transformer ratios may not be so obvious.

**Example 1.1**   Plot 480-V Fuse with 208-V Breaker

*Situation.*   Fuses are applied to protect a 225-kVA lighting transformer with a 480-V primary and a 208-V secondary (Fig. 1.9).

*Requirements.*   Plot the time-current characteristic of both devices. For this and the other examples of this chapter, we ignore any NEC requirements that may have bearing on the time and current margins.

**solution**   We have two voltage levels to deal with. Obtain Siemens-ITE TCC# TD-7108 and Bussman TCC#s: 233 and 234.

1. We arbitrarily pick 208 V as the base voltage, and, since we have no fixed constraints, we will start with the 208-V breaker.

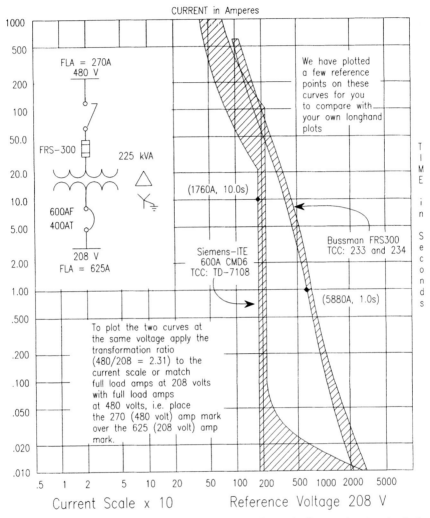

**Figure 1.9** Plot of 480-V fuse with 208-V breaker with circuit diagram inset and calculations.

2. It is always a good idea to give the TCC a good "read" before plotting anything. Orient yourself to the units and length of the time and current axes. The current scale is indicated in "Multiples of Circuit Breaker Continuous Current Rating." The upper band asymptotically approaches 1 times the circuit breaker continuous current rating. Note that the time scale is indicated in seconds throughout beginning at 0.001 s. The first cycle mark is indicated at the 0.016-s point.

3. Mark the 0.010-s point on the target plot. Mark the 400-A point on the target plot. Note that even though the circuit breaker *frame* rating is 600 A, we shall set the *trip* point lower than the frame rating. We do this to give you a better

sense of the distinction between a breaker's frame rating and the variety of current levels at which it may be programmed to trip.

4. Using a light box or a window with enough light to show the source curve underneath the target plot, match the 400-A point on the target plot with the 1.0 on the source plot while also matching up the 0.010-s points of the source and target plots. You may match the 400-A points on either the upper or lower scale; it makes no difference but using the upper scale will give you a better sense of the trip time asymptotically approaching 400 A. You will notice that on the lower current scale the tripping band begins at five times the circuit breaker continuous current rating.

5. Trace the source plot onto the target plot. Note that there are three different "tails" to the manufacturer's TCC. Trace the 240-V tail since this is the voltage closest to 208 V.

6. At this point we have simply traced a 208-V device onto a 208-V target plot. To normalize the 480-V fuse onto the 208-V target plot, we ask ourselves the question: "How many amp at 208 V do we have for every 1 A at 480 V?" The answer is the transformation ratio 480/208 = 2.31. Then we need only line up the 1.0 on the 480 source curve scale with 2.31 on the 208 current scale. We can choose any current value: 10 A, 100 A, or even the transformer full-load current. As long as we keep this relationship in mind, we will be able to normalize devices of any voltage onto our 208-V plot.

7. Trace the 300-A characteristic by interpolating between the 200- and 400-A fuse curves.

**Example 1.2**    Plot the Fuse and Circuit Breaker at 480 V

*Situation.*    A new 1500-kVA substation shall be connected to a 13.2-kV distribution feeder that is protected by an upstream overcurrent relay with settings you know (Fig. 1.10).

*Requirements.*    The substation shop drawings have come to you with a 100E primary fuse already specified. Plot both the relay and the fuse time-current characteristic in order to get a feeling for the coordination relationships.

**solution**    Refer to Fig. 1.10. We obtain the TCCs of the General Electric IAC 53 relay and the S&C SM-5 fuse. The IAC 53 relay uses curve GES-7002B. For reasons we shall discuss in detail later, a complete picture of the tripping characteristics of the primary fuse will require two curves: TCC 153-4 (standard speed minimum melting) and TCC 153-4-2 (standard speed total clearing time). This manufacturer and others frequently print fuse curves in matched pairs of different colors. Try holding them both up to the light to see how the minimum and total curves compare for each fuse size. You should see that these curves are nearly parallel for times beyond 600 s (10 min), and you should see all the total clearing curves converge toward the 1 cycle mark (0.016 s).

Since both devices are operating at 13,200 V, it would be easiest to plot them at 13,200 V. We will do this in the next example. For now, we will plot them both at 480 V in order to extend our focus on how to normalize TCCs to voltages that are different from operating voltages. We will start with the relay curve because it is a fixed constraint.

**Plotting the relay curve.**    We ask ourselves the question: "1 amp at 13,200 V is equal to how many amps at 480 V?" The answer, of course, is the transformation ratio, in this example, 13,200/480 = 27.5.

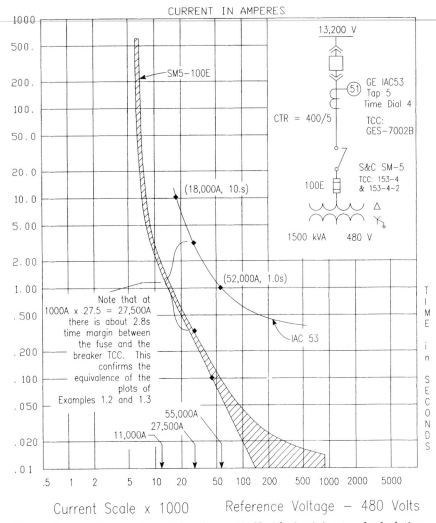

**Figure 1.10**   Plot of fuse and circuit breaker at 480 V with circuit inset and calculations.

If you get stuck on determining the order in which you need to ask yourself this question, you can reason, using your intuition about primary and secondary voltage and current relationships: Since we have decided to plot at 480 V, we know that there will be more current at the secondary voltage than at the primary voltage. (This is a step-down transformer.)

Tape the source curve to a light box or a window. Find the 27.5-amp mark on the current scale of the (blank) 480-V target paper and align this 27.5-A mark over the 1-A mark of the source TCC current scale. The IAC 53 has a vertical hash mark printed just below the 1 × "Multiples of Pickup Setting" to make this alignment a little easier.

At this point, it is worthwhile just staring at what you have done. You should have a 480-V log-log scale taped over a 13,200-V log-log scale. Make sure the time scales align as well. We have not made any adjustments for relay pickup yet. The IAC time-current characteristic curves lie neatly in the middle of the paper. The 275-A mark on the target paper lies over the 10-amp mark on the source paper, the 2750-A mark lies over the 100-A mark, and so on. If we wanted to shift the sources back and forth on our target paper, we need only relabel the decade marks on the preprinted target plot current scale accordingly. For example, by adding zeros to the preprinted target plot (effectively multiplying by 10, 100, and so on), the source curves would shift to the left. By subtracting zeros (effectively dividing by 10, 100, and so on), the source curves would shift to the right. There will be situations when we will need to do this.

After you feel comfortable with these scaling relationships, you are ready to make the necessary correction for relay pickup. From the information we are given about the relay settings, we know that the relay will begin to pick up at the tap setting times the current transformer ratio:

$$\text{CTR} \times \text{Relay Tap} = \frac{400}{5} \times 5 = 400 \text{ A}$$

It is important to realize that these are 400 A at 13,200 V. From what we know about the transformation ratio, 400 A at 13,200 A is equal to $27.5 \times 400 = 11,000$ A. Align the 11,000-A mark on the target paper over the 1.0 on the source curve paper. If you try to do this, you will notice that *you do not even have* an 11,000-A mark on the preprinted target paper current scale. You need to add 3 zeros to all the preprinted decade marks on the target paper. Thus, 1 becomes 1000, 10 becomes 10,000, and so on. This puts the 11,000 mark just about in the middle of the paper. Following through now, orient the 11,000 mark over the 1.0 on the source curve paper, match up the time scales, and draw the curve that corresponds to time dial setting 4.0. The endpoints of medium voltage relay curves require some attention, but let us defer this discussion to later chapters.

While you have the target paper taped over the source curve paper, you might like to look through a few other points to see how they align. For example, the 10× multiple of pickup setting mark on the source curve should align with the 110,000 mark on the target paper. The 5× multiple of the pickup setting mark on the source curve should align with the $400 \times 27.5 \times 5 = 55,000$-A mark on the target paper.

**Plotting the fuse curve.**   The fuse is applied at 13.2 kV also. The same 27.5 alignment factor applies, but a reading of the TCCs reveals that the current scale is laid out in actual amperes. You may actually find an actual ampere scale easier to work with. Even though there is no 1-A mark on this TCC, we can just as easily use the 100-A mark. Since we know that 100 A at 13,200 V is equal to $100 \times 27.5 = 2750$ A at 480 V, we need only match the 100-A mark on the source curve with the 2750-A mark on the target paper. You may draw either the minimum melt or the total clearing time curve first, but you must draw both. Make sure the time scales align. When you plot both, you should notice that the total clearing curve makes a kind of tail on the fuse curve. Again, the endpoint of any curve we draw requires some attention, but for now stop drawing your curve where the source curve ends.

In many circumstances, coordination studies are undertaken after a circuit is built, or at least after parts have been ordered by the electrical contractor (in the case of new construction). This reduces a great deal of the work to a simple matter of obtaining the time-current characteristic curves from the manufacturer's representative. Sometimes, contractor shop drawings will indicate manufacturer protective devices catalog numbers, sometimes you will just have to go to the site and get the nameplate information yourself.

**Example 1.3**   Plot a Fuse and a Circuit Breaker at 13.2 kV

*Situation.*   Same circuit as in the previous example (Fig. 1.11).

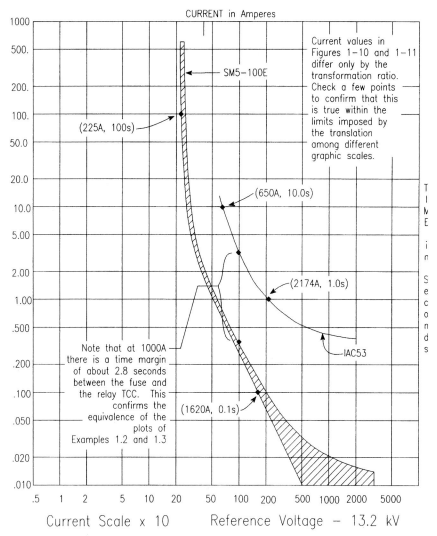

**Figure 1.11**   Plot of fuse and a circuit breaker at 13.2 kV with circuit inset and calculations.

*Requirements.* Plot the relay and fuse time-current characteristic curves at 13.2 kV on the same sheet of log-log paper.

**solution** It is the more common approach to plot time-current characteristic curves at the voltage at which the majority of the devices are applied. Since we do not need to deal with any transformation ratio, we need only attend to the differences in the way the relay and fuse curve current scales are laid out.

We label our coordination study at 13.2 kV. We compute the full-load amperes of the substation:

$$\frac{1500 \text{ kVA}}{\sqrt{3} \times 13.2 \text{ kV}} = 65.8 \text{ A}$$

*Tracing the relay TCC.* We regard the relay tripping characteristic as a fixed constraint. One reason for advancing the practice of coordinating devices from load to source is that, on existing systems, you may make more work for yourself if changing one relay setting means that will have to recheck coordination with other devices. Of course, if you are laying out a new system from scratch, you may well develop your coordination studies from source to load in order to determine some of the design constraints on downstream switchgear.

We note that the IAC 53 relay current scale is laid out according to "Multiples of PickUp Setting." If the relay is set to pick up at 400 A, then by aligning the 1.0 on the IAC 53 curve with the 400-A mark on our target paper we have correct alignment. This is the most common way of aligning the curves, and the manufacturer has printed a long vertical hash mark to indicate the 1.0 multiple of pickup setting.

Align the target paper 400-A mark over the 1.0 and align the time divisions. Only after these are aligned do you find the Time Dial = 4 curve and trace it. On the left end of the IAC curve we begin at the 1.5 times the pickup setting. We draw it to the 2400-A mark on the right end of the curve. For the purpose of this exercise, we assume the upper limit of fault current at 2400 A.

*Tracing the fuse curve.* The fuse curve is composed of two parts: the left and right boundaries or the minimum melting time-current characteristic curves. We must obtain both from the manufacturer.

Again, we may use the current scale as-is since the fuse current scales are in actual "Current In Amperes." We align the 100-A mark on the S&C TCC with the 100 A mark on the target paper. The minimum curve has an extremely inverse characteristic. The maximum curve stretches into the high current region.

We have not used the 1500-kVA transformer secondary full-load current rating thus far (1802.8 A). There is another way of proceeding with getting the fuse and circuit breaker on the same sheet of paper as long as your light source can shine through three sheets of paper:

- Mark the full-load ampere point = 65.8 A on the primary fuse time-current characteristic.

- Mark the full-load ampere point = 1802.8 on the secondary circuit breaker time-current characteristic.

- Align the two on a light table, place the target paper over each, and draw.

**Example 1.4**    Plot 34.5-kV breaker with a 13.2-kV and 2.4-kV breaker

*Situation.*    When a fault occurs on a 2.4-kV distribution feeder, the fault current flows through three breakers in series as shown in Fig. 1.12. We are given tap and time-delay information.

*Requirements.*    Normalize on 34.5 kV. Use Asea-Brown-Boveri (ABB) MMCO/MCO TCC# 619611.

solution    There are two transformation ratios to deal with.

$$\frac{34.5}{13.8} = 2.5 \quad \text{and} \quad \frac{34.5}{2.4} = 14.4$$

At 34.5 kV we have Tap 0.5 × 2000/5 = 200 A
At 13.8 kV we have Tap 0.5 × 1200/5 = 120 A
At 2.4 kV we have Tap 0.5 × 800/5 = 80 A

Plotting breaker A is easy since our reference scale is 34.5 kV. We simply overlay the 200-A mark on the target paper over the 1.0 on the "Multiples of Tap Value Current" scale on the source curve.

Plotting breaker B requires normalizing the 120-A pickup at 13.8 kV to its 34.5-kV equivalent. This is 120/2.5 = 48 A. We overlay the 48-A mark on the target paper over the 1.0 on the "Multiples of Tap Value Current" scale on the source curve.

Plotting breaker C requires normalizing the 80-A pickup at 2.4 kV to its 34.5-kV equivalent. This is 80/14.4 = 5.6 A. We overlay the 5.6-A mark on the target paper over the 1.0 on the "Multiples of Tap Value Current" scale on the source curve.

Figure 1.12 contains a few reference points for you to confirm that your B curves are normalized correctly.

*Remarks.*    It is common practice to specify overcurrent relays with progressively greater inversity from source to load not only because the time-current characteristics are less likely to miscoordinate but also because the "run" and "rise" of current versus time varies. Circuits operating at different voltages are subject to faults of varying magnitudes and frequency; thus the rises and runs of the relays that protect them require special attention.

At least one manufacturer has developed the a method for its line of molded case low-voltage circuit breakers so that coordination of molded case breakers can be established (when applied at the same voltage) and so that time-current characteristic curves need not be printed for every circuit breaker continuous ampere rating. The curves are printed with arrows on them so that you simply line up two reference points on the horizontal axis and look for daylight. The reference points are already computed for you. These reference points assume a base current rating of, for example, 10,000 A, for an entire family of breakers whose time-current characteristic curves appear on a single tissue. The method only works when you are dealing with devices applied at the same voltage.

The practice of choosing an arbitrary base current in order to center your curves on the log-log paper is fairly common among overcurrent

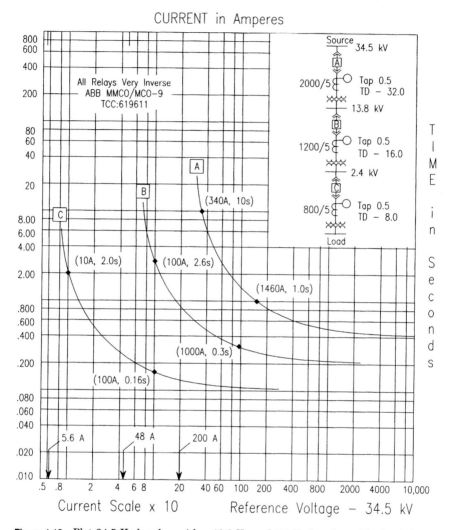

**Figure 1.12**  Plot 34.5 Kv breaker with a 13.2-Kv and 2.4-Kv breaker with circuit inset and calculations. Instrument transformers should be located to include the breaker within the protected zone. A faulted breaker may not be isolated by the successful operation of the bus protection system when a power source exists on the line side of a faulted breaker. The fault is still energized from this source and other relay systems must also operate to isolate the fault.

Circuit breaker failure is detected by providing each circuit breaker with a fault detector that, working with the bus relays, initiates a timer to trip another circuit breaker. This detection system can trip local breakers directly or it can initiate remote tripping of lines by direct transfer trip, by stopping carrier, or line blocking schemes by sending permissive signal where required.

coordination specialists. In this book we shall use the transformation ratio explicitly in all our normalization calculations in order to retain the sense of the circuit under study.

## Bibliography

Blackburn, J. L., and J. V. Kresser, "Line and Circuit Protection," Chap. 10, *Applied Protective Relaying,* Westinghouse Electric Corporation, 1982.

Central Station Engineers, *Electrical Transmission and Distribution Reference Book,* Westinghouse Electric Corporation, 1964, p. 413.

"IEEE Recommended Practice for Protection and Coordination of Industrial and Commercial Power Systems," Chap. 14, *ANSI/IEEE Std. 242-1986* (Buff Book), 1986.

### General references

Blackburn, J. L., "Introduction and General Philosophies (of Protective Relaying)," Chap. 1, *Applied Protective Relaying,* Westinghouse Electric Corporation, 1982.

Davies, T., *Protection of Industrial Power Systems,* Pergamon Press, Ltd., Oxford, 1984.

Horowitz, S. H., *Protective Relaying for Power Systems,* IEEE Press, New York, 1980.

Institute of Electrical and Electronics Engineers, Inc., *IEEE Guides and Standards for Protective Relaying Systems,* The Institute of Electrical and Electronics Engineers, Inc., 1978.

Mason, C. R., *The Art and Science of Protective Relaying,* John Wiley and Sons, New York, 1956.

St. Pierre, Conrad, and Tracey Wolney, "Standardization of Benchmarks for Protective-Device Time-Current Curves," *IEEE IAS,* July/Aug. 1986.

Warrington, A. R. C., *Protective Relays: Their Theory and Practice,* Chapman & Hall, London, 1962.

### Further reading

Broadwater, Robert P., "Expert System for Integrated Protection Design with Configurable Distribution Circuits," *T-PWRD,* April 1994.

Enns, Mark (Chair of Working Group D10 of Line Protection Subcommittee, Power System Relaying Committee), "Potential Applications of Expert Systems to Power System Protection," *T-PWRD,* April 1994.

"When Protection Does Not Protect," *Business Week,* July 18, 1964.

# General Considerations

# 2

# Basic Short-Circuit Calculations

## 2.1 Foreword

You cannot safely coordinate tripping characteristics of overcurrent devices without the assurance that the devices have sufficient interrupting capacity. You cannot have this assurance without calculating short-circuit current. The first order of business in any overcurrent coordination study takes place off the log-log paper doing the kind of calculations that are the subject of this chapter. We will provide examples of the most practical calculation methods for coming up with numbers to assist us in the selection of devices strong and fast enough to withstand and interrupt the largest fault currents we can expect. We will discuss fault currents so low that they either completely elude the sensing methods available to us or cannot be distinguished from normal load currents.

## 2.2 Basic Longhand Calculations

For protection design, we will need values for short-circuit current in three-phase, single-line-to-ground, and line-to-line faults. In this chapter, we will focus on the basic longhand calculations for each of the foregoing. Electrical people who have access to power system analysis software need to learn these basic maneuvers not only to verify by longhand their computer-generated results for small subsystem analysis but also to know how to set up the subsystem boundaries so that time is not wasted building a model that is too large for the purpose. Unless you are proficient in the basic longhand maneuvers, you will be wasting your time trying to enter all the data that power systems analysis software requires.

For example, if you simply need to specify the short-circuit withstand rating of a 200-A 208-V lighting panel fed from a power panel which is itself fed from a breaker in a unit substation (itself fed from a larger bulk distribution substation fed by your utility), you probably can make some reasonable assumptions about short-circuit currents closer to the 200-A lighting panel. In the absence of other information, you can be guided by the interrupting rating of the nearest upstream device (or the impedance of the next upstream transformer) so that you do not need to know, for instance, the X/R ratio and MVA short-circuit current availability at the utility service entrance.

---

### The Usual Simplifying Assumptions

- The Thevenin equivalent voltage at the point of fault may be taken to be 1 per unit or 100% of system rated voltage. The physics of a fault does not allow the voltage to remain at 100% of nominal very long but the assumption is applied in order to have enough potential to drive current through the fault.
- Transformer self-cooled kVA ratings shall be the basis for full-load amperes except where otherwise noted.
- Prefault load currents and harmonic components of short-circuit currents can be ignored.
- Motoring of small induction machines may be ignored.
- All dynamic loads are considered to be on-line when the fault occurs.
- Ignoring the resistive component of the Thevenin equivalent impedance results in a more conservative short-circuit calculation than when you include it. If you want to include it then you should include it in your low-voltage system calculations since the resistive component is more dominant than in medium-voltage systems.

---

Most short-circuit calculations require knowledge of sequence components. The calculation of Example 2.1 involves symmetrical component theory, but the theory is implicit enough so that you can practically do the calculation in your head. The example involves a building substation, but the calculation method can be applied to, for example, short-circuit current flows between two interconnected 500-bus systems between the United States and Canada, as long as you can reduce the two 500-bus systems to a single impedance.

**Example 2.1**   Simple Three-Phase Bolted Fault Calculation

*Situation.*   A three-phase bolted fault occurs on the load side of a secondary breaker in a 1000-kVA, 13,200/480-V unit substation as shown in Fig. 2.1.

*Requirement.*   Determine the maximum symmetrical short-circuit current on the load side of the transformer secondary breaker.

**solution**   Transformer nameplate data that indicates percent impedance to be 5.75 percent. Assume that the fault occurs at 100 percent rated voltage (480 V). Then,

$$\frac{100\%}{5.75\%} \times 1201 \text{ (full-load secondary A)} = 20{,}886 \text{ A}$$

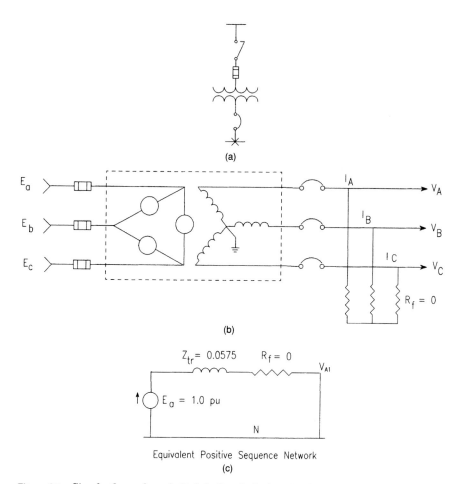

(a)

(b)

$Z_{tr} = 0.0575$    $R_f = 0$

$E_a = 1.0$ pu

$V_{A1}$

N

Equivalent Positive Sequence Network
(c)

**Figure 2.1**   Simple three-phase bolted fault calculation: (*a*) One line diagram of three-phase bolted fault on load side of breaker. Impedances on either side (primary or secondary) of any given transformer may be referred to the opposite side of the transformer by either multiplying or dividing an impedance by the square of the transformer turns ratio. In this case, the given nameplate impedance is already referred to the secondary side. (*b*) Three-line diagram of three-phase bolted fault. (*c*) From symmetrical component theory we need only the positive sequence equivalent network. For a three-phase bolted fault under these conditions all nine sequence networks can be reduced to the Phase A positive sequence network.

*Remarks.*    For a large category of service transformer applications, fault current at the secondary breaker is 10 to 20 times full-load current of the transformer secondary. We have ignored fault impedance, fault current asymmetry, and the effect of system grounding on this result. This calculation method is frequently called the *infinite bus* calculation because it assumes a source of zero impedance (at 100 percent rated voltage) or infinite ability to supply fault current from buses outside the partition. A more rigorous description would be to call it the *first cycle symmetrical* short-circuit fault calculation.

In order to specify protective devices based on the method indicated in Example 2.1, we will need to be mindful of the impedance of the circuit between the source and the point of fault (ignoring, for the moment, the impedance of the fault itself). The point on the voltage wave at which the short circuit must occur to produce maximum asymmetry (and thereby increase the short-circuit duty on our protective devices) depends on the X/R ratio. *Maximum asymmetry* is obtained when the short circuit occurs at a time angle equal to 90 + θ (measured forward in degrees from the zero point of the voltage wave) where the tan(θ) equals the X/R ratio of the circuit. *Minimum asymmetry* (or symmetry) will occur when the fault occurs 90 degrees from that point on the voltage wave.

For example, for a circuit with Z = 1.0 + j1.0, the X/R ratio is 1.0. Since the tangent of 45 degrees is 1.0, the maximum offset occurs at 90° + 45° = 135° from the zero point of the voltage wave. The application of X/R ratio information to the results of an infinite bus short-circuit calculation will be discussed in detail in Chap. 3.

---

### Transformer Nameplate Impedance Data

Transformer impedance is expressed as a voltage percentage. It is the percentage of rated primary voltage that must be applied to cause rated secondary current to flow into a short-circuit at the secondary terminals. For example, a three-phase, 13,200/480-V, 1000-kVA transformer with a 5.75 percent impedance would require only 13,200 × 0.0575 = 759 V on the primary to cause rated secondary current (equal to 1201 A) to flow. Then 100 percent of rated primary voltage will cause 100/5.75, or 17.39 times rated secondary current to flow into a bolted fault.

---

## 2.3   Beyond the Infinite Bus Calculation

If you were in the business of making protective devices for electrical power systems, you would embrace any analytic model that gives you more handles on the way a power system is behaving. Microprocessor control designers look for the leading and/or falling edges of digital input quantities; power system protection specialists look for changes in the relationship among analog quantities. Subtle changes in these quantities are the signatures of short circuits or overloads. The analytic tool that has provided these handles for nearly 100 years is symmetrical component theory.

The application of symmetrical component theory gives electrical protection specialists three handles for *each phase* of a three-phase system. These (3 × 3 = 9) nine-phase decompositions are called the positive, negative, and zero sequence components, and they can be applied to all the quantities in Ohm's law: voltage, current, and impedance in terms of only one reference phase, for instance, phase A.

The reason Example 2.1 works is that for *three-phase bolted faults only* the nine-sequence impedances can be expressed in terms of the phase A-positive sequence impedance. We have also ignored fault impedance. In terms of sequence components the solution equation reduces to

$$I_A = E/(Z_1 + Z_2 + Z_0 + Z_f)$$

$$I_B = \mathbf{a}^2 I_A$$

$$I_C = \mathbf{a} I_A$$

In other words, the fault in $I_B$ and $I_C$ is the same as $I_A$ multiplied by some factor of the operator $\mathbf{a}$ that rotates the vector operand 120°.

We need sequence components to analyze any kind of unbalanced fault of which the single-line-to-ground fault is the most common. The most general expression of a single-line-to-ground fault is.

$$I_{slg} = \frac{3E_{ln}}{Z_1 + Z_2 + Z_0 + 3Z_g}$$

where $E_{ln}$ = line to neutral voltage
 $Z_1$ = positive sequence impedance
 $Z_2$ = negative sequence impedance
 $Z_0$ = zero sequence impedance
 $Z_g$ = ground return impedance

**Example 2.2**   Simple Line-to-Ground Fault Calculation

*Situation.*  A single-line-to-ground fault occurs at the same location in the switchgear of Fig. 2.1.

*Requirements.*  Calculate fault currents with and without fault resistance. See Fig. 2.2. Develop a general solution for fault voltages and currents.

**solution**   Most of the information we will need to solve this problem will not appear on the transformer nameplate, in particular, the sequence impedances of the transformer. We can either consult with the manufacturer or we can use information provided in NEMA or IEEE publications.

From Wagner and Evans (1932) and Blackburn (1987), we know that the positive, negative, and zero sequence network must be connected in series as shown in Fig. 2.4. It is common practice to assume that for passive circuit elements such as buses, cables, and transformers that $Z_1 = Z_2$. Let us assume that the zero sequence impedance is *three times* the positive and negative sequence impedance. The significance of the assumption that $Z_0 \leq 3Z_{1,2}$ will be discussed in detail in Chap. 4.

In sequence component solutions, it is customary to assume that the fault occurs from phase A to ground. Assume a prefault voltage of $V = 1.0\angle 90°$ or $j1.0$ per unit.

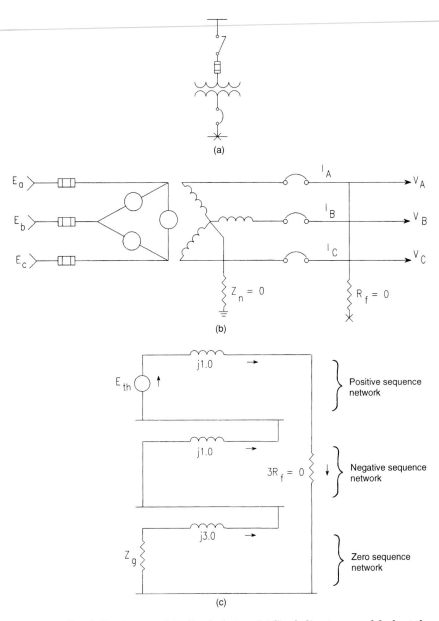

**Figure 2.2**  Simple line-to-ground fault calculation: (*a*) Single line-to-ground fault at the same location on the switchgear as Example 2.1. (*b*) Three-line diagram of single-line-to-ground. (*c*) Equivalent sequence network. In existing technical literature on practical single-line-to-ground calculations you will see a number of assumptions about zero sequence impedance when measured zero sequence impedance information is unavailable. Most of them assume that positive and negative sequence impedances are equal and that zero sequence impedance is a (usually small) integral multiple of the positive sequence impedance. Refer to the table of Fig. 2.3.

*Without Fault Resistance*

With $X_1 = X_2 = 1.0$ and $X_0 = 3.0$ per unit.

$$I_0 = I_1 + I_2 = I^f = \frac{j1.0}{j(1.0 + 1.0 + 3.0)} = 0.2 + j0.0$$

$$I_a^f = 3I_0 = 0.6 + j0.0 \qquad I_b = I_c = 0$$

So, if our base current is 1201 A, then the single-line-to-ground fault current would be $1201 \times 0.6 = 720.6$ A. We would use this number to program the substation main breaker ground-fault pickup.

With $I_0 = 0.2$ and noting the direction of current flow through the sequence impedances in Fig. 2.2, we have

$$V_0 = -(0.2)(j3.0) = -j0.6$$

$$V_1 = j1.0 - (0.2)(j1.0) = j1.0 - j0.2 = j0.8$$

$$V_2 = -(0.2)(j1.0) = -j0.2$$

Note that $V_0 + V_1 + V_2 = 0$. Since $[\mathbf{V_{abc}}] = [\mathbf{A}][\mathbf{V_{012}}]$

$$\begin{matrix} \mathbf{V_a} & = \\ \mathbf{V_b} & = \\ \mathbf{V_c} & = \end{matrix} \begin{bmatrix} 1 & 1 & 1 \\ 1 & a^2 & a \\ 1 & a & a^2 \end{bmatrix} \begin{bmatrix} \mathbf{0.6\angle -90°} \\ \mathbf{0.8\angle 90°} \\ \mathbf{0.2\angle -90°} \end{bmatrix} = \begin{bmatrix} \mathbf{0\angle 0°} \\ \mathbf{1.25\angle -46.12°} \\ \mathbf{1.25\angle 133.9°} \end{bmatrix}$$

Thus, voltages in the remaining phases are 125 percent of their prefault value.

*With Fault Resistance*

$$3R_f = 3$$

$$I_0 = I_1 = I_2 = I = \frac{j1.0}{3.0 + j5.0} = 0.14706 + j0.08824$$

$$I_a^f = 0.44118 + j0.2641 = 0.5145\angle 30.96° = 3I_0$$

With $I_b = 1201$ A, then the single-line-to-ground fault would be $1201 \times 0.5154 = 617.9$ A. We would use this number to program the main breaker ground fault pickup.

Again,     $I_b = I_c = 0$ and $I_0 = 0.1715\angle 30.96°$

$$V_0 = -j3I_0 = 0.2647 - j0.44118 = 0.5145\angle -59.0362°$$
$$V_1 = j1.0 - jI_0 = 0.08824 + j0.8529 = 0.8575\angle 84.0938°$$
$$V_2 = -jI_0 = 0.08824 - j0.14706 = 0.1715\angle -59.0362°$$

$$\begin{matrix} \mathbf{V_a} & = \\ \mathbf{V_b} & = \\ \mathbf{V_c} & = \end{matrix} \begin{bmatrix} 1 & 1 & 1 \\ 1 & a^2 & a \\ 1 & a & a^2 \end{bmatrix} \begin{bmatrix} \mathbf{0.5145\angle -59.0362°} \\ \mathbf{0.8575\angle 84.0938°} \\ \mathbf{0.1715\angle -59.0362°} \end{bmatrix} = \begin{bmatrix} \mathbf{0.5145\angle 30.9628°} \\ \mathbf{1.3105\angle -37.2982°} \\ \mathbf{1.0517\angle -130.968°} \end{bmatrix}$$

$$(3I_0) \times R_f = (3 \times 0.1715) \times 1 = 0.5145\angle 310° = V_a \angle 310°$$

*Remarks.* We will need to be aware of how voltages change under fault conditions to successfully apply voltage relays. It is worthwhile to compare fault voltages with and without grounding with Fig. 2.3.

As you can see, the calculation of a single-line-to-ground itself is as simple as Ohms' law. It is the sequence impedance information that is hard to come by. When you do have the information you need, you must be mindful of the conditions under which the single-line-to-ground fault will be greater than the three-phase bolted fault of Example 2.1. We can express the condition mathematically as follows:

$$\text{With } I_{\text{slg}} = \frac{3E}{(Z_1 + Z_2 + Z_0)} \text{ and } I_{3\phi} = \frac{E}{Z_1}$$

dividing the right-hand term by 3 and equating denominators

$$\frac{E}{\dfrac{(Z_1 + Z_2 + Z_0)}{3}} = \frac{E}{Z_1}$$

| Type of Fault | Current Ratio* | | Voltage Ratio | |
|---|---|---|---|---|
| | L | G | L-G[†] | L-L[‡] |
| LL | 0.69–1.15 | ..... | 0.67–1.20 | 0.58–1.04 |
| SLG | 0.00–2.00 | 0.00–2.00 | 0.58–1.97 | 0.67–1.20 |
| DLG | 0.69–2.02 | 0.00–3.00 | 0.00–1.80 | 0.00–1.04[§] |

Based on $\dfrac{R_1}{X_1} = \dfrac{R_2}{X_1} = 0$ and $0 \le \dfrac{R_0}{X_1} \le \infty$

$\dfrac{X_2}{X_1} = 0.5$ to $1.5$ and $0 \le \dfrac{X_0}{X_1} \le \infty$

L = Line
G = Ground

*Reference is the three-phase short-circuit current.
†Reference is the normal line to neutral voltage.
‡Reference is the normal line-to-line voltage.
§These voltages are identical; only the line-to-ground voltage curves have been plotted.

**Figure 2.3**  Range of fault currents and voltages. Two systems of the same voltage, which, for particular fault locations yield identical results with the infinite bus fault calculation, may have radically different voltages and currents for unbalanced faults. The ratios of sequence impedances have an important bearing on many applications and may result in higher currents than for three-phase short-circuit or higher voltages than for ordinary operation. Wagner & Evans (p. 22) contains a chapter entitled "Power System Voltages and Currents Under Fault Conditions," which is replete with plots of X0/X1 versus current, or R0/X1 versus voltage for various types of faults. Some of the most useful results appear in the table in Fig. 2.3. (*Adapted from Wagner and Evans*, Symmetrical Components.)

so that the condition for $I_{slg} = I_{3\phi}$ is

$$\frac{Z_1 + Z_2 + Z_0}{3} = Z_1$$

In practice, both the single-line-to-ground fault and the double-line-to-ground fault can produce a greater fault current than the three-phase fault especially where synchronous generators have solidly grounded neutrals (or low impedance neutral impedances) and on the wye grounded side of the delta-wye grounded transformer banks of the three-phase, three core design. More on this is in Chaps. 4 and 7.

### 2.3.1  Line-to-line short-circuit current

We are now in a position to calculate another commonly occurring fault, the line-to-line fault. As long as $Z_1 = Z_2$ (which is usually the case for passive circuit elements), you may simply multiply the three-phase bolted fault short-circuit current by $\sqrt{3}/2$. In terms of Example 2.1, the line-to-line short-circuit current on the load side of the secondary breaker would be $20,886 \times 0.866 = 18,087$ A.

### 2.3.2  Voltages and currents under unbalanced fault conditions

The ranges of voltages and currents under unbalanced fault conditions are controlled principally by the ratio of $Z_0$ to $X_1$, that is, by the method of system grounding and the values of the grounding impedances. When we discuss the subject of grounding in more detail, we shall see that a classification of systems into grounded or ungrounded without further restrictions is unsatisfactory because it takes into account only the impedance between the ground and the neutral points of apparatus, instead of the total effective zero sequence impedance that includes line and apparatus impedance as well as that of grounding resistors and reactors.

The ranges of line currents, ground currents, line-to-ground voltages, and line-to-line voltages that exist on a system under unbalanced fault conditions are summarized in Fig. 2.3.

One of the most important facts brought out in this figure is that the line-to-ground voltage may rise to *twice* the normal line-to-neutral voltage, i.e., to a value somewhat greater than the normal line-to-line voltage—a fact that is not generally appreciated. It is well to note that the ratios of line current and ground current to the three-phase short-circuit current may be as great as 2.0 and 3.0, respectively, and that the ground current of a double-line-to-ground fault may be 50 percent greater than the maximum value of a single-line-to-ground fault.

According to Anderson (1973), it is usually the case that SLG is most severe, with the LLL, DLG, and LL following in that order. In general, since the DLG fault value is always somewhere in between the maximum and minimum, it is usually neglected in the distribution system fault calculations.

The faults most commonly studied in industrial and commercial protection practice are classified as shunt faults. These networks report only the Thevenin equivalents that correspond to the boundary conditions that define the type of fault. It is very important that the fault point be carefully defined and that ground or fault impedances be included (if any). There are other fault configurations (involving open phases) classified as compound faults that are commonly investigated in utility transmission short circuit studies.

The diagrams of Fig. 2.4 are adapted from Wagner and Evans, *Symmetrical Components*. The most recent, comprehensive treatment of the subject appears in Blackburn (1993).

## 2.4   Fault-Current Sources

Fault-current waveforms are far more complex than the simplified representation indicated in Fig. 1.4. The waveform in that diagram results from the superposition of several different sources, all of which involve rotating machinery, local or remote. There are two other phases involved, and this determines the RMS value of current and voltage through the first cycle and beyond. There are also asymmetries to deal with; fault currents are composed of symmetrical (steady state) and transient components.

While the RMS value of the symmetrical component may be determined from Ohm's law, the transient component can only be determined from information about the Thevenin impedance at the point of fault. It is customary to express the Thevenin impedance in terms of a ratio of reactance to resistance or X/R ratio (from $Z_{th} = R_{th} + jX_{th}$). When you superpose the symmetrical and transient components of all the sources that contribute current to a short circuit, the picture of a fault-current waveform resembles the waveforms shown in Fig. 2.4. Once again, for clarity, only one phase is shown.

One of the most thorough discussions of this subject, with oscillographs and diagrams, appears in Anderson (1973) and Beeman (1953). Just about every textbook that deals with fault analysis contains a diagram representating fault-current waveforms in a variety of detail so they will not be repeated here.

### 2.4.1   Utility contribution

The prospective MVA short-circuit contribution of the utility at your service drop is one measure of the "stiffness" of the utility system. The

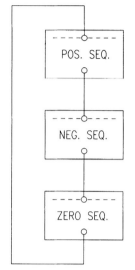

Single—Line—Ground Fault

Eq. (a) $I_f = \dfrac{3 \times E_{L\text{-}N}}{x_1 + x_2 + x_3}$

Boundary Conditions: $V_A = 0$

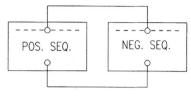

Line—to—Line Fault

Eq. (b) $I_f = \dfrac{\sqrt{3} \times E_{L\text{-}N}}{x_1 + x_2}$

Boundary Conditions: $V_A = V_B$

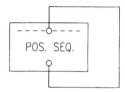

Three Phase Fault

Eq. (c) $I_f = \dfrac{E_{L\text{-}N}}{x_1}$

Boundary Conditions: $V_A = V_B = V_C = 0$

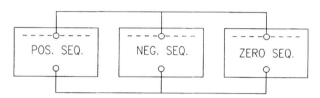

Double—Line—Ground Fault

Eq. (d) $I_f = \dfrac{3 \times E_{L\text{-}N} \times x_2}{x_1 x_2 + x_0 x_1 + x_0 x_2}$

Boundary Conditions: $V_A = V_B = 0$

**Figure 2.4** Sequence networks for most common types of faults: (a) single-line-to-ground fault, Eq. (a); (b) line-to-line fault, Eq. (b); (c) three-phase fault, Eq. (c); (d) double-line-to-ground fault, Eq. (d). In the sequence networks shown, all connections have been made at the point on the circuit where the fault occurs. The boxes represent sequence impedances that have already been reduced. Voltage source E appears in the positive sequence network. Phase A is the reference phase.

higher the MVA, the greater the available fault current. There is always some impedance in any electrical power source, and the effect of it is to reduce the amount of fault current that will flow into your switchgear. Your utility will advise the maximum available short-circuit kVA or amperes that its system can produce at your service connection. Available fault current can be stated in three ways:

- KVA (or MVA) with X/R Ratio
- Symmetrical amperes with X/R Ratio
- Maximum short-circuit in MVA plus an R + jX

The basic formula that applies is the following:

$$\text{Xpu or Rpu} = \frac{\text{Actual Ohms} \times \text{Base MVA}}{(\text{base kV})^2}$$

If your utility gives you service drop impedance information in ohms, then you simply divide the line-to-line voltage of your service drop by the ohmic data that the utility gave you to get short-circuit MVA. For a feeder whose voltage you know and whose reactance you know, you need only divide the square of the line-to-line voltage by the given impedance to get short-circuit MVA.

**For three-phase faults**

$$\text{MVA}_{sc} = \frac{\sqrt{3} \times I_{3\phi} \times kV}{1000}$$

where $I_{3\phi}$ is the total three-phase fault current in amperes and kV is the system line-to-line voltage in kilovolts. From this

$$I_{3\phi} = 1000 \ \text{MVA}_{sc} / \sqrt{3} \times kV$$

$$Z_{\text{ohm}} = Vln/I_{3\phi} = 1000 \ kV / \sqrt{3} \times I_{3\phi} = kV^2 / \text{MVA}_{sc}$$

Substituting, $\text{Zpu} = \text{MVA}_b \times Z_{\text{ohm}} / kV^2$. Therefore, the positive sequence impedance to the fault location is

$$Z_1 = \text{MVA}_b / \text{MVA}_{sc} \ \text{pu}$$

$Z_1 = Z_2$ in many situations where active sources do not dominate circuit behavior. $Z_1$ can be assumed to be $X_1$ unless X/R data are provided to determine an angle.

**For single-phase-to-ground faults**

$\text{MVA}_{slg} = $ single-line-to-ground short-circuit MVA $= \sqrt{3} \times I_{slg} \times kV / 1000$

where $I_{slg}$ is the total single-line-to-ground fault current in amperes, and kV is the system line-to-line voltage in kilovolts.

$$I_{slg} = 1000\ MVA_{slg} / \sqrt{3} \times kV$$

However,

$$I_{slg} = I_1 + I_2 + I_0 = 3V_{ln}/Z_1 + Z_2 + Z_0 = 3V_{ln}/Z_g$$

where $Z_g = Z_1 + Z_2 + Z_0$ (from classical symmetrical component equivalent circuit for single-line-to-ground fault). $Z_g = 3\ kV^2 / MVA_{slg}$ in ohms

$$Z_g = \frac{3MVA_b}{MVA_{slg}}\ pu$$

Then $Z_0 = Z_g - Z_1 - Z_2$ or in most practical cases, $X_0 = X_g - X_1 - X_2$, since the resistance is usually very small in relation to the reactance.

---

### Computing X and R of a Transformer When Only Z Is Known

From time to time you may need to enter X and R into a computer program to do a short circuit analysis. Let's say you only know that the 1000-kVA transformer impedance is 5.75 percent. To determine X and R to the input screen you must make an assumption about X/R ratio. Using the data supplied in the Appendix, you can see that for a 1-MVA transformer the typical X/R ratio is about 4.5. Use this as the X/R quantity in the following equations.

$$R = \frac{Z}{\sqrt{1 + \left(\frac{X}{R}\right)^2}}$$

$$X = R\left(\frac{X}{R}\right)$$

$$R = 1.247\ ohms$$

$$X = 5.625\ ohms$$

Be careful of the per unit ohmic values. The Z is usually given in percent of the transformer base. In the absence of specific information, most circuit analysis software use a default X/R ratio such as X/R = 30 for medium voltage circuits

---

**Example 2.3**   Working with Utility Short-Circuit Information

*Situation.*   You buy power at 34.5 kV. You are planning an expansion to your distribution network and need to determine the impedance of the utility source in order to estimate short-circuit current. The local utility gives you the following information: $MVA_{3\phi} = 679$ MVA and $MVA_{slg} = 711$ MVA on a 100-MVA base. X/R ratio is 22. You buy power at 34.5 kV.

*Requirements.*   Determine source reactance at the utility service point.

**solution**   With $MVA_b = 100$ MVA, the total reactance to a three-phase fault occurring at the service drop would be

$$Xpu = MVA_b/\text{Utility Fault Capability}$$

$$= 100/679 = 0.1473 \ \Omega \ pu$$

$$Rpu = 0.1473/22 = 0.0067 \ \Omega \ pu$$

$$Zpu = 0.1473 + j0.0067 = 0.1474 \angle 26.04° \ \Omega$$

The sequence impedances for a single-line-to-ground fault occurring at the service drop would be

$$X_1 = X_2 = 100/679 = 0.1473 \ pu$$

$$X_g = 3 \times 100/711 = 0.4219 \ pu$$

$$\text{Since } X_0 = X_g - X_1 - X_2$$

$$X_0 = 0.4219 - 0.1473 - 0.1473 = 0.1273 \ pu$$

---

## Impedances of Single-Phase Transformers in Three-Phase Transformer Banks

For three-phase type transformer units, the nameplate specifies the impedance in percent on the three-phase kVA rating and the kV line-to-line voltages. Where several kVA ratings are specified, the impedance of the *ambient* rating (without fans or pumps) should be used.

For individual single-phase transformers, that are in common use in electrical customer services, the transformer impedance is normally specified on the single-phase kVA and the rated winding voltages of the transformer. When three such units are used in *three-phase* systems, then the three-phase kVA and the line-to-line kV bases are required. Thus, when three individual single-phase transformers are connected in the power system the individual nameplate percent or per unit impedance will be the leakage impedance, but on the three-phase kVA, base and the system line-to-line kV (Stevenson, 1982).

---

It is important to remember that all fault current—even the fault current that appears at your service drop—is generated by rotating machinery. The utility contribution to a fault as shown in Fig. 2.5 is ultimately fault current generated by remote generators or motors. Now, let us consider fault current from local rotating machines. Our strategy will be to continue to determine the subtransient impedance of the device in order to apply Ohm's law on a per unit basis.

### 2.4.2   Generator contribution

Under fault conditions, generator reactances change. These changing reactances are responsible for the changing current waveform that we see for generators and motors in Fig. 2.5. Field excitation voltage and speed remain substantially constant within the first few cycles after the fault. The expression of the variable reactances at any instant after a fault involves a multiterm formula with time as the independent variable. A more complete discussion than we have space for here may be found in Bergen, and in Blackburn. For our purpose, it will be sufficient to divide steady-state kVA by subtransient reactance to estimate generator fault current contribution.

---

### Reactances of Rotating Machines

- The direct-axis *sub*transient reactance $X_d''$ is the apparent reactance of the stator winding the instant the short-circuit occurs. $X_d''$ usually determines the current magnitude during the first cycle after the fault occurs.
- The direct-axis *trans*ient reactance $X_d'$ is the apparent initial reactance of the stator winding when only the field winding is considered (damping or amortisseur windings ignored). The direct-axis transient reactance determines short-circuit current magnitude in the range up to 30 to 130 cycles depending upon the design of the machine.
- The synchronous reactance $X_s$ is the apparent reactance that determines the current flow when a steady state condition is reached. It is not effective until several seconds after the short-circuit occurs. Most fault protection devices, such as circuit breaker or fuses, operate before steady state conditions are reached. Therefore, generator synchronous reactance is seldom used in calculating fault currents for the application of these devices.

For any rotating machine the amount of short-circuit current may be estimated from the following equation:

$$I_{sc} = \frac{\text{Motor/Generator FLA} \times 100}{\%X_d''}$$

The restrictions on its application are similar to the restrictions we placed upon the application of the "infinite bus" short-circuit calculation.

---

#### 2.4.3    Motor contribution

The fault-current contribution of induction motors results from generator action produced by mechanical inertia driving the motor after the fault occurs. Because protective devices require at least a quarter cycle (and up to 30 cycles and beyond), the motor is a generator until the device opens the circuit.

**Synchronous motors.**    Synchronous motors supply current to a fault in much the same manner as synchronous generators. This fault current diminishes as the motor slows down and the motor field excitation decays. The variable reactance of a synchronous motor is discussed in much the same terms as the reactances of generators. Numerical values of the reactances, also given in per unit on the machines' base, will usually be different for the motor mode of operation than in the generator mode of operation. An examination of Table A.4 "Modification Factors for Momentary and Interrupting Duty Calculations" reveals that in the case of an interrupting calculation (and assuming a synchronous plant generator), the reactance in the motor mode of operation is 1.5 times greater than the reactance in the generator mode of operation.

**Induction motors.**    In contrast to the synchronous motor, the field flux of the induction motor is produced by induction from the stator rather than from a direct-current field winding. This flux decays on removal of source voltage resulting from a fault, so that the contribution of an induction motor drops off at a rapid exponential rate. As a consequence, induction motors are assigned only a reactance that is equivalent to the synchronous machine subtransient reactance $X_d''$. This reactance will be about equal to

$$X_d'' = \text{FLA/LRA} = \text{Motor FLA/Motor LRA}$$

and hence the initial fault-current contribution will be about equal to the full voltage starting current of the particular kind of machine. However, the resistance in small motors may be large enough to cause significant decay in their fault-current contribution before the first peak of fault current is experienced.

Wound-rotor induction motors normally operate with their rotor rings short circuited and will contribute fault current in the same manner as a squirrel cage induction motor. Occasionally, large wound-rotor motors are operated with external resistance maintained in their rotor circuits. This gives them short-circuit time constants that are so low that their fault contribution is insignificant. However, a specific investigation should be made before neglecting the contribution from wound-rotor motor.

In general, then,

$$I_{sc} = \frac{\text{Motor FLA} \times 100}{\%X_d''}$$

A running induction motor will, when a fault is applied at its terminals, dissipate the electrical energy stored in its magnetic field into the fault in accordance with the short-circuit time constant of the motor and the external system impedance between the motor and the fault. Induction-motor short-circuit time constants by themselves are short (1 to 3 cycles). Typically, external system impedance results in overall time constants of less than eight cycles. Consequently, induction motors are not considered in the calculation of short-circuit fault currents for time-overcurrent relays that operate in three cycles or more. It should be noted that these current values of short-circuit current are expressed in symmetrical amperes and that, after three cycles, any dc transient current has decayed to zero.

Induction motors 250 hp and above are considered to be large motors, motors 50 to 250 hp are considered to be medium, and motors 50 hp and below are considered to be small (Huening, 1982).

If it is not practical to calculate fault current for each small motor below 50 hp separately, it is usual practice to combine them all at each location. In the case of low-voltage motors, consider all motors at each location that may be running even though at partial load. ANSI standards permit neglecting motors less than 50 hp when considering medium-voltage circuit breaker applications.

To estimate the short-circuit contribution of induction machines 50 hp and below, assume that the motor contribution to the fault current will be *four times* the full-load running current of each motor. This simplification is possible because of the relatively rapid decay small induction motor short-circuit current we see in Fig. 2.5. This simplification is the only situation in which load current is used as the basis for estimating short-circuit current.

A typical design situation arises in which you might need to estimate the interrupting duty required of a unit substation breaker without knowing the particulars about the nature of the loads connected to it. A *worst case* estimate might proceed as follows:

- For a 480/277-V substation, assume the connected motor load equals 100 percent of system kVA, that is, 1 hp = 1 kVA. This is reasonable because 480-V substations are commonly designed to feed heavy motor loads exclusively. Then *four times* normal load current for which the substation main breaker and bus structure are sized would be added to the short-circuit current available on the secondary side of the transformer (typically 12 to 25 times normal load current). A contribution of four times rated current corresponds to first cycle impedance of 1/4 = 0.25 per unit based on motor rated kVA and voltage.

- For a 208/120-V substation, assume that motor load is 50 percent of the system kVA. Again, with 1 hp = 1 kVA, *two times* normal load current for which the substation main breaker and bus structure are sized would be added to the short-circuit current available on the secondary side of the transformer (typically 12 to 25 times normal load current). This is reasonable because 208/120-V substations commonly carry a mixture of lighting and motor loads.

Table A.3, "Multipliers for Source Short-Circuit Current Contributions," summarizes all the foregoing information. Huening (1982) contains a detailed discussion of induction motor contribution to a fault. Example 2.5 will put all this information together for the case of a three-phase bolted fault.

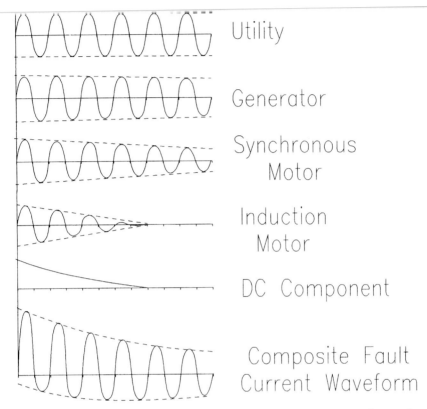

**Figure 2.5** Schematic representation of fault current waveforms—one phase only. The lower the X/R ratio, the sooner fault current will decay. Said another way: the higher the X/R ratio, the longer it will take fault current to decay to a level that is within the interrupting rating of the protective device. The waveforms shown indicate that short-circuit current from sources located remote from the point of fault have slower ac current decay compared to local sources. This must be taken into account where the calculated short-circuit current is adjusted to reflect the system X/R ratio at the point of fault. The dc component of fault current will paralyze any (ac) transformer; thus, when system X/R ratios change radically over the life of a power circuit, attention must be given into the input/output characteristics of the instrument transformers.

## 2.5   The Fault Power Method of Short-Circuit Calculation

The so-called MVA method, applied by many experienced protection specialists who have mastered per unit and ohmic methods, employs fault *powers* to compute short-circuit currents. We have already used the method to some extent in the earlier examples involving utility short-circuit contributions, and we develop it at length here. The beauty of it lies in the fact that you use circuit element information in almost the same form that it appears on nameplates with almost no ohmic or per unit conversions. It is applied by calculating the admittance of each component of a circuit with its own infinite bus in terms of MVA. We can then combine pairs of circuit element MVAs in series and parallel according to the product-over-sum rule from basic network theory for combining the admittance and/or impedance of two circuit elements. Series MVA combinations are computed like impedances in parallel. Parallel MVA combinations are computed like impedances in series. In the following development, super-scripts will indicate a specific circuit element and/or iterative fault power, and subscripts will indicate a positive, negative, or sequence fault power.

$$\text{Series: } MVA^1 \text{ and } MVA^2 = \frac{MVA^1 \times MVA^2}{MVA^1 + MVA^2}$$

$$\text{Parallel: } MVA^1 \text{ and } MVA^2 = MVA^1 + MVA^2$$

The MVA method is best illustrated by example. Given the circuit of Fig. 2.6a, we want to determine the three-phase fault current at F:

**Step 1: Convert all circuit elements to short-circuit MVAs.**    The short-circuit MVA of each circuit element is equal to its MVA rating divided by its own per unit impedance or reactance.

$$\text{For the utility: } 1000/1 = 1000 \text{ MVA}$$

$$\text{For the utility feeder: } (34.5)^2/5 = 238 \text{ MVA}$$

$$\text{For the utility transformer: } 15/.07 = 214$$

$$\text{For the customer motor: } 5/0.2 = 25$$

**Step 2: Combine MVAs.**    Since we have more than two circuit elements, we perform the calculations iteratively.

$$MVA^1 \text{ and } MVA^2 = \frac{1000 \times 238}{1000 + 238} = 192 \text{ MVA}$$

Let 192 MVA be the *new* MVA$^1$. Then

$$MVA^1 \text{ and } MVA^3 = \frac{192 \times 214}{192 + 214} = 101 \text{ MVA}$$

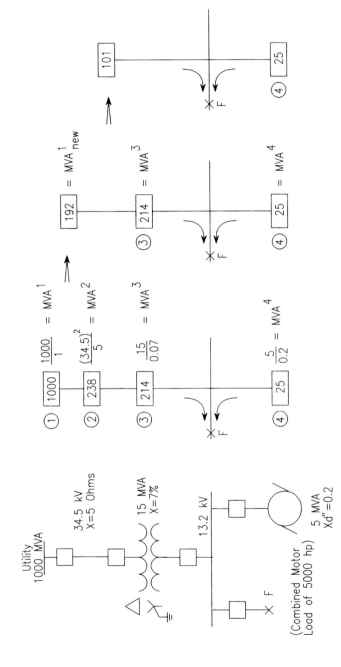

**Figure 2.6a** MVA Method Example. In applying this method we need to be mindful of the meaning of superscripts and subscripts. MVAs with subscripts indicate sequence fault powers. MVAs with superscripts indicate iteration number.

Going this far with the calculation will allow you to determine the three-phase fault current at the 13.8 bus without motor contribution.

**Step 3: Convert MVA to symmetrical fault current**

$$I_1^f = \frac{101 \times 1000}{\sqrt{3} \times 13.2} = 4430 \text{ A (LLL } without \text{ motor contribution)}$$

We assume that fault current on the load side of the feeder breaker is the same as the fault current on the bus. But we want the fault on a feeder with a motor back-feeding fault current into it so we must combine the MVAs in parallel by adding them thus

$$\text{MVA}^1 + \text{MVA}^4 = 101 + 25 = 126$$

$$I_{sc} = \frac{126 \times 1000}{\sqrt{3} \times 13.2} = 5526 \text{ A (LLL } with \text{ motor contribution)}$$

At this point, it should be obvious how quickly the method may be applied, and, because of its iterative nature, how it lends itself to a computer solution. The method does not require a common MVA base as required in per unit methods. It is not necessary to convert impedances from one voltage to another as required by the ohmic method. Best of all, you do not need to deal with anything but large whole numbers.

You may apply the method to compute single-line-to-ground, double-line-to-ground, and other shunt faults as well. Referring again to the circuit of Fig. 2.6a, we know that the fault at the 13.2-kV bus is 126 MVA. Assuming that the positive and negative impedances are equal, we can say that the positive sequence fault power is equal to the negative sequence fault power, so that

$$\text{MVA}_1 = \text{MVA}_2 = 126$$

Now a single-line-to-ground fault on the 13.2-kV bus would have only the transformer and the motor contributing to zero sequence MVAs. The delta connection on the secondary of the transformer blocks any zero sequence power contribution from the utility. Therefore, our MVA block diagram may be redrawn to indicate flow of zero sequence fault power only. See Fig. 2.6b.

$$\text{MVA}_0^{trans} = \text{MVA}_1 = \text{MVA}_2 = 214$$

Assuming that the transformer zero sequence reactance is equal to its positive and negative sequence reactances is another common assumption in industrial practice. The zero sequence reactance of a

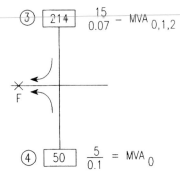

$$\text{MVA}_0^{\text{mot}} = \frac{5}{0.1} = 50 \text{ MVA}$$

**Figure 2.6b** Zero sequence fault power flow.

motor is about *one half* its positive zero sequence reactance (Ref. IEEE Red and Buff Books). Therefore

$$\text{MVA}_0^{\text{mot}} = \frac{5}{0.1} = 50 \text{ MVA}$$

The total zero sequence fault power then is equal to the sum of the motor and transformer fault powers because of the parallel connection.

$$\text{MVA}_0^{\text{trans}} + \text{MVA}_0^{\text{mot}} = 214 + 50 = 264$$

The single-line-to-ground fault power is obtained by the upper connection diagram shown in Fig. 2.6c. This connection diagram follows from symmetrical component theory. Since these are three branches in parallel, the simplest approach is to take one branch out of the circuit and solve for its MVA value and then multiply the value by 3.

$$\text{MVA}_1 \text{ and MVA}_2 = \frac{126 \times 126}{126 + 126} = 63 \text{ MVA}$$

$$\text{MVA}_{1,2}^{\text{new}} \text{ and MVA}_0 = \frac{63 \times 264}{63 + 264} = 51 \text{ MVA}$$

$$\text{MVA} = 3 \times 51 = 153 \text{ MVA}$$

$$I_{\text{slg}} = \frac{153 \times 1000}{\sqrt{3} \times 13.2} = 6710 \text{ A (SLG with motor contribution and no neutral impedance)}$$

If you wanted to limit the flow of ground-fault current with an impedance of, for instance, 1.0 ohm, you could reformulate the network of Fig. 2.6c with a reactor MVA of

$$\frac{(13.2)^2}{1.0} = 174 \text{ MVA}$$

Then

$$\text{MVA} = 3 \times \frac{(51 \times 174)}{(51 + 174)} = 118 \text{ MVA}$$

$$I_{slg} = \frac{118 \times 1000}{\sqrt{3} \times 13.2} = 5189 \text{ A (SLG with motor contribution and neutral impedance)}$$

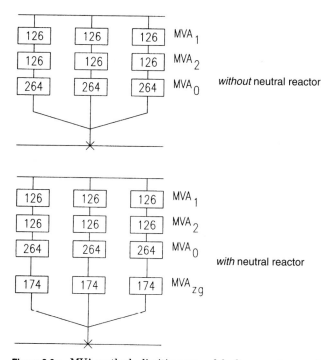

**Figure 2.6c**  MVA method—limiting ground fault-current example.

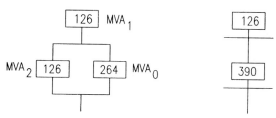

**Figure 2.6d**  MVA method—double-line-to-ground fault-current example.

You can work this problem in reverse, specifying a value of single-line-to-ground current (to the same value as three-phase fault current, for instance) in order to specify the fault-current-limiting reactor in ohms.

In Fig. 2.6$d$ you can compute double-line-to-ground fault current from the following formulas:

$$MVA_{x1} = \frac{MVA_1 + (MVA_2 + MVA_0)}{MVA_1 \times (MVA_2 + MVA_0)}$$

and

$$MVA_{x0} = MVA_{x1} \times \frac{MVA_0}{(MVA_0 + MVA_2)}$$

So that the MVA sequence connection diagram can reduce to Fig. 2.6$d$ and that

$$MVA_2 + MVA_0 = 126 + 264 = 390$$

$$MVA_1 = \frac{126 \times 390}{126 + 390} = 96 \text{ MVA}$$

$$MVA_0 = 96 \times \frac{264}{264 + 126} = 66 \text{ MVA}$$

$$MVA_f^{dlg} = 3 \times MVA_{x0} = 3 \times 66 = 195 \text{ MVA}$$

$I_f^{dlg} = 8550$ A (LLG fault with motor contribution and no neutral impedance)

You can come up with numbers for the determination of interrupting duty for the very common main-tie-main switchgear arrangement with all fault-current sources going full tilt by proceeding in the same manner we have shown and applying the delta-wye/wye-delta conversion formula indicated in App. item A.5.1. A more complete discussion of this method appears in Yuen (1974) and IEEE Brown Book (1990) along with a comparison of the results of the MVA method with the ohmic and per unit methods. It may be applied to far more complex circuits with reasonable accuracy and lends itself to an iterative algorithm that can be programmed into a handheld computer if you do not have access to a workstation-based short-circuit analysis program. Although you need to be careful about the reasonableness of your assumptions about sequence impedances and do not need to have detailed information about fault-current decrements, the example given should make clear the MVA method's effectiveness in terms of speed, accuracy, and economy.

## 2.6   Very Low Level Fault Currents

Because of the nature of their operation, overcurrent devices have a singular difficulty in sensing low-level fault currents compared to, for example, protective devices based on the differential principle. Our strategies for discriminating among overcurrent devices is complicated by the fact that when fault current is low, no device may sense that anything is wrong.

Minimum fault currents exist in a situation such as the short circuit of (initially) only one turn of a transformer winding or, more commonly, during periods of maximum system impedance. These conditions may include minimum generation, equipment outages on the supplying utility, equipment outages within the industrial plant, minimum load periods during which induction and synchronous machines are disconnected from lines, high impedance type of faults such as may occur in low-voltage systems or as turn-to-turn faults in motors or transformers. Protective device selectivity based only on maximum fault considerations may fail under minimum conditions.

One of the classical failure modes of an electrical distribution circuit is the arcing fault. The arcing fault originates in the failure of insulating materials, and it can sneak up on you, burning (or "tracking") slowly enough so that you can hardly distinguish the fault current from normal load current. Arcing phase-fault currents are found to be as low as 38% of the bolted fault current calculated for the same circuit (Dunki-Jacobs, 1972.) Arcing ground-fault current can be much smaller. The magnitudes of this current may be so low that the time-delay characteristics of the overload protective devices confuses the low-magnitude arcing fault with the moderate overload or temporary inrush current and allows it to persist for lengthy periods. For example, a 200 percent overcurrent on a fuse might require 200 s or more before the fuse opens.

For faults electrically "close" to the source secondary switchgear, the bolted single-line-to-ground fault current is roughly equal to the three-phase bolted fault current. Therefore, probable arcing fault current is about four to eight times the source transformer full-load current (Smith, 1982). That would mean that for our canonical 1000 kVA, 480-V building level unit substation with a full-load current of 1201 A, arcing faults within in the unit substation switchgear itself will be about 4800 to 9600 A. In practice, you would probably want to set the pickups on your protective devices much lower than this. In fact, the NEC is very specific about the pickup, time delays, and coordination margins between ground fault protective devices. More on this is in Chap. 4.

## 2.7   Single-Phase Short-Circuit Calculations

We will be able to apply the same principles for single-phase calculations that we have applied for three-phase calculations but with some important differences. We will have to compensate for the effect of single-phase impedance, and, where the single-phase system is derived from a three-phase utility source, the single-phase impedance may be normalized with respect to the three-phase base. Other considerations:

- The impedance of the ground return path in single-phase faults varies widely. The neutral conductor may not carry part of the current, or there may be a grounding conductor in parallel with the metallic raceways. Therefore, it is recommended practice to carry out short-circuit calculations by assuming that the impedance of the neutral, the ground conductor, or both, is equal to the impedance of the line conductor. This assumption errs on the side of safety.

- Impedance components using the three-phase calculations are line-to-neutral values for sources, devices, and conductors. When we combine them, we do so vectorially. In single-phase faulted circuits current flows "out" in one path and "returns" in the other. Impedances are in series so impedances must be *doubled*.

A complete discussion of this topic appears in Farrell and Valvoda (1992). Some manufacturers have developed tables to assist you in the selection of devices for the protection of single-phase transformers. See General Electric (1981).

## 2.8   Computer Modeling of Fault Dynamics

Your approach to the application of computer software to calculate short-circuit current will be influenced somewhat by whether you use it to study only your own power system or whether you use it to study many different systems. A consulting engineer who has "cross-system" experience with computer software may have a very different point of view than the senior engineer of a large industrial distribution system who only knows his or her own system in great detail, especially with respect to the relative accuracy of input data and the interpretation of the output data produced by computer software. The best short-circuit studies are produced from situations in which there is a judicious combination of the talents of the people who know the power system under study and the talents of people who are proficient in preparing actual field data for use by computer software.

Contemporary software goes beyond the enterprises calculating short-circuit currents, motor-starting voltage drops, and the like into actual circuit *management*. The same input data that you use to compute short-circuit currents can be used to keep track of protective devices and calibration schedules, fuse inventory control, thus an integrated package.

There are three ANSI-IEEE standards that apply to the calculation of fault current values that are used for the application of switchgear and related protective devices.

- ANSI C37.13 applies to low-voltage switchgear.

- ANSI C37.5 applies to medium- and high-voltage switchgear rated at *total* short-circuit current levels.

- ANSI C37.010 applies to medium- and high-voltage switchgear rated at *symmetrical* short-circuit current values.

These standards require analysis of both the three-phase and single-line-to-ground faulted networks.

### 2.8.1  Input data

Electrical power engineers need only number the buses in some kind of reasonable, hierarchical manner and put reasonable data in the input forms to run a multibus short-circuit study. There are on-line libraries of NEMA and IEEE standards even for this.

It is easy to underestimate the time it takes to pull together field data that you can have some confidence in. For example, you may never really know if the cable orientation of an underground circuit is such that it has the same impedance throughout its length. To a larger extent than you might have imagined, your input data will have to be verified by the reasonableness of your output data.

### 2.8.2  Output

In the previous section, we indicated that many faults will dampen over time if the fault-current source impedance changes over the life of the fault. The transition from momentary to interrupting fault current is of particular interest, and this takes place from the first half cycle to about the fifth cycle (the typical clearing time of a medium-voltage circuit breaker). There are some situations in which it would be helpful to know what fault currents might be farther out, particularly, if we want to coordinate backup protection so that backup protection is enabled only after fault current has decayed below a particular value. Some software manufacturers provide fault-current figures out to 99 cycles. Let us have a look at two crude intervals that should be of particular concern to us. The reader should be aware that ANSI, IEEE, DIN, and IEC each has a slightly different methodology for calculating fault currents in each of the following intervals that is the result of different assumptions. The following is adapted from the IEEE Red and Buff Books.

**0 to 3 cycle maximum.**  The purpose of studying this interval is to determine the maximum currents to which instantaneous, extremely short-time relays or direct-acting trips should respond. The calculation procedure to determine these relay operating fault currents calls for the representation of all rotating equipment (generators and motors) by their equivalent subtransient reactance $X_d''$. Passive system components (transformers, reactors, cables, regulators, busway) are represented by either their reactances or impedances, depending on the calculating technique employed.

If you are using electromechanical relays, it is important to take into account the fact that instantaneous relays of the plunger and clapper designs respond to dc as well as ac current. It is therefore necessary to account for the dc transient current that is usually present when an ac fault is initiated.

**3 to 60 cycle maximum.**  The purpose of studying this interval is to determine the maximum current to which time-overcurrent relays operating in approximately 3 cycles (0.05 s) or more should respond.

It should be noted that the magnitude of the 0 to 3 cycle short-circuit current, calculated previously, is controlled by the subtransient reactances $X_d''$ of synchronous machines (generators and motors) as well as the contribution of induction motors, which is determined by the subtransient reactance of the induction motors (or locked rotor impedance).

The reactance of a synchronous machine varies from the low value of subtransient reactance to the high value of synchronous reactance $X_d''$ in accordance with a short-circuit decrement curve. From the subtransient reactance value, reactance increases rapidly in the first few cycles to a value identified as a transient reactance. The composite effect of the individual decrements of the synchronous machines is sufficiently complex to preclude a simple analytical study. Suffice it to say that for calculating the 3 to 60 cycle short-circuit fault current, a resolution using subtransient generator reactances $X_d''$ and transient synchronous motor reactances $X_d'$ will result in a conservative or realistic value. Still another aspect accounts for a further reduction in short-circuit current.

Knowledge of maximum and minimum short-circuit currents are necessary to set instantaneous tripping correctly. Computing maximum short-circuit levels at all points in a system is easier than computing the minimum short-circuit level.

**0 to 3 cycle minimum.**   The purpose of these studies is to determine the minimum short-circuit feeder currents to which instantaneous, extremely short time relays, or direct-acting trips should respond. The calculation procedure is the same as that in maximum except that the minimum systems operating conditions must be assumed (maximum impedance)

**3 to 60 cycle minimum.**   The purpose of these studies is to determine the minimum short-circuit fault currents to which time-overcurrent relays operating in approximately 1 s or less should respond. The calculation procedure is the same as that indicated above except that minimum systems operating conditions must be assumed (maximum impedance)

On industrial power systems supplied by a utility, the extended-time short-circuit current is essentially the same as the 3 to 60 cycle maximum short-circuit current. When local generators contribute to a large fraction of the short-circuit current, however, a severe decrement of short-circuit current may occur. An extended-time short-circuit study may be particularly useful in evaluating the operation of generator overcurrent relays with voltage restraint.

In magnitude, the extended-time short-circuit current is the steady-state current after all transients have disappeared and is a function of the generator excitation ceiling voltages and the generator synchronous reactances.

In addition to the output indicated in Fig. 2.7, a very useful tool is to have an entire branch contribution map. The unit substation motor backfeed situation of Example 2.5 is a small, but pertinent example of the effect of branch contributions. Every branch will have a different current contribution into the fault. Fault analysis software will compute distribution factors for branch contributions and will locate them on a map for you to compare with protective device withstand and interrupting ratings.

Every program has a slightly different manner in which input data is prepared. You may well have to deal with phase-fault and ground-fault situations differently (as you should). Some software manufacturers even include a dc short-circuit program to help you protect the power circuits that actually protect power circuits.

## 2.9   Overview of Methodologies

Whether or not we apply computer software to calculate short-circuit current, we must not forget that the results are only estimates because both the numerator and the denominator of our Ohm's law formulation ($I_{sc} = 1.0/Z_{pu}$) are only estimates. Unless you actually measure the sequence impedances, your answer depends on the industry accepted "best guess"

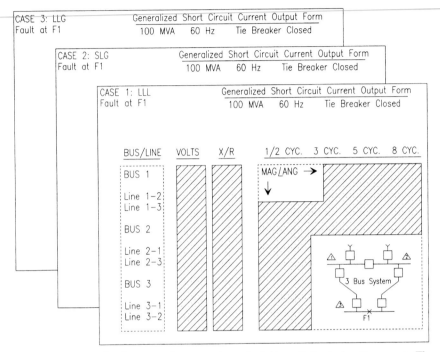

**Figure 2.7**  Generalized output for computer calculation of short-circuit current. The input and output data files for an electrical power network need to be nurtured over weeks, months, and years. Allow yourself one hour of time for seek and/or confirm impedance information for every bus and/or branch record. It is helpful when output displays at least some of the input information. A complete RMS short-circuit report should include the following results for both phase and ground fault situations: instantaneous peak asymmetrical, instantaneous dc component, instantaneous ac symmetrical component (1/2 cycle), 1-3-5-8 cycle RMS asymmetrical, steady state ac symmetrical component. There has been some effort in the industrial and professional organizations to standardize computer software input/output data preparation methodologies.

in the IEEE and/or manufacturer tables. We have assumed that voltage remains at 1.0, but actually voltage is fairly dynamic and, systemwide, is likely to be 95 to 105 percent of its nominal value when the fault occurs (except at the fault itself). Even if our models and assumptions were correct, the sensing elements in our protective devices cannot reproduce voltage and current waveforms with 100 percent accuracy, and the matter of accuracy itself is dependent on the level of fault current.

In low-voltage systems, the error in omitting resistances of all parts of the circuit except cables and small ampere rating buses is usually less than 5 percent. However, the resistance of cable circuits is often the predominant part of the total impedance of a cable. When appreciable lengths of cable are involved in the circuit through which short-circuit current flows in a low-voltage system, the resistance *and* the reactance of the cable circuits should be included in the impedance diagram (Beeman, 1953). In medium-voltage systems, we can usually get away with ignoring resistance.

The flow charts for the E/Z and E/X fault analysis appear in Figs. 2.8 and 2.9. They are a handy guide for the key decisions that need to be made when following industry standards for fault calculations. The reader is encouraged to consult with the references indicated in the Appendix. There is a great deal of literature of short-circuit current calculations, and we can only give you a flavor of the quantitative results and qualitative reasons we need to carry on with the business of coordinating overcurrent protective devices. Figure 2.10 should give you a better feeling for how we shall use the numbers we calculate by longhand or read from a computer printout. The axis that plots current indicates protective device sensitivity. The axis that plots time indicates delay. As the inverse characteristic implies, there will always be a tradeoff between sensitivity and time delay.

To achieve selectivity between two protective devices in series, their time-current characteristic must maintain a minimum coordination time over the entire range of possible fault currents. The available fault current at the downstream device determines the upper limit of the range of coordination. With the same pickup settings and time-current characteristic curves, the effect of higher fault currents is to increase the range of coordination, raise the time delay, and slow down the overall tripping times.

To a great extent, your choice of short-circuit calculating method will depend on the application principles that govern the proper use of a given protective device. For example, for the application of low-voltage circuit breakers and both medium- and low-voltage fuses to motor circuits, only first cycle calculations are necessary. The background of circuit breaker-rating structures as well as the characteristics of short-circuit currents must be understood to enable you to select the proper rotating machine reactances and multiplying factors for the dc component to determine the short-circuit current magnitude for checking the momentary and interrupting duties.

The rating structures of all protective devices are designed to tell the application engineer how the device will perform under conditions where the short-circuit varies with time. The particulars involved is the subject of Chap. 3.

## 2.10  Solved Problems

**Example 2.4**  Plant Generation in Parallel with Utility

*Situation.*  An institutional heating plant can use by-product steam to generate electricity for its own electrical load, as shown in Fig. 2.11a–c.

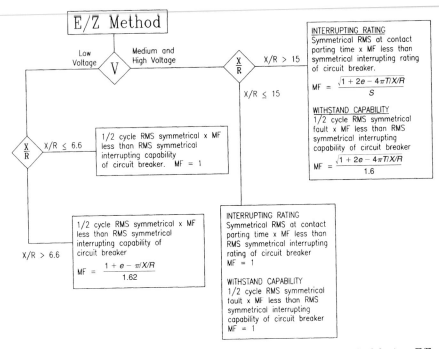

**Figure 2.8** Flow chart for IEEE, ANSI, and IEC fault analysis methodologies, E/Z Method. User notes: (1) for E/Z Method, refer to *IEEE Transactions on Industry Applications,* Jul/Aug 1985; (2) $T$ = contact porting time in cycles, $S$ = capability factor; (3) flowchart adapted from *EDSA User Manual,* courtesy of EDSA Micro Corporation.

*Requirements.* Calculate three-phase and single-line-to-ground fault levels with and without plant generation for a fault on the load side of a critical distribution feeder. The distribution feeder is connected to the same bus as the generator and utility service tie.

**solution**    First establish base values. With $MVA_b$ = 100 MVA = 100,000 kVA and Vpu = 1.0

$$I_b = 100{,}000/(\sqrt{3} \times 4.16 \text{ kV}) = 13{,}389 \text{ A}$$

Next convert the impedances.

For the utility: Zpu = 100/1000 MVA = 0.1 pu

For the service transformer: $(7/100)(100/10) = 0.7$ pu

For the generator: $Z_{1,2}$pu $= (0.1)(100/5) = 2.0$ pu

$$Z_0 \text{pu} = (0.05)(100/5) = 1.0$$

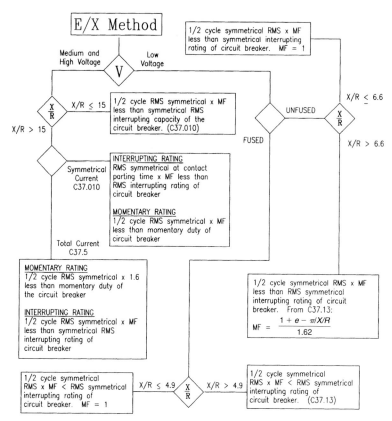

**Figure 2.9**   Flow chart for E/X Method. User notes: (1) for E/X Method, use X″ from ANSI C37.13; (2) Flow chart adapted from *EDSA User Manual,* courtesy of EDSA Micro Corporation. MF = 1 unless indicated otherwise.

*Without Plant Generation*

*Three-phase bolted fault*

$$Ipu = 1.0/Zpu = 1.0 / (0.1 + 0.7) = 1.25$$

$$I_{3\phi} = 13,389 = 1.25 = 16,736 \text{ A}$$

*Single-line-to-ground fault.*   (From second equation, p. 43.) Since the transformer is solidly grounded $Z_g = 0$. Taking $Z_1 = Z_2 = Z_0 = 0.7$ pu for the transformer

$$Z_1 = Z_2 = 0.1 \text{ and } Z_0 = 0 \text{ for the utility}$$

$$Ipu = 3(1.0)/(0.1 + 0.7) + (0.1 + 0.7) + (0.7) = 1.304$$

Then

$$I_{slg} = 13,389 \times 1.304 = 17,464 \text{ A}$$

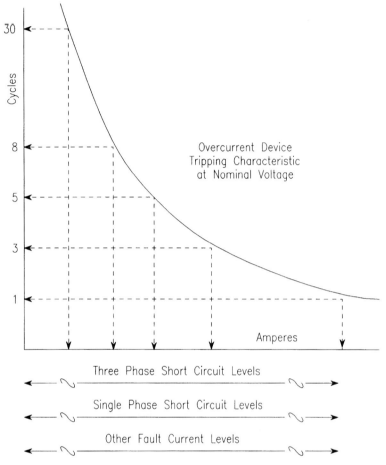

**Figure 2.10** How short-circuit numbers will be applied to the constraints of an overcurrent coordination study. The principle that underlies all decisions in electric circuit protection involves a choice between switchgear with the mechanical strength to withstand available fault current during the clearing interval or switchgear that is smart enough to interrupt the circuit before fault current ever reaches the mechanical (thermal) limits of the switchgear.

*With Plant Generation*

*Three-phase bolted fault.* Now the source impedances are in parallel. For the two branches:

$$Zpu = (0.8)(2.0)/(2.8) = 0.5714$$

$$Ipu = Vpu/Zpu = 1.0/(0.5714) = 1.75 \text{ A}$$

$$I_{3\phi} = 13,389 \times 1.75 = 23,343 \text{ A}$$

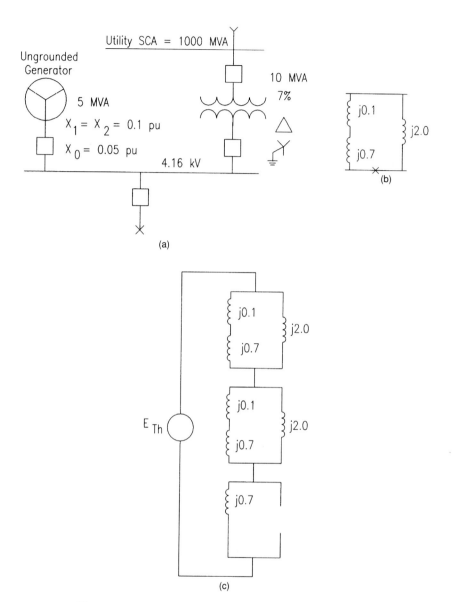

**Figure 2.11**  Plant generation in parallel with utility: ($a$) one-line diagram for Example 2.4; ($b$) impedance network for three-phase bolted fault of Example 2.4; ($c$) impedance network for single-line-to-ground fault of Example 2.4.

*Single-line-to-ground fault.* We need the classical single-line-to-ground sequence network. The generator is ungrounded so that there is an open circuit in the zero sequence network.

$$Z_1pu = (0.8)(2.0)/(2.8) = 0.5714$$

$$Z_2pu = 0.5714$$

$$Z_0pu = 0.7$$

$$Ipu = (3 \times 1.0)/(0.5714 + 0.5714 + 0.7) = 1.628$$

$$I_{slg} = 1.628 \times 13,389 = 21,797 \text{ A}$$

**Example 2.5**  System Short-Circuit Study Using Complex Reduction Method

*Situation.*  Given a utility service interconnect with customer-owned generation in Fig. 2.12.

*Requirements.*  Calculate three-phase fault magnitude at bus 2.

solution  Normalize all source and load impedances on a base of 100 MVA. For a three-phase bolted fault, we only need positive sequence impedances. For a fault at bus 2, construct a Thevenin equivalent network as shown in Fig. 2.13a and b.

**Step 1:  calculate the per unit impedance values**

*Utility*

$$Z_{ut} = MVA_b/kVA_{source}$$

$$= 100,000/400,000 = 0.25 \text{ p.u.}$$

$$\text{Given } \frac{X}{R} = 7$$

$$\text{Then } \Theta = \tan^{-1}\left(\frac{X}{r}\right)$$

$$Xpu = Z_{ut} \times \sin(\Theta)$$

$$= 0.24749 \ \Omega$$

$$Rpu = Z_{ut} \times \cos(\Theta)$$

$$= 0.03536 \ \Omega$$

*750-hp Induction Machine*

$$Z_{machine} = Z_m \times MVA_b/kVA_{motor}$$

$$\text{Assuming 1 hp = 1 kVA then}$$

$$Xpu = X_d'' \times MVA_b/kVA_{motor}$$

$$= 0.250 \times (100,000/750)$$

$$= 33.3333 \ \Omega$$

$$\text{Since } \frac{X}{R} = 20$$

$$Rpu = X_d''/(X/R) \times MVA_b/kVA_{motor}$$

$$= (0.25/20) \times (100,000/750)$$

$$= 1.6666 \ \Omega$$

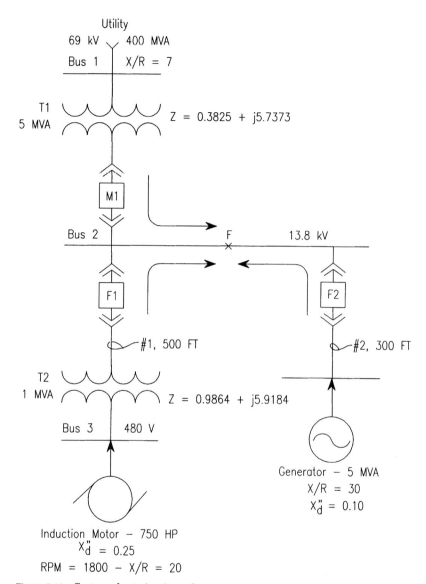

**Figure 2.12**   System short-circuit study.

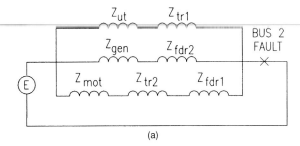

(a)

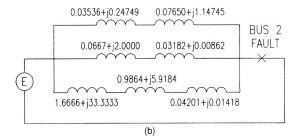

(b)

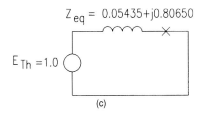

(c)

**Figure 2.13**  (*a*) Equivalent network for fault at Bus 2; (*b*) normalized impedances for fault at Bus 2; (*c*) Thevenin equivalent circuit.

$$5\text{-}MVA\ Generator$$

$$Z_{machine} = Z_m \times MVA_b/kVA_{gen}$$

$$Xpu = X_d'' \times MVA_b/kVA_{gen}$$

$$= 0.100 \times (100,000/5000)$$

$$= 2.0000\ \Omega$$

$$Rpu = X_d''/(X/R) \times MVA_b/kVA_{gen}$$

$$= (0.100/30) \times (100,000/5000)$$

$$= 0.0667\ \Omega$$

*5-MVA Transformer*

$$\text{Zpu} = (Z\%_{\text{tr}} \times \text{MVA}_{\text{b}})/(100 \times \text{kVA}_{\text{tr}})$$

$$\text{Xpu} = 5.7373 \times (100{,}000/(100 \times 5000))$$

$$= 1.14745 \ \Omega$$

$$\text{Rpu} = 0.3825 \times (100{,}000/(100 \times 5000))$$

$$= 0.07650 \ \Omega$$

*1000 kVA Transformer*

$$\text{Zpu} = (Z\%_{\text{tr}} \times \text{MVA}_{\text{b}})/(100 \times \text{MVA}_{\text{tr}})$$

$$\text{Xpu} = 5.9184 \times (100{,}000/(100 \times 1000))$$

$$= 5.9184 \ \Omega$$

$$\text{Rpu} = 0.9864 \times (100{,}000/(100 \times 1000))$$

$$= 0.9864 \ \Omega$$

*Feeder #1*

$$\text{Zpu} = Z_{\text{f}} \times \text{MVA}/(\text{kV11}^2 \times 1000)$$

$$R_\Omega/1000 \ \text{ft} = 0.1600 \qquad X_\Omega/1000 \ \text{ft} = 0.0540$$

$$\text{Xpu} = (500/1000) \times 0.0540 \times 100{,}000/(13.8^2 \times 1000)$$

$$= 0.01418 \ \Omega$$

$$\text{Rpu} = (500/1000) \times 0.1600 \times 100{,}000/(13.8^2 \times 1000)$$

$$= 0.04201 \ \Omega$$

*Feeder #2*

$$\text{Zpu} = Z_{\text{f}} \times \text{MVA}_{\text{b}}/(\text{kV}_{\text{ll}}^2 \times 1000)$$

$$R_\Omega/1000 \ \text{ft} = 0.2020 \qquad X_\Omega/1000 \ \text{ft} = 0.0547$$

$$\text{Xpu} = (300/1000) \times 0.05407 \times 100{,}000/(13.8^2 \times 1000)$$

$$= 0.00862 \ \Omega$$

$$\text{Rpu} = (300/1000) \times 0.2020 \times 100{,}000/(13.8^2 \times 1000)$$

$$= 0.03182 \ \Omega$$

*Remark.* There is nothing straightforward about getting accurate feeder impedances. Among the usual considerations involving the kind of conductor, insulation, and shielding, feeder impedances are affected by orienation among themselves and among other conducting materials. You must start with manufacturer data and make adjustments according to the kind of cable you have and the orientation of the phases.

**Step 2: network reduction for fault at bus 2.** Combine the series impedances shown in Fig. 2.13*b*. The equivalent circuit after combining the series impedances in shown in Fig. 2.13*c*.

**Tabulation of Impedance Values**

| Element | Rpu | Xpu |
|---------|---------|-----------|
| $Z_{ut}$ | 0.03536 | j0.24749 |
| $Z_{motor}$ | 1.6667 | j33.3333 |
| $Z_{gen}$ | 0.0666 | j2.0000 |
| $Z_{tr1}$ | 0.07650 | j1.14745 |
| $Z_{tr2}$ | 0.98639 | j5.91836 |
| $Z_{fdr1}$ | 0.04201 | j0.01418 |
| $Z_{fdr2}$ | 0.03182 | j0.00862 |

Now combine the parallel impedances to determine the Thevenin equivalent impedance. (The arithmetic of combining the parallel impedance values is left to the reader.)

$$Z_{thev} = 0.05435 + j0.80650 = 0.8083\angle 86.14°$$

**Step 3:   calculate the three-phase fault current**

$$I_{base} = 100,000/(13.8 \times \sqrt{3})$$

$$= 4183.8 \text{ base A}$$

$$I_f = (1.0/Z_{thev}) \times I_b$$

$$= 4183.8/0.8083$$

$$= 5176 \text{ A}$$

This is the *symmetrical* fault current at the instant the fault occurs. To determine asymmetrical fault current, we can use X/R = 0.80650/0.05435 = 14.84 and look up an asymmetry factor in Table A.2. We can see from our table that this X/R ratio falls between 16.623 and 14.251 in the short-circuit X/R ratio column. The $M_m$ asymmetry factor associated with this is about 1.525 thus yielding an estimate of 1.525 × 5176 = 7896 A asymmetrical three-phase bolted short circuit current. This is what we should use to program our instantaneous devices.

*Remarks.*   A more rigorous solution would involve

- the application of different impedances as the fault progressed beyond t = 0.0
- separate reduction of R and X networks
- utility short-circuit current contributions kept separate from local sources such as on-site generators

The foregoing discussion is sufficient to get us started coordinating overcurrent devices. The Appendix contains a crib sheet containing the most commonly used per unit and fault power network conversion formulas. From now on, we will assume that you will be able to determine short-circuit current by longhand, by computer, or by a combination of each. We will have a chance to refine our calculations and their interpretation in the application situations that lie ahead.

# Bibliography

Anderson, P. M., *Analysis of Faulted Power Systems,* Iowa State University Press, Ames, Iowa, 1973.

Beeman, *Industrial Power Systems,* McGraw-Hill, New York, 1953.

Bergen, A., *Power Systems Analysis,* Prentice-Hall, New York, 1986.

Blackburn, J. L., *Protective Relaying: Principles and Applications,* Marcel Dekker, Inc., New York, 1987.

Blackburn, J. L., *Symmetrical Components for Power Systems Engineering,* Marcel Dekker, Inc., New York, 1993.

Dunki-Jacobs, J. R., "The Effects of Arcing Ground Faults on Low Voltage System Design," *IEEE Transactions on Industry Applications,* May/June 1972.

Farrell, George, and Frank Valvoda, "Single-Phase Short Circuit Calculations: A Step-by-Step Guide," *Consulting-Specifying Engineer,* March 1992.

General Electric Company, "Short-Circuit Current Calculations," Application Information GET-3550F-0489 BLC, 1981.

Huening, Jr., Walter C., "Calculating Short-circuit Currents with Contributions from Induction Motors," *IEEE Transactions on Industry Applications,* March/April 1982.

*SKM Comparison of Calculation Procedures for Fault Analysis,* SKM Systems Analysis, Calif.

Smith, R. L., "Practical Low Voltage Equipment Ground Fault Protection for Solidly Grounded Systems with Wye-connected Source Transformers," *IEEE Transactions on Industry Applications,* March/April 1982.

Stevenson, Jr., W. D., *Elements of Power Systems Analysis,* 4th ed., McGraw-Hill, New York, 1982.

Wagner, C. F., and R. D. Evans, *Symmetrical Components,* original edition published in 1933 by Westinghouse Electric Corporation. Reprinted in 1982 by Kriegar Publishing, Malabar, Fla.

Yuen, Moon H., "Short Circuit ABC—Learn It in an Hour, Use It Anywhere, Memorize No Formula," *IEEE IAS,* March/April 1974.

## General references

Calabrese, G. O., *Symmetrical Components Applied to Electric Power Networks,* The Ronald Press Company, New York, 1959.

Farrell, George, and Frank R. Valvoda, *Protecting Electrical Systems,* series published in *Consulting-Specifying Engineer,* 1990–1992. Series available in reprint.

"Guide for Calculation of Fault Currents for Application of AC High Voltage Circuit Breakers Rated on a Total Current Basis," *ANSI/IEEE Standard C37.5-1979,* IEEE Service Center, 1979.

St. Pierre, Conrad, "Sample System for Three-Phase Short-Circuit Calculations," *IEEE Transactions on Industry Applications,* March/April 1990.

*A Simple Approach to Short-Circuit Calculations,* Bussman Division of Cooper Industries, Bulletin EDP-1.

Simpson, Ronald H., "Multivoltage Short-Circuit Duty Calculation for Industrial Power Systems," *IEEE IAS,* vol. 1A-22, March/April 1986. The author of this paper was recognized by the IEEE for distinguished work on this topic. This paper is among the most recent papers that pull together all of the common assumptions made by practicing industrial electrical power system designers. The paper provides a detailed flowchart for making decisions regarding momentary and interrupting specifications for protective devices.

Stagg, and El-Abiad, *Computer Methods in Power Systems Analysis,* McGraw-Hill, New York, 1968.

*Westinghouse Consulting Guide.* Front-end material contains practical examples of short-circuit calculations.

## Further reading

Bengiamin, N. N., and F. H. Holcomb, "PC-based Power Systems Software: Comparing Functions and Features," *IEEE Computer Applications in Power,* Jan. 1992. This article discusses the theory behind power flow and short-circuit calculations and tabulates comparisons among the most recent versions of 10 different software packages.

Clarke, Edith, *Circuit Analysis of AC Power Systems,* General Electric Co., Schenectady, N.Y., 1943, 1953.

Hartman, "Understanding Asymmetry," *IEEE Transactions on Industry Applications,* July/Aug. 1985.

Reichenstein, Hermann W., et al., "Relationship of X/R, Ip, and I'rms to Asymmetry in Resistance/Reactance Circuits," *IEEE Transactions on Industry Applications,* March/April 1985.

Tylavsky, Daniel J., "Improvements in Fault Current Calculation Techniques for DC Systems," *IEEE Transactions on Industry Applications,* Sept./Oct. 1985. This paper will give you some insight into the methods of performing short-circuit calculations for the dc power systems common in the mining industry. Much of the theory and modeling techniques will be familiar to the reader who has some feeling for how lumped parameter models have been developed for ac power systems. From this basis some advancements are proposed regarding calculation methodologies for short-circuit contributions from dc rectifiers.

# 3

# Design and Application Principles

## 3.1 Foreword

In this chapter, we discuss protection design from the device application standpoint. This approach is common in a great deal of the literature on power system protection: a protective device in search of a circuit. In Part 2 of this text, we shall approach the subject of protection design from the circuit point of view. From the circuit point of view, we shall think in terms of finding which protective device applies to our circuit rather than the other way around. It is natural to begin with the fuse since the fuse was the first protective device invented.

The following is a passage from the patent Thomas Edison was granted in 1880 for a device called a "Safety Conductor for Electric Lights"

> The safety device consists of a piece of very small conductor . . . [having] such a degree of conductivity as to readily allow the passage of the amount of current designed for its particular branch. If an abnormal amount of current is diverted through a branch, a small safety wire becomes heated and melts away, breaking the overloaded branch circuit. It is desirable, however, that the few drops of molten metal resulting therefrom should not be allowed to fall upon carpets and furniture and also that the small safety conductor should be relieved of all tensile strain; hence I enclose the safety wire in a jacket or shell of nonconducting material.

Edison's fuse was a one-shot device that could not distinguish between an overcurrent condition that was persistent in nature and one that was not. The early fuse was refined for special applications that now number in the hundreds. It is no exaggeration to say that protective devices have genealogies of their own. Refer to App. Figs. A.11 and A.12 for a look at fuse families.

Circuit breakers were developed because electricity users needed a device that would open all three phases during the same cycle and would not destroy itself after operation. However, at the low and medium voltages, circuit breakers do not interrupt current as fast as fuses. Circuit breakers also require more space. On the other hand, fuses are limited in the amount of current they can carry at certain voltages. And even though they may be relatively inexpensive and easy to install, they cannot be tested as easily as a circuit breaker; you can imagine that circuit breaker testing is very important in, for instance, nuclear power plants.

The choice between a fuse or a circuit breaker is a choice we will face throughout this text and is a choice encountered all throughout the literature on electrical circuit protection. The role that agencies such as ANSI, IEEE, NEMA, IEC, and others have on the testing and rating of protective devices will be an element that will have to be considered in a great many application situations. Standards established by such agencies have facilitated the application of electrical equipment, but we must remember that the standards may only establish minimums (not the norm) and that many situations require the application of principles that exceed minimum requirements.

## 3.2   Device Selection Considerations

When you need to choose between the specification of a fuse or a circuit breaker, your decision will most likely be affected by

- how much money is in the budget you have to work with
- what kind of switchgear is already installed
- what the local utility wants
- user operating requirements and access
- (architectural) space

It cannot be said that fuses are superior to circuit breakers or vice versa, especially when all of the foregoing may preclude the construction or renovation of a new facility on the basis of economics alone. If the choice is between reducing the electrical construction budget or not having a facility at all, the electrical equipment industry has more than enough safe, economic options from which you may choose.

### 3.2.1   Nominal voltage and continuous current ratings

Your decision making should begin with consideration for the voltage at which the device will be applied and how much current the device must carry under normal operating conditions. Voltage *ratings* are specified to equal or exceed actual system voltages. Circuit breakers or fuses rated 120/240 V are suitable for systems having no more than 120 V phase-to-ground. A similar condition exists for circuit breakers rated at 277/480 V. Circuit breakers or fuses having a single voltage rating such as 250 or 600 V can be safely applied on systems having up to that voltage phase-to-phase or phase-to-ground. Circuit breakers and fuses should never be applied on systems having any voltage in excess of their voltage rating. The same applies for protective devices operating at medium voltage (and is particularly important for proper application of medium-voltage, current-limiting fuses). In the case of medium-voltage breakers, ANSI C37.06 requires that special consideration be given to the ratio of rated maximum voltage to the lower limit of operating voltage. The required symmetrical and asymmetrical interrupting capabilities vary in inverse proportion to the operating voltage. A so-called "K-Factor" is determined and, for operating voltages below 1/K times rated maximum voltage, the required symmetrical interrupting capability of the circuit breaker shall be equal to K times the rated short-circuit current.

The NEC defines a continuous load as a load in which the maximum current is expected to continue for 3 hours or more. The distinction between continuous and noncontinuous becomes particularly important in the design of motor circuits. (See also "Duty" in NEC Art. 100 for the distinctions made among intermittent, periodic, short-time, and varying duty.)

Some rules regarding continuous current ratings are as follows:

- UL standards require that a fuse be able to continuously carry 110 percent of its rated current at an ambient temperature of 25°C.

- UL standards require that a circuit breaker be able to carry 100 percent of its rated current at an ambient temperature of 40°C.

The NEC Sec. 220-10(b) requires that the rating of the overcurrent device for a feeder supplying a continuous load shall not be less than 125 percent of the continuous load current. In effect, this means that the protective device cannot be continuously loaded beyond 80 percent (= ampacity/1.25) of its rating. There is an exception, however; where UL has approved overcurrent protective devices for operation at 100 percent of their rating, then the feeder can be loaded to 100 percent of its ampacity rating.

Known examples of protective devices that have UL approval for 100 percent continuous operation are:

- Some large bolted pressure switches rated above 600 A that use class L fuses

- Some molded case breakers of the type that are assembled as an integral unit in a supporting and enclosing housing made of insulating materials.

- Some low-voltage power circuit breakers of the draw-out heavy steel frame type that handle large blocks of power.

### 3.2.2   Protective device withstand ratings

*All* properly applied electrical equipment is designed to *withstand* faults. Only some electrical equipment is designed to interrupt fault current. The distinction between the two is commonly confused in everyday conversation about electric power circuits. The notion of fault withstand and the necessity for a withstand rating is discussed early in the NEC but only implicitly.

> *110-10. Circuit impedance and other characteristics.*   The overcurrent protective devices, the total impedance, the component short-circuit withstand ratings, and other characteristics of the circuit to be protected shall be so selected and coordinated as to permit the circuit protective devices used to clear a fault without the occurrence of extensive damage to the electrical components of the circuit.

The NEC requires two principal short-circuit ratings for system components up to 600 V: withstand and interrupting. Noninterrupting components have only withstand ratings. Devices that interrupt current, especially overcurrent operated protective devices, may have one or both. Devices such as circuit breakers have the mechanical capability of closing (and latching) into an already faulted circuit. Proper application of the NEC virtually guarantees coordination of withstand capabilities in circuits less than 600 V.

### 3.2.3   Protective device interrupting ratings

Interrupting ratings are also discussed early in the NEC. NEC 110-9 states:

> Equipment intended to break current at fault levels shall have an interrupting rating sufficient for the system voltage and the current which is available at the line terminals of the equipment.
> Equipment intended to break current at other than fault levels shall have an interrupting rating at system voltage sufficient for the current that must be interrupted.

NEC Art. 100 defines interrupting rating as:

> The highest current at rated voltage that a device is intended to interrupt at standard test conditions.

FPN: Equipment intended to break current at other than fault levels may have its interrupting rating implied in other ratings, such as horsepower and locked rotor current.

The *interrupting rating* is the current that the breaker can interrupt successfully at a specified voltage. This current is defined as the RMS value of short-circuit current (including asymmetry due to the dc component) that is flowing one-half cycle after the short circuit occurs. It is often called the *momentary rating,* and it is this current to which instantaneous devices respond. In three-phase circuits, it is the average of the RMS value's asymmetrical current in the three phases. This value has been termed the average RMS asymmetrical current (sometimes referred to as the three-phase, average total RMS current).

- The standard interrupting duty cycle of a circuit breaker with *instantaneous tripping* for fault currents consists of an opening operation, followed after a 15-s interval by a close/open operation.

- The standard interrupting duty cycle of a circuit breaker with *delayed tripping* for fault currents consists of an opening operation, followed after a 15-s interval by a close/open operation, the tripping being delayed by the associated tripping devices.

At the end of any performance at or within its interrupting rating, the circuit breaker should be in substantially the same mechanical condition as at the beginning and should be capable of withstanding rated voltage in the open position and of carrying rated current at rated voltage for a limited time (but not necessarily without exceeding the rated temperature rise).

Breakers equipped with trip units that provide time-delay tripping for fault currents must not be applied on systems in which the available fault current can exceed the short time rating because the breaker can exceed the short time rating and because the breaker may not be capable of closing into and latching against the mechanical forces developed by the fault current when it exceeds the short-time rating of the breaker.

Never assume that the physical interchangeability of a protective device means that the fuse or circuit breaker has the same interruption capacity. The same 1000-A device may be available with two different interrupting capacities. This is done in the spirit of giving system designers economic options. The price we pay for these choices, however, comes in terms of the attention we must pay to the details of testing and rating protective devices. Refer to Love (1991) for an engaging discussion of this subject.

Application of power circuit breakers for switching duty may require derating of the circuit breaker in any of the fundamental operating characteristics that have been cited in the foregoing discussion. Particular attention should be given to breakers intended for use in capacitor, reactor, and/or arc furnace switching. Automatic reclosing and fast bus transfer will pose additional items for concern. You may still be able to select a circuit breaker based on mainstream criteria, but you should confirm with the manufacturer that circuit breakers' evaluated capabilities will meet the needs of your application. In many cases, you may simply need to select the next higher circuit breaker. In some cases, you may need to select another manufacturer.

## 3.3  Asymmetry in Protective Device Ratings

If faults did not have power factors, then we would not have to figure X/R ratios into our decisions about which device to pick from a manufacturer's catalog at all. We could simply apply a protective device anywhere on a circuit on the basis of its symmetrical interrupting rating and move on to the next design problem. But faults *do* have power factors that are well below normal steady-state operating power factors, and X/R ratios vary from place to place on a circuit. Let us state a general principle and then move on to specifics.

*As long as the X/R ratio at a given point in a circuit is equal to 15 or less, the asymmetrical short-circuit duty never exceeds the symmetrical short-circuit duty by a margin greater than that by which the circuit breaker's asymmetrical short-circuit capability exceeds its symmetrical capability.*

This statement says a great deal about the response of the circuit at the fault point and the industry standards that apply to a protective devices applied at low or medium voltage.

In systems up to 600 V, device-interrupting ratings usually are stated in symmetrical amperes. Devices are selected with the interrupting ratings equal to or greater than a system's available symmetrical short-circuit current. This is not always a safe practice, nor does it meet the intent of the NEC.

In systems over 600 V, knowledge of the X/R ratio can give us some feeling for the extent to which fault current will decay within the three- to five-cycle time frame. If the X/R ratio will cause fault current to dampen to a value below the rating of the breaker, then we have some assurance that the faulted circuit may be interrupted safely.

The subject has been the focus of considerable study over the years. Electrical system power factors usually exceed those of the test circuits, and device-interrupting ratings usually may be selected on the basis of available symmetrical current as long as the circuit is not too reactive.

Short-circuit power factors lower than those applied in the UL test circuits most often are caused by equipment such as current-limiting reactors, current-limiting busway, high-impedance transformers, large induction motors, and on-site generation at utilization voltage. X/R ratios may reach 20:1 in circuits containing such equipment (a short-circuit power factor of 5 percent). The highest short-circuit X/R ratio applied in any of the 600-V-or-less test circuits is 6.6 (a short-circuit power factor of 15 percent).

Many authorities recommend that when available short-circuit current exceeds 75 percent of a device's symmetrical interrupting rating, the available asymmetrical current should be determined.

The calculation of symmetrical short-circuit current duties is normally sufficient for the application of circuit breakers and fuses over 1000 V because they have published symmetrical current-interrupting ratings. The ratings are based on the first-cycle symmetrical current, determined at one-half cycle after fault inception, and incorporate an asymmetrical capability as necessary for a circuit X/R ratio of 6.6 or less (short-circuit power factor of 15 percent or greater). A typical system served by a transformer rated 1000 or 1500 kVA will usually have a short-circuit X/R ratio within these limits. For larger or multitransformer systems, it is advisable to check the X/R ratio; if it is greater than 6.6, the circuit breaker or fuse application should be based on asymmetrical current limitations.

*Interrupting and Short-Time Ratings.*   Interrupting ratings for low-voltage circuit breakers are normally stated in *symmetrical* amperes. The ratings are based on the assumption that the X/R ratio of the typical low-voltage system is 6.6. As indicated, the RMS value of the asymmetrical current one-half cycle after the fault occurs is 1.33 times the RMS value of the symmetrical fault current on a per-phase basis. However, on three-phase circuits, if the fault occurs at the instant of time that causes the maximum offset of current in one phase, then because of the 120° phase relationship, the other two phases cannot also experience maximum offsets. Therefore the asymmetrical rating of a low-voltage breaker is *approximately* 1.17 times its symmetrical rating (or an average of one-half the 1.33). Breakers originally rated only in asymmetrical amperes and standard values, such as 25,000 or 50,000, were selected. The symmetrical ratings are based on these values and therefore become 22,000 or 42,000 A, and so on. When you specify interrupting capacities of circuit breakers, you should give some thought to whether the X/R ratio at the point of application will remain below 15.

Table A.2 is a tabulation of asymmetry factors keyed to X/R ratios. Table 3.1 is a tabulation of asymmetry factors keyed to the type of protective device.

**TABLE 3.1    Summary of Protective Devices and Their Ratings**

| A.F. | Protective device | X/R | Operating time | Ratings |
|---|---|---|---|---|
| LV $M_a$ | Molded Case bkrs | 6.6 | ½ cycle | SI, ASI |
| LV $M_a$ | Power bkrs | 6.6 | ½ cycle | SI, ASI |
| LV $M_m$ | Fuses | 6.6 | ½ cycle | SI, ASI |
| MV $M_m$ | Air bkrs | 10–20 | 3–8 cycles | C&L, SI |
| MV $M_m$ | Vacuum bkrs | 10–20 | 3–8 cycles | C&L, SI |
| MV $M_m$ | Fuses | 10–20 | ½ cycle | SI, ASI |

SI = Symmetrical Interrupting, ASI = Asymmetrical Interrupting, C&L = Close and Latch.
A.F. (Asymmetry Factor) = $I_{asymm}/I_{symm}$.
$M_m$ = Maximum single-phase RMS current at ½ cycle.
$M_a$ = Average three-phase RMS current at ½ cycle.

## 3.4    Fuse Application Principles

In general, the voltage rating of a fuse can be higher but never lower than the system voltage. If you find yourself in a situation in which the system voltage is around 40 percent of the fuse voltage rating, you should consult with the manufacturer to determine if you have all the application information you need to make the appropriate specification. The manufacturer may well offer a fuse closer to your system voltage that you do not know about.

The voltage rating of a fuse is a function of its capability to open a circuit under an overcurrent condition. Its voltage rating determines the ability of the fuse to suppress the internal arcing that occurs after a fuse link melts and an arch is produced. If a fuse is used with a voltage rating lower than the circuit voltage, arc suppression will be impaired and, under some fault current conditions, the fuse may not clear the overcurrent safely. For example, conventional current-limiting fuses have an arc voltage at rated interrupting capacity of three times fuse voltage rating. If the basic impulse level of the switchgear components is adequate to withstand the arc voltage, the higher-voltage-rated fuse may be used.

### 3.4.1    Low-voltage fuses

A low-voltage fuse of any labeled voltage rating will always perform satisfactorily on lower-service voltages. For example, a 600-V class fuse will work just as well at 250 as at 480 V. The continuous current rating of a fuse should be selected so that it clears only on a fault or an overload and not on current inrush.

You should not assume that a lower ampere rating of a fuse necessarily means better protection. For example, a 225-A time-delay Class K5 fuse appears to offer better short-circuit protection than, say, a 400-A non-time-delay Class K1 or Class J fuse. In this particular case, the converse is true (Paape, 1976). You need to look at the manufacturer's time-current characteristics of the fuse in order to determine the suitability of the fuse for your application. If you compare the time-current characteristic curves of the Class K and Class J fuses you will see that "better protection" has a different meaning in different regions of the time-current plot. In general, the nominal rating of a fuse refers to the asymptotic value of current to which the minimum melting threshold "converges." An overcurrent that is sustained just below the minimum melting threshold will remain infinitely long—never actually converging, never actually opening the fuse. Ambient temperatures and types of enclosures affect fuse performance and should be considered.

**Fuse short-time rating.**   Industry standards also specify maximum operating times at certain overload values such as 135 and 200 percent of rating and for time-delay qualification, minimum opening time at a specific overload percentage. Within these parameters and from various other overcurrent test data, manufacturers construct time-current curves. Normally, such curves are based on available RMS currents 0.01 s and above, and on either the average melting, minimum melting, or total clearing time.

**Fuse let-through considerations.**   In applications involving high available fault currents, the operating characteristics of the current-limiting fuse limits the actual current that is allowed to flow through the circuit to a level substantially less than the prospective maximum. The peak let-through current of a current-limiting fuse is the instantaneous peak value of the current though the fuse during fuse opening. The let-through $I^2t$ of a fuse is a measure of the thermal energy developed through the entire circuit during fuse opening. The let-through $I^2t$ of a fuse is a measure of the thermal energy developed through the entire circuit during clearing of the fault. Both values are important in evaluating fuse performance and can be determined from peak let-through and $I^2t$ curves supplied by the manufacturer. A let-through current value considerably less than the available fault current will greatly reduce the magnetic stresses (which increase as the square of the current) and thus reduce fault damage in protected equipment. In some cases, it becomes possible to use circuit elements with withstand

and interrupting ratings less than the maximum fault current available. You can do this if the fault is cleared extremely quickly.

The low peak let-through current and $I^2t$ levels can be achieved with current-limiting fuses because of their extremely fast (often less than one-quarter cycle) speed of response when subjected to high fault current. But peak let-through values alone cannot determine the comparable effectiveness of current-limiting fuses. The product of the total clearing time and the effective value of the let-through current squared $I^2t$, or thermal energy, should be considered as well.

The melting $I^2t$ of a fuse does not vary with voltage. However, arcing $I^2t$ is voltage-dependent and the arcing $I^2t$ at 480 V, for example, will not be as great as that at 600 V (Fig. 3.1).

**Fuse series ratings.** Fuses are commonly applied on the power source side of a circuit breaker in order to increase the circuit breaker's interruption capacity. Although the proper selection of a fuse to protect the circuit breaker, starter, or cable circuit will generally prevent equipment failure during a fault condition, some apparatus design practices allow damage to bimetals, contacts, and other parts. Unless the combination has been specifically tested and rated as a unit, the application of a fuse of a given interrupting rating in a switch or other fusible device does not confer that rating on the equipment involved. A switch, for example, might not withstand the let-through energy of a current-limiting fuse during certain fault-current conditions. When a combination rating is not available, the rating of the fuse or the device, whichever is less, should be applied.

### 3.4.2   Single-element low-voltage fuses

Single-element fuses have a high-speed response to overcurrent and provide security in the protection of nonmotor loads. If you applied a single-element fuse to a motor load, the circuit would operate normally as long as the motor inrush current did not exceed the fuse rating.

The NEC refers to single-element fuses as "non-time-delay fuses" and states in Table 430-152 that they should not be sized with ratings in excess of 300 percent of the full-load current of the motor. However, Exception No. 2 in Art. 430-52 permits ratings to be increased up to 400 percent of full-load current. The same problem of nuisance openings could occur where single-element fuses are applied in other inductive load applications such as transformers or solenoids.

### 3.4.3   Dual-element low-voltage fuses

The use of dual-element fuses with two distinct series-connected sections that provide instantaneous for short-circuits and another time-

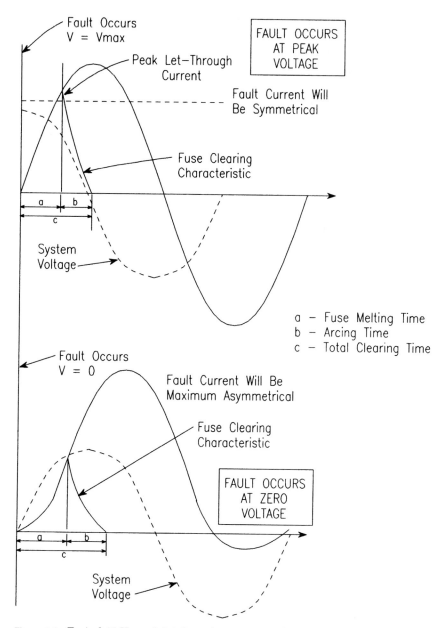

Fault Occurs
V = Vmax

FAULT OCCURS
AT PEAK
VOLTAGE

Peak Let–Through
Current

Fault Current Will
Be Symmetrical

Fuse Clearing
Characteristic

a  b

c

System
Voltage

a – Fuse Melting Time
b – Arcing Time
c – Total Clearing Time

Fault Occurs
V = 0

Fault Current Will Be
Maximum Asymmetrical

Fuse Clearing
Characteristic

FAULT OCCURS
AT ZERO
VOLTAGE

a  b

c

System
Voltage

**Figure 3.1** Typical 60-Hz peak let-through current as a function of available RMS symmetrical current. The instantaneous value of fault current has no physical meaning but it can be calculated to indicate an absolute maximum value and the nature of current decay. In order to calculate this maximum fault current, it is assumed that the instant of fault occurs when the current wave is going through the zero point. This gives the maximum value of the decaying dc component. It will then take ½ cycle for the current wave to assume its maximum value. Thus, the value of fault current at the ½ cycle represents the actual maximum total asymmetrical RMS value.

delayed operation for normal loads may not always be acceptable in an industrial environment because of the lengthy downtime associated with replacing a fuse. However, an opened fuse provides more incentive to determine the cause of a fault than a circuit breaker.

### 3.4.4  Low-voltage current-limiting fuses

The clearing time of a current-limiting fuse is on the order of one-quarter cycle. These are among the fastest clearing devices available (some specialty fuses will interrupt at a nominal one-eighth cycle). When applying current-limiting fuses in compliance with the NEC, there shall be no mistake of inserting a non-current-limiting fuse into a current-limiting fuseholder. A fuseholder that will take only Class R, H, or K fuses will take only Class R, H, or K fuses.

Class R low-voltage fuses are available up to 600 A at 250 or 600 V. They provide current limitation on the order of 200,000 A.

Class H fuses have a much reduced current-limiting capability on the order of 10,000 A.

Class K fuses have varying degrees of current limitation somewhere between these extremes (on the order of 50,000 A).

The damaging effects of the high-magnitude ground faults, phase-to-phase faults, three-phase faults, and phase-neutral fault can be reduced substantially by the use of current-limiting overcurrent devices. These devices reduce both the peak let-through current and the time of opening once the current is sensed. For example, a ground fault of 20,000 A will open a current-limiting fuse in less than one-half cycle. In addition, the peak let-through current is reduced to a value much less than 20,000 A.

The increasing proportion of loads that are comprised of power diodes, silicon-controlled rectifiers, and other semiconductor devices (uninterruptible power supply, or UPS, systems, ac and dc solid-state motor drives, and the like) require overcurrent protection suited to circuit elements with relatively low short-circuit withstand capabilities and would be damaged by low and moderate through-fault currents. The method of coordinating these fuses with the semiconductor is identical to the method we apply in any other coordination situation except that the semiconductor fuse curves lay differently on the log-log paper and the application voltages are a little different.

For example, given that a manufacturer's data sheet indicates a silicon-controlled-rectifier withstand is 1000 $A^2$s on a system of 480 V with 12,000 A available at the load terminals, you would find that one manufacturer's FBP 60 fuse, applied at 500 V, would protect the SCR since the clearing $I^2t$ let-through is 760 $A^2$s at the load terminals (Crnko, 1979).

### 3.4.5  Medium-voltage fuses

Application voltage, continuous current rating, and interrupting capacity are the principal characteristics of medium-voltage power fuses, whether the fuse is a current-limiting or non-current-limiting (expulsion) type fuse. There are tradeoffs involved in the proper application of either. For example, the current-limiting fuse has comparatively high interrupting capacity; however, the range of voltages for which it may be applied properly is much more limited than an expulsion fuse. An expulsion fuse may be applied over a greater range of voltages than a current-limiting fuse but has somewhat lower interrupting capacity.

There are tradeoffs between continuous current ratings and interrupting capacities as well. For example, current-limiting fuses work well for overcurrent protection on systems with normal continuous currents up to about 200 A. However, the higher the continuous current, the larger the fuse requirement and, consequently, the longer it takes to interrupt. This increase in fuse opening time permits the fault current to rise to potentially damaging levels and therefore limits the fuse to applications to below 200 A at some voltage levels. Still, fuses open in fractions of a cycle and are ideal for situations in which a distribution network grows incrementally because fuses require comparatively little space.

Unlike most low-voltage fuse time-current characteristic curves that are represented on one sheet of log-log paper, the time-current characteristics of medium-voltage power fuses require two separate sheets of log-log paper (sometimes printed in separate colors), either of which represent the following:

*Minimum melt curve.*   The minimum melt curve of a fuse is a plot of the minimum time versus current required to melt the fuse link.

*Total clearing curve.*   The total clearing curve is a plot of the maximum time versus current required to melt the fuse link and extinguish the arc.

**Expulsion type.**   Expulsion fuses designed to be applied above 600 V are commonly called fuse cutouts or power fuses. Expulsion fuses have a nice bend in the middle range of their time-current characteristic tripping curve that makes it easier to coordinate them with inverse relays with a smooth time-current characteristic. This type of fuse is generally applied in utility distribution system cutouts or disconnect switches but may be applied in customer-owned service equipment as well.

In general, the fuse cutouts are selected based on the following data:

- The type of system for which they are selected, e.g., overhead or underground, delta or grounded-wye system

■ The maximum available fault current at the point of application

■ X/R ratio at the point of application

Many manufacturers prepare their (symmetrically rated) cutout application tables on the basis of assumed maximum X/R ratios.

In 1951, a joint study by the EEI and NEMA established standards specifying preferred and nonpreferred current ratings for fuse links of distribution fuse cutouts and their associated time-current characteristics in order to provide interchangeability for fuse links. The reason for stating certain ratings to be preferred or nonpreferred is based on the fact that the ordering sequence of the current ratios is set up so that a preferred size fuse link will protect the *next higher* preferred size.

These same standards also classify the fuse links as type K (fast) and type T (slow). The difference between these two fuse links is in the relative melting time, which is defined by the speed ratio as

$$\text{Speed ratio} = \frac{\text{melting current at 0.1 s}}{\text{melting current at 300 or 600 s}}$$

Here, the 0.1 and 300 s are for fuse links rated 6 to 100 A, and the 0.1 and 600 s are for fuse links rated 140 to 200 A. Therefore the speed ratios for type K and type T fuse links are between 6 and 8, and 10 and 13, respectively.

It is important to realize that the operating principle of expulsion-type fuses is chemical in nature. Gases are released rapidly during the interruption period and, unless equipped with silencing attachments, the operation can be quite noisy. When applied in metal clad switchgear enclosures, you need to follow manufacturer recommendations that are designed to prevent phase-to-phase flashovers between internal live parts.

**Current limiting.** The time-current characteristic curve of a current-limiting fuse does not tuck as neatly under a relay-tripping curve, but it has other advantages, some of which will become apparent in the coordination studies in later chapters. It does not make the noise that an expulsion fuse without a silencer will make. It also has a higher interrupting capacity.

When applying a medium-voltage, current-limiting fuse of a given-voltage rating on a circuit of a lower-voltage rating, consideration should be given to the magnitude and effect of overvoltages that will be induced due to the zero current forcing action of the fuse during the interruption of high-magnitude fault currents.

For example, you need to be careful about installing a 14.4-kV current-limiting power fuse in a 4.8-kV unit substation transformer primary disconnect switch. Even though the 14.4-kV fuse may fit into the 4.8-kV clip, it would still be more prudent to install a current-limiting fuse closer to the nominal primary voltage. For some manufacturers, this may range from 2.4 to 5.5 kV.

It was mentioned earlier that one of the limitations of fuses of either low or medium voltage is that their ease of application comes at the cost of having limited continuous current rating. You will not find it easy to specify a 2000-A fuse on any circuit, for example. That kind of design situation will require a breaker. To meet the needs of specifiers who need the convenience of fuses, manufacturers have developed a very fast, high-interrupting, high-continuous current-carrying "fuse" that combines electronic and pyrotechnic technology. IEEE work-groups have been formed to establish standards for this device that, for the time being at least, we will call a *triggered current limiter.* Because of space limitations and the relative newness of the technology, we cannot dwell on the subject. The reader is encouraged to consult fuse manufacturers for detailed information.

## 3.5   Low- and Medium-Voltage Breaker Application Principles

### 3.5.1   Low-voltage breakers

The nominal ratings of circuit breakers reflect considerable study of the mechanical, electrical, and thermal capabilities of those circuit breakers by industry organizations such as the National Electrical Manufacturers Association, Underwriters Laboratories, or American National Standards Institute. The following is a brief description of the basic ratings.

- *Voltage.*   Circuit breakers are designed and marked with the maximum voltage at which they can be applied. They can be applied on any system in which the voltage is lower than the breaker rating. (For example, a 600-V-rated breaker can be applied on 120, 208, 240, 277, and 480-V systems.)

- *Frequency.*   Circuit breakers are normally suitable for use in 0- (dc), 50-, and 60-Hz electrical distribution systems. Some UPS applications require 400-Hz protective devices. Although the trip units may be rated for application on 400-Hz systems, the maximum continuous current rating of the breaker itself is dependent on the thermal performance of the frame. The higher the continuous current rating at 60 Hz, the larger the derating factor required for 400-Hz application.

- *Continuous current.*   Standard molded-case circuit breakers are calibrated to carry 100 percent of their current rating in open arc at a given ambient temperature (usually 25 or 40°C). In accordance with the NEC, these breakers, as installed in their enclosures, should not be continuously loaded over 80 percent of their current rating. Low-voltage power circuit breakers and certain molded-case circuit breakers are specifically approved for 100 percent continuous duty. These breakers can be continuously loaded to 100 percent of their current rating in a 40°C ambient when installed in their proper enclosures.

- *Interrupting rating.* The short-time current rating (or short-circuit current rating, as it is referred to for a low-voltage power circuit breaker) is commonly expressed in RMS symmetrical amperes. It may vary with the applied voltage and is established by testing per UL or ANSI standards.

- *Short-time rating.* The short-time current rating specified the maximum capability of a circuit breaker to withstand the effects of short-circuit current flow for a stated period, typically 30 cycles or less, without opening. *This provides time for downstream protective devices closer to the fault to operate and isolate the circuit.* This was one of the first significant features offered by the solid-state trip units over thermal-magnetic breakers.

  The short-time current rating of a low-voltage power circuit breaker without instantaneous trip characteristics is equal to the breaker's short-circuit interrupting rating. Most molded-case circuit breakers are not provided with a short-time rating; however, some higher-ampere-rated molded-case circuit breakers are provided with a short-time current rating in addition to the short-circuit interrupting rating. Circuit breakers with an instantaneous trip function should not be applied where continuity of service requires only long- and short-time-delay functions.

- *Control voltage.* This is the ac or dc voltage designated to be applied to control devices intended to open or close a circuit breaker. These devices can normally be supplied with a voltage rating needed to meet a particular control system. Some shunt trip circuit breaker applications will require a remote 120-V ac source. In other situations, you may need a 24- or 48-V dc battery to operate the circuit breaker.

### 3.5.2  Medium-voltage breakers

For medium-voltage circuits in the 200- to 3000-A range, circuit breakers are most commonly applied. Though circuit breakers are able to withstand higher continuous current, circuit breakers are not current-limiting and are relatively slow interrupting devices (three to five cycles at medium voltage). For applications where available fault currents have increased because of expanding power requirements, simply replacing the circuit breakers may not be adequate protection for other underrated equipment on the system. The ideal device would be a fast, high-continuous current, high-interrupting capacity fuse. Such products are now entering the market. They are called current-limiting protectors and interrupting capacities on the order of 120 kA at 3000 A continuous for voltages in the 2.8- to 38-kV range.

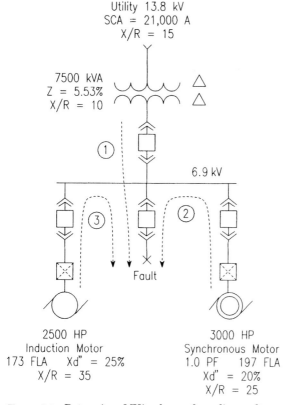

**Figure 3.2** Determine MVA class of medium-voltage breaker. Application of the proper circuit breaker requires a definition of its duty requirements that can be compared with the choice of ratings and capabilities offered by the manufacturer. The mother standards for the determination of fault duty for the application of medium-voltage breakers is C37.010 and C37.06. In this circuit, the secondary voltage is 6.9 kV. The results of fault duty calculations (performed in detail at the end of Chap. 8) indicate that either an 8.25-kV or a 15-kV circuit breaker might reasonably be applied. For economic reasons, the 15-kV switch is the more economical selection.

The methods for applying ANSI standards for selecting medium-voltage breakers are best learned by example. We will postpone our numerical treatment of the fault duties involved in the circuit of Fig. 3.2 until we reach Chap. 8, which dwells on the details of protecting medium-voltage circuits exclusively.

## 3.6 Sensing Elements

We need to remind ourselves that the only level of current that counts on a time-current characteristic curve is the current that the trip unit or relay actually sees. While breakthroughs occur every day in the processing of analog information that comes from power circuit-sensing elements, the laws of electromagnetism proffer tradeoffs with regard to the way power system behavior can be observed and controlled.

In recent years, some research engineers have undertaken work to discover the manner in which power system behavior might be economically observed with traveling waves, thus eliminating the need for local sensing that is now accomplished with instrument transformers. It is probably fair to say that the possibility of full-scale industrial and commercial adoption of traveling wave sensing at the low- and medium-voltage levels during the time frame within which this text has usefulness is quite remote. In other words, the application of faster and cheaper microprocessors to process the traveling waves generated by short circuits is well within the limits of present technology and, while the prospect of electric power system switchgear without instrument transformers for protective relaying is quite exciting, we cannot wait for it.

The beauty of a fuse is that it is both the interrupting and the sensing element. Chemistry intervenes so that we do not have to concern ourselves with the appropriate matching of sensing and interrupting elements. Many low-voltage circuit breakers may be regarded as having integral sensing and interrupting elements, but a large class of low- and medium-voltage switchgear requires separate sensing elements. In low-voltage circuit breakers, these elements are called *sensors* in order to distinguish them from *instrument transformers* that operate in medium-voltage breakers. For the moment, let us discuss instrument transformers because the application principles will apply to sensors as well. The background for this discussion will be derived from the mother standard for all instrument transformers: ANSI-IEEE C57.13.

### 3.6.1  Essential facts about instrument transformers

- Instrument transformers are just like any other kind of transformer to the extent that they can be connected in delta or wye, in series and in parallel. They have a high and a low side, a specific phase order and polarity.

- Instrument transformers are modeled in lumped parameter fashion just like any other transformer except that there is slightly different terminology between the corresponding parameters. The exciting branch of the potential transformer is typically ignored in practical models. In current transformers the exciting branch *cannot* be ignored.

- The load on an instrument transformer is expressed in terms of voltamperes just like power transformers; however, the term *burden* is used in connection with instrument transformers.

- The term *burden* describes the impedance connected to the transformer secondary winding but may also specify the voltamperes delivered to the load. Thus, an instrument transformer delivering 5 A to a resistive burden of 0.1 ohm may also be said to have a burden of 2.5 VA at 5 A (by $P = I^2/R$).

- Instrument transformers are unlike most power transformers because they have little or no continuous overload capability; they must be sized to carry the estimated design or peak load on the circuit.

- Most current transformers are sized to give a little less than 5 A at maximum load. In the United States, current transformer secondary windings currents have been standardized at 5 A. In Europe, 1 A is quite common.

- Multiratio instrument transformers have fixed ratios that are the same among all electrical manufacturers who follow ANSI-IEEE standards as minimums.

- Instrument transformers can be loaded with relays and wattmeters together. There does not necessarily have to be a separate circuit for protection and metering (energy management) functions, but many switchgear designers prefer to keep them separate when budgets allow.

### 3.6.2  Voltage transformers

The typical voltage transformer is a conventional transformer with a high ratio and a low energy requirement. The primary windings carry very small currents under normal conditions. Because the transformers are physically small compared with power transformers, they have magnetic cores of small cross-sectional area, thereby forcing the primary windings (because of the high ratio) to be constructed of many turns of fine wire. This is why potential transformers are more vulnerable to damage from transients than power transformers.

Voltage transformers are primarily for line-to-line service though they are commonly applied line-to-ground or line-to-neutral at a winding voltage equal to the primary voltage rating divided by $\sqrt{3}$. In medium-voltage circuit applications, potential transformers with 69-V secondary windings are in common use. The connection of the secondary depends on the relay application. A schematic of a potential transformer application to ground fault protection appears in Fig. 4.9.

For protective relaying applications, ratio and phase angle inaccuracies of standard potential transformers are so small they can be neglected if the burden falls within the potential transformer's thermal voltampere rating. (Thermal voltampere rating corresponds to the full-load rating of a power transformer.)

Potential transformers must be fused. At medium-voltage fuses, the rule is to select a fuse size 300 percent of the potential transformer primary full-load current or the next standard larger size.

Potential transformers come with magnetizing inrush currents designated as 10X or 12X or 15X. Assume a 0.1-s settling time. They have emergency voltage ratings on the order of 125 percent of the nameplate rating so that under such conditions protective devices connected to them will operate. Some manufacturers cite an emergency time rating (such as 1 min) as well.

### 3.6.3  Current transformers

The measure of a current transformer's performance lies in its ability to reproduce accurately the primary current in secondary amperes both in wave shape and in magnitude at maximum and minimum current levels. The nature of the problem of current transformer specification is that we usually cannot have 100 percent accuracy at both maximum and minimum current levels. Current transformers that are applied to power circuits for protective relaying applications must be able to withstand currents 10 to 20 times more than normal load current during faults. As with power transformers, there is a mechanical and a thermal aspect to this.

Physics tells us that there will be some error between input and output. The extent of the error is a function of

- The shape and magnitude of the power input signal, i.e., the fault current trace. (Some fault currents hardly resemble sinusoids.)

- The NEMA accuracy class of the current transformer. (We will get to these in a moment.)

- The total connected impedance of the sensing circuit including current transformer, the control wire, and the relay. (Electromechanical relays are more of a burden than microprocessor-based relays.)

- Its transformer's performance on the symmetrical ac component and its performance on the offset dc component seen in Fig. 2.5.

The general principle in all current transformer applications is to *select a current transformer that has the highest ANSI accuracy classification at a burden rating equal to or greater than the maximum burden to be connected to its secondary.* To apply this principle, we need to review some of the basic terminology.

Current transformer performance specifications have changed over the years. There is the old and the new way. The old way predates 1968 and is still important to us now because of the existing installed base of switchgear. It discriminated among current transformers with the code letter L or H, which indicated Low or High impedance.

The new way of describing current transformer involves the use of a formula or use of excitation curves:

- *Formula.* From classical electromagnetic analysis comes the fundamental transformer equation:

$$V_s = 4.44 \times f \times A \times N \times B_{max} \; 10^{-8} \text{ volts}$$

$V_s$ = the rms symmetrical secondary induced voltage
f = frequency in Hz
A = cross-sectional area of the iron core in in$^2$
N = number of turns
$B_{max}$ = flux density, lines/in$^2$

The quantities necessary to use this equation are not normally available to anyone other than instrument transformer specialists.

- *The current transformer excitation curves.* The mother standard, ANSI-IEEE C57.13, recognizes the difficulty in making such calculations on the basis of lumped parameter circuit models so it classifies current transformers that have significant leakage flux within the transformer core at *Class T* current transformers. (Before 1968 these were designated as Class H.) Wound current transformers, those that have one or more primary winding turns mechanically encircling the core, are usually CT. The performance of current transformers constructed like this are best determined by test. Figure 5 of ANSI-IEEE C37.13-1978 plots current against current.

Current transformers constructed to minimize the leakage flux in the core, such as through the bar and bushing types, have an equivalent circuit that is easier to model. These CTs have performances that can be calculated so that they are designated Class C (Class L before 1968). C means that the percent ratio correction can be calculated (Fig. 4 of ANSI-IEEE C57.13-1978). It plots families of excitation curves with secondary exciting amps against secondary exciting volts.

The classification number indicates the secondary terminal voltage that the transformer will deliver to a standard burden at 20 times normal secondary current without exceeding a 10 percent ratio correction. The ratio correction should not exceed 10 percent at any current from 1 to 20 times rated current at standard burden indicated as the basis of relay accuracy ratings. The standard designated secondary terminal voltages at 10, 20, 50, 100, 200, 400, and 800 V.

So the meaning of C200 would be interpreted as

$$10\% \text{ accuracy inferred} \times 20 \times \text{normal current} \times \text{secondary amp}$$

$$\text{by } E = IR, 200 \text{ V} = 20 \times 5 \times \text{B2.0}$$

The meaning of T-100

$$\text{by } E = IR \qquad 100 \text{ V} = (20 \times 5) \times \text{B1.0}$$

the secondary output voltage is 100 V, and the maximum burden limitation is B1.0.

**Current transformer saturation.**    At high currents, the magnetic circuits of relays begin to saturate, and the burden impedance decreases as the secondary current increases. You must calculate the current transformer burden for each value of secondary current for which you want to know the current transformer's accuracy. The problem of relay performance with low-ratio current transformers applied to circuits with high fault currents is particularly onerous. Any CT below the C100 rating ought to be given special attention.

The accuracy of a current transformer is usually expressed in terms of a ratio correction factor (rcf): actual input/output ratio is quality to marked ratio times rcf. See App. Figs. A.16 to A.18. An rcf curve plots rcf against multiples of primary or secondary rated current. CT core saturation is the major influence in CT ratio error. The rcf curve is calculated for a particular burden; for each burden, you will need a separate curve. Manufacturers furnish rcf curves for all CT types.

Burden ratings of current transformer were formerly expressed in terms of voltamperes, but it is more accurate to express burden in terms of impedance of the load and its resistance and reactance component, which is now standard. It is usually enough to add series burden impedances arithmetically. Any inaccuracy will be on the safe side.

**Phase relationships.**    Is the sensed voltage in current in phase with the load current? Instrument transformers can sense load current but can be connected in such a fashion as to shift the angle, such as 30°.

**Burdens.** On solidly grounded systems, ground relay taps lower than 1.0 should be avoided because of the high current transformer burden caused by very low tap settings. The performance of current transformer on inrush currents to motors and transformer can result in a current in the grounded relay circuit and is of particular interest with respect to the use of an instantaneous grounded relay. Very low (less than 8 to 10 A) grounded relay instantaneous settings may cause incorrect tripping of a feeder when a motor is started. In a delta system, simultaneous phase-to-ground faults involving different phases on separate feeders will result in a current in the current transformer neutral relay circuit of the feeders involved.

Unlike a power transformer, the primary current of a current transformer is not determined by the burden on its secondary. It is determined by external conditions (such as lead wire) in series with the primary. The secondary winding, with its many turns and high impedance, is intended for a rather narrow range of external burden.

Current transformers do not always perform exactly in accordance with their ratios. This difference is caused by minor variations in manufacture, differences in secondary loadings, and differences in magnetic history. Where there is a prolonged dc component in the primary fault current, such as invariably occurs close to generators, the current transformers will not saturate equally, and a substantial relay-operating current can be expected to flow. Hence, if overcurrent relays are applied, they have to be set so that they do not operate on the maximum error current, which can flow in the relay during an external fault. To meet this problem without sacrificing sensitivity, the percentage differential type relay is usually applied.

**Basic relay tap—current transformer calculations.** The basic calculation for an electromechanical relay is the following:

$$\text{CT Ratio} \times \text{Relay Tap} = \text{Relay Pickup}$$

For example, a 13.8-kV breaker with a 400/5 CT and a relay tap of 4 will have an overcurrent pickup of $400/5 \times 4 = 320$ A. You will need to work this equation in reverse also. Given that cable ampacity is 320 A, what size CT should you select and at what tap shall you set the pickup on the relay?

The basic calculation for a microprocessor-based relay will differ among manufacturers and may have slightly different terminology. The current transformer may be factored into the equation as a simple multiplier such as 80 (for the example above) times a range of pickup values from 0.1 to 10.0.

In general, the following rules should be kept in mind.

- The pickup current of a relay is the rating of the current tap in use. Relays have fixed tap current ranges that may be selected for different circuits. For electromechanical relays, typical tap ranges are 0.5 to 2, 1.5 to 6, and 4 to 16 A. If you look at the nameplate of a relay, you will see the amp range clearly indicated.

- The low current coils rated 0.5 to 2 and 1.5 to 6 A are applied wherever low-current pickup is present. Low-current coils are primarily intended for residual connection in the neutral phase of the short-circuit relay current transformers to detect ground-fault currents.

- Low-current relays impose heavier burdens on their current transformers than middle-range relays.

*Example:* A relay operating with a 6-A tap setting connected to the secondary of a 200/5 current transformer would see $2400/(40 \times 6) = 10$ multiples of its pickup setting with 2400 A flowing in the primary of the current transformer.

Another way of saying the same thing follows. Given a circuit with 2400 A flowing through it, if you apply a 200/5 current transformer, then the 2400 A will be scaled down to $2400/40 = 60$ A. This is the current that the relay receives from the current transformer. Now the relay does not have to do anything with this current unless you program it to do something with it. But suppose you did want to do something with the relay at the 2400-A level. Your choices are indicated in a special way on the horizontal scale. If you chose to program the relay to act at 10 times the minimum closing current, then you would choose the $60/10 = 6$ A tap.

For solid-state relays, the "tap ranges" are programmable, typically, with DIP switches that may or may not be visible from the front. Some manufacturers allow you to work with the relay pickup level explicitly—the standard CT secondary turns ratio of 5 already assumed.

**Current transformer lead resistance configurations.**   The burden on current transformers varies depending on the kind of fault that occurs. This happens because fault current does not have to be picked up by all current transformers in order to trip a breaker. For a three-phase fault, all current transformers will be involved, and the resistance of all three sensing device leads must figure into our calculations. But for a single-line-to-ground fault, only one current transformer will be involved and therefore the resistance of only one lead. In differential schemes, the location of the relay with respect to the CT that defines the protected zone will usually minimize the effect of lead burden on CT saturation. Depending on how the current transformers are connected (the lead burden of delta-connected current transformers is three times that of the wye-connected current transformers, for example) and depending on how long the current transformer wiring is, the resistance (and therefore the burden) on our current transformers can vary considerably for the full range of faults that are normally encountered on bulk distribution power systems.

As a general rule, you should distribute CT burden among all three phases. If several CTs are available on a breaker, consider locating some relays to another CT. Keep CT leads short. If this is not feasible, then use larger wire sizes; the incremental cost is not likely to be budget-busting. When auxiliary CTs must be used, consider the burden amplification effect.

We will go into greater depth on this subject with a numerical example in Example 8.3.

## 3.7   Transformer Through-Fault Protection

Transformer damage is cumulative, and the fact is that the number of through faults to which a transformer can be exposed is inherently different for different transformer applications. For example, transformers with secondary-side conductors enclosed in conduit or isolated in some other fashion, such as those typically found in industrial, commercial, and institutional power systems, experience extremely low incidence of through faults. In contrast, transformers with secondary-side overhead lines, such as those found in utility distribution substations, have a relatively high incidence of through faults, and the use of reclosers or automatic reclosing circuit breakers may subject the transformer to repeated current surges from each fault. Thus, for a given transformer in these two different applications, a different through-fault protection curve should apply depending on the type of application. For applications in which faults occur infrequently, the through-fault protection curve should reflect primarily thermal damage considerations since cumulative mechanical damage effects of through faults will not be a problem. For applications in which faults occur frequently, the through-fault protection curve should reflect the fact that the transformer will be subjected to both thermal and cumulative mechanical damage effects of through faults.

In using the through-fault protection curves to select the time-current characteristics of protective devices, the protection engineer should take into account not only the inherent level of through-fault incidence but also the location of each protective device and its role in providing transformer protection. As noted, substation transformers with secondary-side overhead lines have a relatively high incidence of through faults. The secondary-side feeder protective equipment is the first line of defense against through faults, and its time-current characteristics should, therefore, be selected by reference to the frequent fault incidence protection curve. More specifically, the time-current characteristics of feeder protective devices should be below and to the left of the appropriate frequent fault incidence protection curves. Main secondary-side protective devices (if applicable) and primary-side protective devices typically operate to protect against through faults in the rare event of a fault between the transformer and the feeder protective devices, or in the equally rare event that a feeder protective device fails to operate or operates too slowly because of an incorrect (higher) rating or setting. The device fails to operate or operates too slowly due to an incorrect (higher) rating or setting. The time-current characteristics of these devices, therefore, should be selected by reference to the infrequent fault incidence protection curve. In addition, these time-current characteristics should be selected to achieve the desired coordination among the various protective devices.

In contrast, transformers with protected secondary conductors (for example, cable, bus duct, or switchgear) experience an extremely low incidence of through faults. Hence the feeder protective devices may be selected by reference to the infrequent fault-incidence protection curve. The main secondary-side protective devices (if applicable) and the primary-side protective devices should also be selected by reference to the infrequent-fault incidence protection curve.

### 3.7.1   Analysis of transformer under short-circuit conditions

Suppose a transformer is designed to carry 30 times its rated current for 1 s. Let us determine the length of time that a current of 20 times the rating can be allowed to flow and find the maximum amount of current that the transformer can carry for 2 s.

Transformers have a definite $I^2t$ limitation because heat equals $I^2R_{eq}$, and $R_{eq}$ is constant for a particular transformer. ($R_{eq}$ represents the total resistance of the primary and secondary circuits.)

$$\text{Hence } 30^2 \times 1 = 20^2 t \qquad t = 2.25 \text{ s}$$

For maximum permissible current for 2 s

$$30^2 \times 1 = I^2 \times 2 \qquad I = 21.21 \text{ times full-load current}$$

With differential relaying available on the order of three to eight cycles, transformer heat damage is limited.

### 3.7.2   Category I transformers

Single-phase: 5 to 500 kVA

Three-phase: 15 to 500 kVA

Refer to Fig. A.13.

This curve may be used for selecting protective devices time-current characteristics for all applications regardless of anticipated level of fault incidence.

- The lower limit of time on the thermal curve is terminated as a function of the impedance of the transformer.

- Above 50 s, the damage curve increases at a rate that terminates at an intercept at approximately 2.2 times the full-load amperes at 1000 s.

- For all the other transformer classes, the termination is at 2 s.

### 3.7.3  Category II transformers

Single-phase: 501 to 1667 kVA

Three-phase: 501 to 5000 kVA

Refer to Fig. A.14

- The left-hand curve in Fig. A.14 reflects both thermal and mechanical damage considerations and may be used for selecting feeder protective device time-current characteristics for frequent fault-incidence applications.

- The right-hand curve in Fig. A.14 reflects primarily thermal damage considerations and may be applied for selecting feeder protective device time-current characteristics for infrequent fault incidence applications.

This curve may also be applied for selecting main secondary-side protective devices (if applicable) and primary-side protective devices time-current characteristics for all applications, regardless of anticipated level of fault incidence.

### 3.7.4  Category III transformers

Single-phase: 1668 to 10,000 kVA

Three-phase: 500 to 30,000 kVA

Refer to Fig. A.15

- The left-hand curve in Fig. A.15 reflects both thermal and mechanical damage considerations and may be applied for selecting feeder protective devices time-current characteristics for frequent fault-incidence applications.

- The right-hand curve in Fig. A.15 reflects primarily thermal damage considerations and may be applied for selecting feeder protective device time-current characteristics for infrequent fault incidence applications. This curve may also be applied for selecting main secondary-side protective devices (if applicable) and primary-side protective devices time-current characteristics for all applications, regardless of anticipated level of fault incidence.

Category IV transformers cover single-phase banks (10,000 kVA) and three-phase (30,000 kVA and above) and are most commonly owned by utilities. We shall not deal with them in particular in this textbook. The reader is referred to Blackburn for more information.

In practice, primary-side protective devices characteristic curve may cross the through-fault protection curve at lower-current levels since low-current overload protection is a function of secondary-side protective devices or devices (Table 3.2). (Refer to appropriate transformer loading guides, ANSI-IEEE C57.91-1981 and C57.92-1981.) Efforts should be made, however, to have the primary-side protective devices characteristic curve intersect the through-fault fault protection curve at as low a current as possible in order to maximize the degree of backup protection for the secondary-side devices.

### 3.7.5  Special consideration
### for transformer connections

When we plot transformer protection "curves," we will almost always have to make some adjustments to the reference current levels we establish with short-circuit information. The foregoing through-fault

TABLE 3.2    Transformer versus Impedance Protection Rules per NEC*

| | | Primary side | | Secondary side | | |
|---|---|---|---|---|---|---|
| | | | | >600 V | | ≦600 V |
| Impedance | Voltage | Circuit breaker | Fuse | Circuit breaker | Fuse | |
| All | >600 V | ≦3X | ≦1.5X | None | None | ≦None |
| ≦6% | | ≦6X | ≦3X | ≦3X | ≦1.5X | ≦2.5X |
| >6% <10% | | ≦4X | ≦2X | ≦2.5X | ≦1.25X | ≦2.5X |
| All | ≦600 V | ≦1.25X | ≦1.25X | | | None |
| | | ≦2.5X | ≦2.5X | | | 1.25X |
| ≦6% | | ≦6X | ≦6X | | | |
| >6% <10% | | ≦4X | ≦4X | | | |

Table courtesy of EDSA Micro Corporation.
  * You might think of the difference between fuses and circuit breakers in terms of the difference in which they sense and open circuits. In general, fuses effectively sense the *rate of change* in current by chemical means. The prospective peak let-through curves are evidence of this. The rate of change in $I^2t$ energy opens the circuit in less than a half cycle before high fault current levels are ever seen. Circuit breakers depend upon an *absolute current level* to open the circuit which inherently requires that all parts of the circuit have the capability to withstand fault current for one or more cycles.

protection curve values are based on winding current relationships for a bolted three-phase secondary fault and may be applied directly for delta-delta connected transformers only. With all other transformer connections we will have to shift our curves left or right. You can confirm this by referring to Fig. 3.3, which indicates the manner in which secondary faults are reflected into the primary (or vice versa). Figure 3.3 is a tabulation of per-unit primary-side current to the per-unit transformer winding current for the most common transformer connections at the low- and medium-voltage levels.

For delta-wye-connected transformers, the through-fault protection curve values must be reduced to 58 percent of the three-phase bolted fault values to provide appropriate protection for a secondary-side single-line-to-ground fault. This is because a bolted single-line-to-ground fault on the secondary of the delta-wye-connected core-type transformer with a solidly grounded neutral will develop as much short-time temperature rise because of short-circuit current in the faulted leg as would be developed with a three-phase bolted fault. The primary protective devices will see only 58 percent as much current during the single-line-to-ground fault as for the three-phase fault and will therefore be slower in clearing the fault, thus permitting the short-time temperature limit to be exceeded.

Positive sequence short-circuit currents are reflected through delta-delta and wye-wye transformers inversely as the voltage ratio for all kinds of faults: three-phase, line-to-line, and single-line-to-ground. This is also true for three-phase fault-current phasing through delta-wye or wye-delta transformers. With these same winding connections, a line-to-line fault will draw but 86.6 percent of three-phase fault current value. On the primary side, 100 percent of the three-phase fault current will flow in one phase with 50 percent of this value in the remaining two lines. So, neglecting the transformation ratio, one relay on the primary line will carry 15.4 percent more current than will flow in the secondary faulted phase. To coordinate correctly, you must allow for this unbalance.

## 3.8   Applications of the Differential Principle

We need to be careful that we do not confuse the NEC requirements for overcurrent and short-circuit protection with the majority of protective devices installed in all switchgear that are based on the overcurrent principle, schemes that employ devices where current is the discriminating quantity among series protective devices. We need to appreciate the fact that the kind of protection that is the principal subject of this book is *not the fastest* protective scheme. The best protection technique has always been differential protection based on our old friend, the Kirchoff Current law.

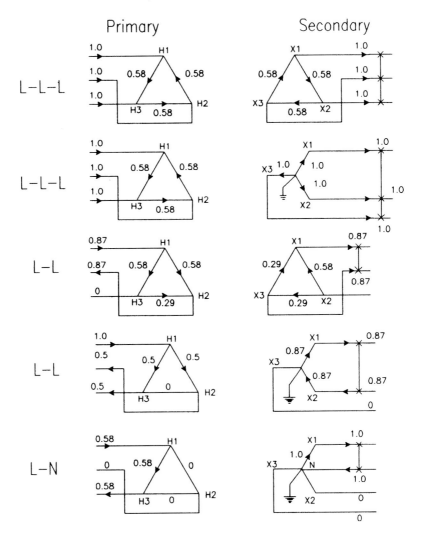

TRANSFORMER CONNECTIONS
(Per Unit Winding and Line Currents Shown)
Adapted from ANSI/IEEE C37.91

$$3 \text{ Phase Fault Current} = \frac{3 \text{ Phase Full Load Current}}{\text{Transformer Per Unit Impedance}} = 1.0 \text{ PU}$$

**Figure 3.3**  Line and transformer winding currents for DY and DD connected transformers. The phase relationships that apply to power transformers also apply in instrument transformer circuits.

Differential protection detects faults early by sensing system imbalances that are the signature of faults; overcurrent protection requires that the fault be in a comparatively advanced state before the fault can be sensed. You can apply differential protection methods to all elements in a power system: generators, buses, cables, transformers, motors, and even combinations of all of these. You can protect transmission lines using the differential principle when you can get both ends of the line communicating.

Figure 3.4a shows the relay circuits for one phase only. For normal operation or for a fault outside the two sets of current transformers, Ip entering the device equals Ip leaving the device in all phases (neglected the small internal leakage current). On a per-unit basis, the secondary current is equal to the primary current minus the current transformer-magnetizing current.

Now the current that drives the relay is the difference between the exciting and the magnetizing currents. With the same type of current transformers, this current will be small at normal load. Differential relays are always set above this maximum value during normal machine operation. If a fault occurs between the two sets of current transformers, one or more of the left-hand currents will suddenly increase, while currents on the right side may either decrease or increase and flow in the reverse direction. Either way, the total fault current will now flow through the relay coil, causing it to operate.

If perfect current transformers were available, an overcurrent relay in the "difference" branch of the circuit could be set to respond very sensitively and quickly. In practice, however, no two current transformers will give exactly the same secondary current for the same primary current. Discrepancies can be traced to manufacturing variations and to differences in secondary loading caused by unequal length of relay leads and unequal burdens connected to the current transformer secondaries. While normally small, the differential current can become appreciable when short-circuit current flows to an external fault. An overcurrent relay would have to be set above the maximum error current that could be expected during an external fault.

The percentage differential relay solves this problem without sacrificing sensitivity. The restraining windings receive the transformer secondary current and desensitize the relay to high external fault currents. The current required for relay operation increases with the magnitude of the external fault current.

The kind of graph you use to apply differential relays plots restraint current versus operating current as shown in Fig. 3.4b. You can define an operating zone and a nonoperating zone as shown in Fig. 3.4a.

There is small, and tolerable, differential current that flows (when transformers automatically change taps under load, for instance) in

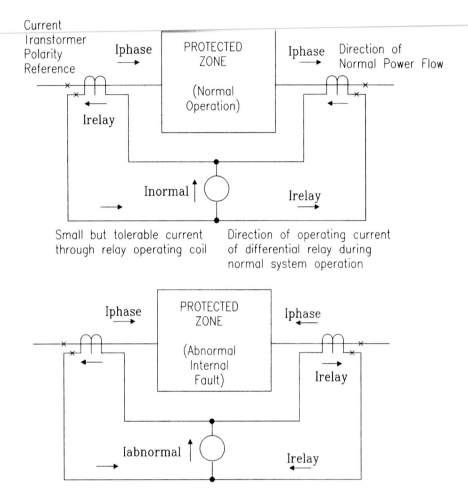

(a)

**Figure 3.4**   The basic differential connection + solid state variable percentage differential relay operating characteristic. This is an extremely general schematic that shows the relationship between current flows for internal and external faults. The major differences between bus differential protection and transformer and/or generator differential protection lies in the number of circuits that lie in the zone and the magnitudes of currents involved in the various circuits that lie within the zone. (*Restraint current graph courtesy of Basler Electric Co.*)

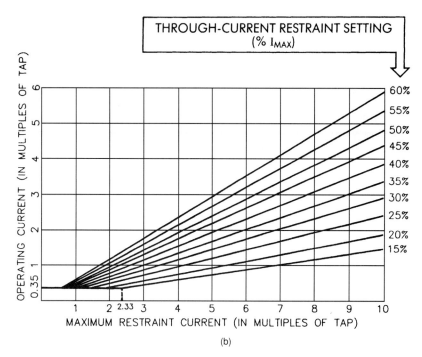

Figure 3.4 *(Continued)*

the relay, and therefore differential relays are designed with adjustments. We do not want mismatches in our sensing elements to fool us into thinking there is something wrong when there is neither. The correct selection and application of current transformers applied in differential protection schemes is critical to their proper operation.

## 3.9 Time and Current Margins Between Overcurrent Devices

We return to the subject of overcurrent protection with some specifics about the time and current margins between overcurrent devices. Keep in mind that these are ideal margins and that we shall frequently encounter situations in which these margins cannot be established or maintained. This is particularly true as the mixture of electromechanical and solid-state devices increases. Faster or slower breakers or *specific device combinations* must be considered so that the real-time arithmetic will vary.

Even though, for example, a medium-voltage relay has a time-current characteristic that is shown as a line, you should allow a ±10 percent zone of tolerance around it. Certain fault modes will tend to shift the medium-voltage overcurrent relay upward (greater clearing time). We show smooth continuous inverse curves, but there may be a trend toward more devices with (segmented) piecewise continuous curves as solid-state overcurrent relays evolve. We will discuss each of the foregoing in greater detail in later chapters.

Coordination can be easily achieved with low-voltage current-limiting fuses that have fast response times. Manufacturers' time-current curves and selectivity ratio guides are applied for both overload and short-circuit conditions, precluding the need for calculating time intervals.

When coordinating inverse time overcurrent relays, the time interval is usually 0.3 to 0.4 s. This interval is measured between relays in series either at the instantaneous setting of the load-side feeder circuit breaker relay or the maximum short-circuit current, which can flow through both devices simultaneously, whichever is the lower value of current. The interval consists of the following components:

Circuit breaker opening time (5 cycles)—0.08 s

Relay overtravel—0.10 s

Safety factor for CT saturation, setting errors, and so on—0.22 s

This safety factor may be decreased by field-testing relays to eliminate setting errors. This involves calibrating the relays to the coordination curves and adjusting time dials to achieve specific operating times.

A 0.355 margin is widely indicated in field-tested systems employing very inverse and extremely inverse time-overcurrent relays.

When solid-state relays are applied, overtravel is eliminated, and the time may be reduced by the amount included for overtravel. For systems using induction disk relays, a decrease of the time interval may be made by employing an overcurrent relay with special high-dropout instantaneous element set at approximately the same pickup as the time element with its contact wired in series with the main relay contact. This eliminates overtravel in the relay so equipped. The time interval often indicated on carefully calibrated systems with high-dropout instantaneous relays is 0.25 s.

When coordinating relays with downstream fuses, the circuit operating time does not exist for the fuse, and the interval may be reduced accordingly. The total clearing time of the fuse should be indicated for coordination purposes. The time margin between the fuse total clearing curve and the upstream relay curve could be as low as 0.2 s where clearing times between 1 s are involved.

When low-voltage circuit breakers equipped with direct-acting trip units are coordinated with relayed circuit breakers, the coordination time interval is usually regarded as 0.3 s. This interval may be decreased to a shorter time as explained previously for relay-to-relay coordination.

When coordinating circuit breakers equipped with direct-acting trip units, the characteristic curves should not overlap. In general, only a slight separation is planned between the different characteristic curves. This lack of a specified time margin is explained by the incorporation of all the variables plus the circuit breaker operating times for these devices within the band of the device characteristic curve.

### 3.9.1 Relays over relays

A time margin of between 0.4 and 0.5 s at the maximum available fault current should be maintained between electromechanical overcurrent relays applied in series. This time includes the breaker operating time (about 0.13 s), relay overtravel or coasting time (about 0.1 s), variations in the manufacture of the devices applied including current transformer performance, and a small safety factor (for example, 0.17 s). For solid-state relays, you may eliminate the allowance for overtravel and add again.

An examination of the time-current characteristic operating curves for the various devices will show that overcurrent relays have a "line" characteristic. The direct trip device and the fuse have a band within which the device will operate. This band is necessary to accommodate the tolerances required for the manufacture of the devices. When a relay is coordinated under the band, the lower limit is applied. This practice will ensure selectivity even if the upper device is operated near the bottom of its band and the lower device is operated near the top of its band. If calibration equipment is not available, relay characteristics should be shown as a band to allow for manufacturing tolerances.

Several curve shapes are available for overcurrent relays. Each of these shapes has its area of being the best for the application. Relays within an electric systems should be compatible, e.g., have the same time-current characteristic so that adequate selectivity can be achieved when the relays are in series. Some combinations of overcurrent relay curve shapes cannot be made to coordinate. The most common and the most versatile characteristic is called the very inverse relay. It will provide time delay over most fuses and other very inverse relays.

Overcurrent relays should also include an instantaneous attachment if the relays are to be indicated in applications other than incoming lines. This instantaneous element, in conjunction with the time-delay element, can help achieve overall selectivity with several steps of protection in series and still not have excessively high operating times on devices nearest the power source.

Shorter time margins are possible among relays with inverse characteristics provided that the available steady-state fault current at the point of application is appreciably greater than the first half cycle, asymmetrical fault current available at the next downstream device. Since the instantaneous trip is responsive to the dc offset current, it must be set just above the asymmetrical fault-current level. The instantaneous setting of the final downstream device must exceed the normal short-time overload current and the initial asymmetrical inrush current. (Refer to Fig. 3.5.)

### 3.9.2   Relays over trip devices or fuses

A time margin of between 0.1 and 0.2 s at the maximum available fault current should be maintained between the relay curve and the trip device or fuse under the relay (Fig. 3.6). The entire operating time including manufacturing tolerances is included in the operating characteristic. The safety margin is 0.1 and 0.2 s.

An inverse time overcurrent relay with definite instantaneous and standard instantaneous attachment can be applied when coordination with trip devices is required. The type of relay follows the general shape of the operating characteristics of the overcurrent trip device to provide minimum time margins for coordination.

It is assumed that the various devices being coordinated are pickup sensitive, with the device closer to the power source having the higher pickup value. When the devices are on different sides of a power transformer, the total plotting ratio should be utilized (the winding ratio, winding connections, and regulation).

### 3.9.3   Fuses over relays

A time margin of between 0.3 and 0.4 s should be maintained between the fuse and relay curves. This time includes the breaker operating time, relay overtravel time, and a safety factor. Again, since overtravel time is not a factor with solid-state relays, you may want to allow 0.2 to 0.25 s as clearance time.

### 3.9.4   Fuses over fuses

**Fuse maximum clearing thermal energy.**   If fuses are applied in series in a circuit, it is essential for short-circuit coordination to verify the clearing $I^2t$ of the downstream fuse. Fuse manufacturers publish fuse-ratio tables (see Fig. 5.2) that provide listings of fuses that are known to operate selectively. Use of these tables permits coordination without the need for full-blown circuit *provided the fuses being applied are all of the same manufacturer.*

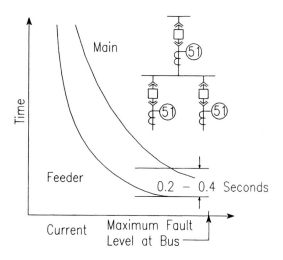

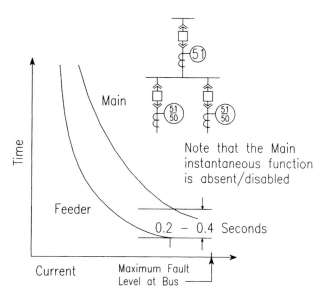

**Figure 3.5**   Relay-relay interval. *51-Only Detail:* During light generation periods, fault currents are reduced and all operating times increase, but, because of the time characteristics of inverse overcurrent relays, the margins between successive relays also need to increase. Several inverse relays in series can be set for the same time for faults immediately beyond the relay and still provide the requisite 0.40-s margin (0.2-s margin for microprocessor-based relays) for faults beyond the next relay because of the lower current value for fault in that location. *50/51 Detail:* Instantaneous devices are typically applied on the final overcurrent protective device supply load or on any protective devices with sufficient circuit impedance between itself and the next downstream protective device.

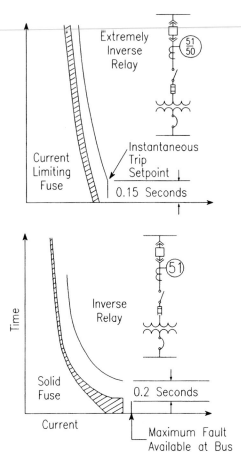

**Figure 3.6**  Fuse-relay interval. The inverse and very inverse characteristics are sometimes more favorable where close coordination with fuses is required. They also make it possible to take advantage of the reduction of maximum fault current as distance from the power source increases. This figure indicates ideal coordination intervals between a relay and a fuse at medium voltage. However, cases in which the medium-voltage upstream relay provides more protection to the transformer than the primary fuses are quite common.

The time margin between two fuses in series should be about 0.1 s at the maximum current at which the two must coordinate. The available fault current will then be low enough so that the larger fuse, at least, is operating in the time-delay portion of the curve and not in the instantaneous or current-limiting arc of the fuse characteristic. The downstream device may operate in the instantaneous or current-limiting area if desirable. Sometimes the use of a current-limiting fuse makes an otherwise impossible coordination problem workable and acceptable. Preloading should be considered in all these applications to ensure that large load currents or starting inrush currents do not cause unnecessary operation of the protective devices.

### 3.9.5  Trip devices over fuses

When coordinating an upstream circuit breaker with a downstream fuse, the let-through energy of the fuse (clearing $I^2t$) must be less than the required amount to release the circuit breaker trip latch mechanism. This is not easily accomplished with many types of circuit breakers. Critical operation occurs in the region for periods of time less than 0.01 s, even though a normal time-current plot would suggest that selective performance exists. Similar problems exist when attempting to coordinate a downstream circuit breaker with an upstream fuse. The clearing time of the circuit breaker can often exceed the minimum melting time of the fuse. Overload coordination for low-magnitude or moderate faults can be established with standard time-current curve overlays.

For protection of a downstream circuit breaker with an upstream fuse during high fault currents, the peak let-through current of the fuse must be compatible with the momentary withstand rating of the circuit breaker. Manufacturers' tables for the selection of fuses to protect circuit breakers are an easy solution provided that such tables are based on current styles, types, and classes of fuses and circuit breakers. UL now series-tests and issues various combinations of fuses and circuit breakers as submitted by different manufacturers. These UL certifications are preferable to manufacturers' data without third-party certification where available.

A clear space between the device characteristics on the plot is usually sufficient to ensure selectivity. The tripping characteristic of both these types of devices includes the arcing time, manufacturing tolerances, and safety factors.

### 3.9.6  Trip device over trip device

The trip devices must be coordinated at their values of pickup for selectivity. These devices are designed to be coordinated over each other with no intentional time delay placed between bands. There is a clear space provided between bands by the manufacturer's design. For example, a long time-delay band of maximum can be placed over a long time-delay band of intermediate downstream, and selectivity will be provided.

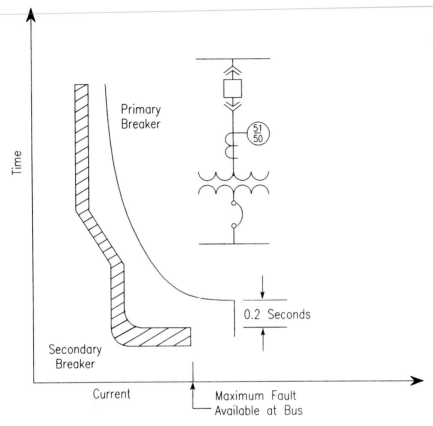

**Figure 3.7**  Low-voltage breaker-relay interval. The figure indicates a molded-case circuit breaker. Not shown is the tripping region at high fault current. Molded-case circuit breakers can be difficult to coordinate in the high-current region. This coordination problem at high-current levels does not exist with fuses on the secondary breaker; however, you may want to provide more ground fault protection than a fuse can offer, thus requiring another specification step when you must specify a ground fault relay with a bolted pressure switch.

### 3.9.7  Instantaneous device over instantaneous device

The term *instantaneous* means that the action of the device is not intentionally delayed in any way. These devices are actuated only by the magnitude of current that passes through the operating coil of an electromechanical relay or the ports of a microprocessor-based relay. In order that any selectivity between instantaneous devices in series may be achieved, there must be a sufficient difference in the current magnitude at the two locations. This difference in magnitude is achieved by having impedance in the circuit. The upstream device must be set at least 150 percent of the current available at the downstream protection location. The downstream device should be set no higher than about 60 percent of the current for which it is expected to operate. The apparently high margin of safety is necessary because instantaneous devices tend to overreach and operate on currents that are apparently lower than the relay setting. Since no time delay is involved, the instantaneous device tends to operate on the instantaneous asymmetrical values. The time-delay relays are restrained until the asymmetrical current has dissipated, but the instantaneous relay will operate on this offset current and hence cause overreach problem.

In general, instantaneous settings for relays should be less than the available symmetrical fault current at the breaker, but greater than the asymmetrical through-fault value at the secondary side of a downstream transformer. When there is no transformer downstream, the instantaneous tap setting should be less than or equal to the available asymmetrical fault current at the next downstream device.

Application of microprocessor-based relays requires some consideration for reset time. Traditional electromechanical relays reset "instantaneously" when current falls below the pickup point and have an inherent time-delayed reset characteristic. Delayed reset characteristics are sometimes required to allow solid-state inverse relays to coordinate the electromechanical inverse relays. The slow reset of an induction disk relay sometimes causes the relay to operate faster than expected if fault current is reapplied by, for instance, a utility recloser.

Microprocessor-based relays reset as instantaneously as the clock speed and software of the microprocessor allow. In some applications you may have to slow down the instantaneous reset, which some manufacturers allow with electromechanical relay emulation (Henville, 1993).

### 3.9.8  Time-delay relay over time-delay relay

The time margin at the maximum available fault current can be shortened, and the total systems operating time reduced by the judicious use of instantaneous elements that cut short the time-delay curve so that any current higher than the pickup of the instantaneous unit will cause the unit to operate before the time-delay element. This allows the coordination point to be moved back to the current value represented by the instantaneous element pickup. The safety margin between devices can be applied at this point instead of at the maximum current value with great advantage because of the inverse nature of the time-delay overcurrent relay.

*Coordinating protective devices across a delta-wye transformer.* When protecting a Δ-Y transformer, an additional 16 percent current margin over all the margins mentioned in this section should be programmed between the primary and secondary protection device characteristic curves, a substation primary fuse and a secondary main breaker, for instance. This helps maintain selectivity for secondary phase-to-phase faults since the per-unit primary current in one phase for this type of fault is 16 percent greater than the per-unit secondary current that flows for a secondary three-phase fault.

As the migration toward microprocessor-based relays continues, the problem of coordinating an induction disk relay with a solid-state relay will present itself with greater frequency. In the early years of the migration, manufacturers were compelled to repackage the tried-and-true electromechanical technology in a digital black box. As the level of comfort with microprocessor technology increases, coupled with the ingenuity of manufacturers who have invested heavily in solving some of the new problems that microprocessor-based protective devices pose to the protection specialist, we shall see the capabilities of devices fundamentally change the way power circuits are designed, rather than the other way around. The potential for better dynamic coordination may lie in the application of overcurrent relays that have a library of hybrid (or even custom piece-wise continuous) time-current characteristics and can adapt to changing circuit topologies, normal load, abnormal voltage, and varying phase- and ground-fault current levels.

### 3.10   Overcurrent Devices

There are various degrees of interactivity in commercial overcurrent coordination software. Some programs have subroutines, macros, or "rule files" that coordinate devices in a manner that is somewhat "automatic" once you establish (or modify) upper and lower device default parameters. Others do not have the automatic feature and are no worse for it, given that results produced "automatically" might create more work in verification.

The information contained in Fig. 3.8 regarding the suggested settings and margins between devices has been developed from several sources. This listing is intended only to get you started, and it should not be construed as the authoritative guideline on the subject. You are likely to discover that these settings and/or margins are impractical or even unallowable by the NEC, depending on the fault-current levels you have to deal with and the variety and manufacturer of the protective devices you must coordinate. Your level of comfort with this listing or a list of your own will come from experience in coordinating overcurrent devices.

### 3.11   Principal Applications for Relays

ANSI-IEEE has assigned numbers to almost 100 devices commonly found in switchgear apparatus. Only a subset of these 100 devices are

| For time-delay device on: | Suggested current setting is: |
|---|---|
| 1. Incoming lines and miscellaneous feeders | Just above maximum permissible operating current, allowing for motor starting |
| 2. Individual motors | Just above locked rotor starting current |
| 3. Transformer feeders to meet NEC requirements | |
|    a. If no secondary breaker | 2.5 per unit transformer rating |
|    b. If there is secondary breaker and the transformer reactance is between 0.6 and 0.10 per unit | 4.0 per unit of transformer rating |
|    c. If there is a secondary breaker and the transformer reactance is not over 0.06 per unit | 6.0 per unit of transformer rating |

*Remark 1:*  If there are several transformers on a feeder without individual primary side fault protection, a relay current setting corresponding to 1.5 times the total full load rating of the several transformers should be ample, except in those cases having large individual motors. However, the setting selected should not be more than six times the full load current of the smallest transformer as required by the NEC.

| For instantaneous devices on: | Suggested current setting is: |
|---|---|
| 1. Transformer feeders | Just above primary current corresponding to maximum initial asymmetrical current for a secondary fault using a 1.6 multiplier for the dc component on 5000 V. This setting should be able to ride through the transformer magnetization current. |
| 2. Motor feeders | Just above the initial asymmetrical current that motors can contribute to a fault on some other current as determined by motor's subtransient reactance and a 1.6 multiplier for 2300 V and above, and a 1.5 multiplier for 600 V and below. If this is not available, use locked rotor current plus 1.0 per unit motor current. |

*Remark 2:*  Low time dial settings in electromechanical relays require special attention. For example, a half tap may cause unnecessary relay operation due to switchgear mechanical vibration. Relay damages and CT saturations have been reported due to improper testing procedure when the instantaneous setting has been over 100 A.

**Figure 3.8**  Suggested current settings of overcurrent relays and direct acting trips for short-circuit protection. (*Adapted from* EDSA User Manual. *Used with permission of EDSA Micro Corporation.*)

relays (Fig. 3.9). The relays themselves can be separated into five categories. The logical performance of these five categories can be defined in terms of the input and the output of the relay. The only relay output of interest is the signal sent to the breaker trip coil. The input of interest, however, comes from either current transformers, voltage trans-

| PURPOSE | RELAY TYPE | | PROTECTED ZONE | | | | | |
|---|---|---|---|---|---|---|---|---|
| | | Feeders | Transmission | Bus | Transformers | Generators | Motors |
| CLEAR FAULTS | Current | 50, 51, 50/51 DFPR | 51TC, 67 67N | 50, 51 (< 35 kV) | 50, 51 | 51/27R 51/27C | 51, 50/51 |
| | Differential | | | | 87T | 87G | 87G |
| | Breaker Failure | | 50 BF | | | | |
| RELIEVE STRESS | Negative Sequence | | | | | 46N | 46N, 47N |
| | Excitation | | | | 24 | 24, 40Q, 60 | 40Q |
| | Temperature | | | | 49 | 49 | 49 |
| | Voltage | 27/59 | | | | 27, 59, 59N | 27, 27/59 |
| RESTORE POWER | Synchronous | 25 | 25 | | | 25, 25A | |
| | SS Reclose | 25/79S | 25/79S | | | | |
| | MS Reclose | 25/79M 79, 79M 25/79TR 0FPR | 25/79M, 79 79M, 25/79TR | | | | |
| PRESERVE SYSTEM | Power | 32R | | | 32R, 32 0/U | 32R, 32 0/U | |
| | Frequency | 81, 81 0/U | | | | 81, 81 0/L | |

**Figure 3.9** Principal applications for relays. A listing of protective devices offered by one manufacturer (*courtesy of Basler*). The devices that are the principal subject of this book lie in the unshaded areas. Electrical people should not be shy about asking manufacturers to custom-build a device to meet the requirements of an application if no off-the-shelf device is available. Protective device manufacturers remain in business because of the remarkable in-house engineering talent that is available for consultation by and application training for electrical designers whose contact with protection engineering is too intermittent to master the art.

formers, or both, and can thereby be used to distinguish relays into the following classes:

1. *Magnitude.*   Overcurrent relays, for example. Overcurrent devices are the backbone of any protection system and comprise about 90 percent of the installed base of relays in the United States. Overcurrent relays are generally indicated on breakers over 1000 V and, to some extent, on low-voltage circuit breakers where greater accuracy is required than can be provided by direct-acting trip coils on the circuit breakers.

2. *Differential.*   When an entire zone of protection of a relay occupies a relatively small physical space near the relay. Differential relaying is regarded as the best kind of protection that money can buy, although its application is limited to applications involving buses, transformers, and motors.

3. *Directional.*   When the zone of a relay must be defined by the direction of current flow with respect to voltage. The quantity that provides the reference phasor is called the polarizing quantity. Typically, voltage is the polarizing quantity, although current signals may be indicated just as well.

4. *Ratio.*   The most familiar application of this principle is in distance relays in which the ratio of voltage/current, tuned to a desired reach down a transmission line with known impedance parameters, determines a trip or block region on a complex plane defined by the impedance of the transmission line itself. Distance relays may be applied to any circuit element (such as a large motor) with known V/I parameters. One of the limitations of distance relays, however, is that the high-speed reach zone is only good for about 80 percent of the transmission line. When two distance relay systems are looking at each other, then only the middle 60 percent of line can be cleared at high speed (in one cycle or less). In this situation, pilot relay systems are indicated.

5. *Pilot.*   When the boundary points of the differential protected zone are not physically close to each other or when the reach of distance relays are not adequate for high-speed clearing, pilot relaying provides a technique for communicating information from a remote zone boundary to the relay at the source terminal. The physical medium for pilot relaying involves the use of pilot current (on the order of milliamps) circulating through telephone lines, audio tone telemetry, or high-frequency signals coupled to the power transmission line itself.

This is a fair ranking (from most to least) of the frequency with which devices operating on the given principles are applied in industrial and commercial distribution systems: overcurrent (magnitude-based) relays most to pilot relays the least. This ranking shall be our guide in how to proportion the focus of our study.

## Bibliography

Crnko, Timothy M., "Current-Limiting Fuse Update—New Style Fuse for Protection of Semiconductor Devices," *IEEE IAS*, May/June 1979.

Henville, C. F., "Combined Use of Definite and Inverse Time Overcurrent Elements Assists in Transmission Line Ground Relay Coordination," *IEEE*, July 1993.

Love, Daniel, "Failure Analysis of Low Voltage Power and Control Circuits," *IEEE IAS*, Sept./Oct. 1991.

Paape, Kenneth L., "Tradeoffs in Motor Branch Circuit Protection," *IEEE IAS*, July/Aug. 1976.

"VacClad-W Medium Voltage Metal-Clad Switchgear," *Westinghouse-Cutler-Hammer Application Guide 32-265*, 1989 (used with permission).

### General references

"Application Guide for Low Voltage AC Nonintegrally Fused Power Circuit Breakers (Using Separately Mounted Current Limiting Fuses)," *ANSI C37.27-1972*.

Cooper Power Systems, *Electrical Distribution Systems Protection Manual*, 3d ed., 1990.

Elmore, W. A., "Instrument Transformers for Relaying," Chap. 5, *Applied Protective Relaying*, Westinghouse Electric Corporation, 1982.

"Guide for Application, Operation, and Maintenance of Distribution Cutouts and Fuse Links, Secondary Fuses, Distribution Enclosed Single-Pole Air Switches, Power Fuses, Fuse Disconnecting Switches, and Accessories," *ANSI/IEEE C37,48-1969*.

Hoerauf, Robert, and David D. Shipp, "Characteristics and Applications of Various Arc Interrupting Methods," *IEEE IAS*, vol. 27, no. 5, Sept./Oct. 1991. This paper addresses the arc interruption considerations in selecting protective devices.

"Selecting Circuit Breakers by Flow Chart," *Specifying Engineer*, Feb. 1985.

"Specifications for Power Fuses and Fuse Disconnecting Switches," *ANSI C37.46-1981*.

"Standard Requirements for Instrument Transformers," *ANSI/IEEE C57.13*. This is the mother standard for all instrument transformers.

"Standards for Industrial Control Equipment," *Underwriter's Laboratory Standard UL508*.

UL Standard 489.

### Further reading

*Determining Current Carrying Capacity in Special Applications*, SQ-D 361.

Elmore, W. A., S. E. Zocholl, and C. A. Kramer, *Effect of Waveform Distortion on Protective Relays*, ABB Power T&D Company, Inc.

Fuller, J. F., E. F. Fuchs, and D. J. Roesler, "Influence of Harmonics on Power Distribution System Protection," *IEEE Transactions on Power Delivery*, vol. III, 1988, pp. 549–557.

Horton, W. F., and S. Goldberg, "The Effect of Harmonics on the Operating Points of Electromechanical Relays," *IEEE Transactions on Power Apparatus and Systems*, vol. PAS-104, May 1988, pp. 1178–1188.

IEEE PES Working Group of the Power System Relaying Committee, "Relay Performance Considerations with Low Ratio CT's and High Fault Currents, *IEEE IAS*, July 1993.

Power System Relaying Committee, "Sine Wave Distortions in Power Systems and the Impact on Protective Relaying," IEEE/PES 84th 0115-6 PWR.

Rice, David E., "Adjustable Speed Drive and Power Rectifier Harmonics—Their Effect on Power System Components," *IEEE Transactions on Industry Applications,* vol. I-22, no. 1, Jan./Feb. 1986.

Roberts, Jeff, and Edmund O. Schweitzer III, "Analysis of Event Reports," presented before the *44th Annual Conference for Protective Relay Engineers,* Texas A&M University, April 15–17, 1991.

Schweitzer III, Edmund O., "Practical Benefits of Microprocessor-Based Relaying," presented before the *Electric Council of New England, Protective Relaying Committee Meeting No. 55,* Stamford, Conn., May 5, 1989.

Smith, R. K., et al., "Solid State Distribution Current Limiter and Circuit Breaker: Application Requirements and Control Strategies," *IEEE Transactions on Power Delivery,* July 1993.

Zocholl, Stanley E., "Integrated Metering and Protective Relay Systems," *IEEE Transactions on Industry Applications,* Sept./Oct. 1989.

# 4

# Ground-Fault Protection

## 4.1 Foreword

Whenever current flows through a path for which it was not intended, we have a ground-fault problem. The word *intended* (or *intentional*) is critical in understanding the subtleties of the subject. Ground faults are the most common kind of fault on any power system. The amount of current that flows through these unintended paths depends on the impedance between the potential difference along the fault path. We try to control these potential differences and impedances with a range of grounding methods that have evolved from practical experience. The whole history of electrical power system development can be understood in terms of when and how grounding methods were devised and applied.

We speak in terms of ungrounded or grounded systems as if the differences were opposite, when actually the terms are only nominal. Grounding can and should be regarded as a continuum, a matter of degree rather than as two states. This continuum ranges from the free-neutral system (very low impedance and high ground-fault current) to the effectively grounded system (very high impedance and negligible ground-fault current). The higher the ground-fault current in relation to the three-phase fault current, the greater the degree of grounding in the system. Effectively (or solidly) grounded systems, for example, will have a line-to-ground short-circuit current of at least 60 percent of the three-phase short-circuit value.

Our concern for grounding methods is due to the need to either specify protective devices to match the level of ground-fault current (if any) or control the flow of ground-fault current to match the sensing capabilities of the protective devices available to us. Choosing which to do would be easy were it not for the fact that the choice we make profoundly affects the way the power system will behave under fault conditions.

Such a choice does not exist for the electrical person who comes to a power system that already exists. The manner in which the power system behaves under fault conditions has already been determined, and the work that lies ahead is mainly in getting to know how much ground-fault current you will have and what your protective devices are capable of seeing and interrupting.

We will deal with specific examples of ground-overcurrent coordination in the specialty chapters of Part 2 of this book. For now, we dwell on the ideas concerning ground-fault protection that will apply to both low-voltage and medium-voltage circuits. Our review of grounding theory and practice will enable us to determine how to set ground-overcurrent protective devices.

- Will there be ground-fault current at all?

- If so, what kind of phase-to-ground-fault current levels can we expect? What are the magnitudes of such currents and what paths do they take?

- How and where do we sense these currents and how and where should they be interrupted?

- What are the tradeoffs between protection and selectivity that are specific to ground-fault protection?

## 4.2  Relevant Theory

There are two things that electricity must do to be useful to us:

- Electricity should flow at a predictable and dependable voltage level, such as 120, 277, or 34,500 V.

- Electricity should follow a predictable and safe path between the generating source and the load.

To meet the first requirement, we have a configuration called the *system ground*. Every new system created by a service transformer or a generator requires the establishment of a new system ground. For the second requirement, we have a configuration called the *equipment ground*. Figure 4.1 illustrates the distinction. As we shall see, the equipment ground system is an essential part of any overcurrent protection system.

The NEC provides us with working definitions.

*System grounding.*   The intentional connection to ground of one of the power current-carrying conductors of the system.

*Equipment grounding.*   The connection to ground of all the non-power-carrying conductive materials that enclose or are adjacent to the

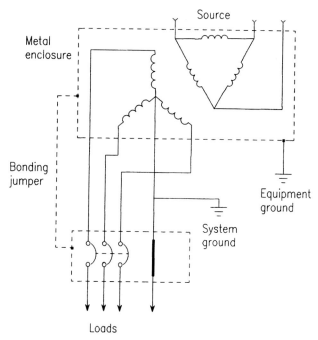

**Figure 4.1**  System and equipment grounding. *System ground-ing* connects the electrical supply, from the utility, the trans-former secondary windings, or from a generator, to ground. System grounding limits voltages due to lightning, line surges, unintentional contact with higher voltage lines, and to maintain the nominal voltage during normal operation. System ground-ing is not intended to conduct ground-fault current that is caused by a ground fault in a circuit.

   *Equipment grounding,* consisting of interconnecting networks of equipment grounding conductors, ensures that all exposed non-current-carrying metallic parts of all structures and equip-ment or near the electrical distribution system are at the same potential (note the bonding jumpers between the enclosures) and that this is the zero reference potential of the earth. Equip-ment grounding conductors are required by the National Elec-tric Code to be run with or enclose circuit conductors and thereby conduct ground-fault currents of sufficient magnitude for fast operation of overcurrent devices.

energized conductors. These conducting materials are typically con-duit and raceways in buildings, grounding conductors pulled through underground cable systems and bonded to primary conductor man-holes, transformer cases, switchgear enclosures, and so on.

   Figure 4.1 shows separate ground connections for each one in order to emphasize the difference in function between the two. In practice, there is a common connection to earth for both grounds.

   Equipment grounding must be adequate if system grounding is to function properly. All parts of equipment capable of conducting should be connected to ground by bonds that can adequately carry ground-fault current from any possible line-to-ground-fault to the appropriate terminal at the system's source (West, 1974). Since the equipment bonding jumpers are installed for the sole purpose of conducting ground-fault current, we are justified in calling these jumpers "ground-fault conductors" or "ground-fault bonding jumpers" instead of "equipment-bonding jumpers." The terms are used interchangeably in the industry, however, causing a certain degree of confusion until you get used to the confusion.

### 4.2.1  Separately derived systems

The notion of a separately derived system is fairly intuitive to electrical people who deal regularly with analytic models of power systems.

- Every voltage level of a distribution system must be grounded independently.
- Neutrals must be grounded at the source, not the load.
- Where transformer secondary winding is wye-connected, ground at the neutral.
- Where the transformer secondary winding is delta-connected, a neutral can be derived from a grounding transformer.

The foregoing are ideas that are more or less taken for granted when computing fault currents and designing protection systems.

The issue of a separately derived system becomes particularly important for protection specialists when dealing with alternate power sources for emergency and standby power systems (see Fig. 4.2). In most situations, you can assume that the service transformer of a facility defines the separately defined system because of the electrical isolation of primary and secondary windings but only if the secondary of the transformer feeds a premises wiring system as defined by the NEC.

> NEC Art. 100: *Separately Derived System.*  A premises wiring system whose power is derived from a generator, transformer, or converter windings and that has no direct electrical connection, including a solidly connected grounded circuit conductor, to supply conductors originating in another system.

The notion of a separately derived system is fundamentally a grounding issue. Art. 250 of the 1993 NEC contains the actual mechanical requirements for grounding separately derived power systems.

### 4.2.2  Stray neutral currents

When electrical systems are not separately derived, "stray" neutral currents result. These stray neutral currents can

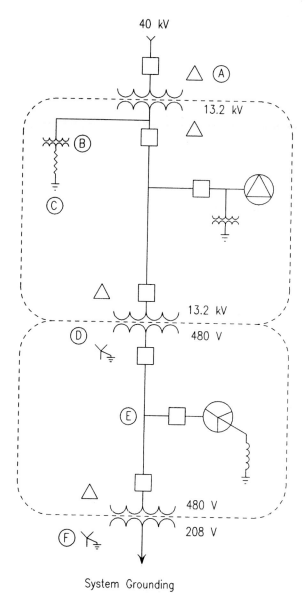

System Grounding

**Figure 4.2** System grounds established in each voltage level. All currents supplied by a transformer must return to that transformer.

- overheat raceways
- interfere with devices that are sensitive to electromagnetic interference
- cause enough arcing to ignite explosive materials

If a grounded neutral circuit conductor is connected to the equipment grounding conductors at more than one point, or if it is grounded at more than one point, the stray neutral current paths will be established. Currents will be flowing wherever potential differences exist. Fault currents will tend to follow a path close to the conductor, such as through conduit, rather than through remote paths, even if the latter has a larger conducting cross section because of the higher reactance of the remote current return path. This is what causes the fault current in the return circuit to split according to the rules of parallel impedances. If we have protective devices ready to pick up excessive ground-fault currents, these stray currents jangling around the faulted circuit may not accumulate to any threshold to trip any circuit breaker. If ground-fault current to drive protective devices is scarce to begin with, let's not provide any other paths for it to "leak" out of the path that enables us to sense it.

Because of the multiple neutral-to-ground connections, two problems can develop.

- If a ground fault occurs anywhere in the systems, then the fault current has two paths of flow—one directly to the grounded neutral of the incoming utility source via equipment-grounding conductors and one to the grounded neutral of the engine-generator set via equipment-grounding conductors and back to the neutral of the incoming utility source via the continuous neutral. The latter path will not tend to actuate the ground-fault sensor, which causes incomplete sensing of the total fault current.

- If the load is imbalanced, the return neutral current has two paths of flow. It can go directly to the service neutral via the neutral conductor or back to the service neutral via the equipment-grounding conductors and the continuous neutral. The current through the latter path would have the same effect on the ground-fault sensor as a ground-fault current and will be carried by the equipment-grounding conductors, which are not provided for this purpose. If the second path has sufficiently low impedance (comparable to the same of the neutral path), an imbalanced load may cause the ground-fault sensor to trip the breaker even though a ground fault or short circuit does not occur.

The grounded service conductor of service-supplied systems should be grounded at the service equipment. If the supply transformer is located outside of the building, the grounded service conductor should also be grounded on the secondary side of the supply transformer, either at the transformer or elsewhere ahead of the service equipment. A grounding connection should *not* be made to any grounded neutral circuit conductor on the load side of the service disconnecting means.

In a separately derived system, the main transformer is on the customer's premises and is used solely to supply power to those premises. A system that is not separately derived is fed from a common utility transformer bank external to the premises and that also supplies other customers. Such may be the case in many shopping malls.

## 4.3 Models of Faulted Circuits

When the NEC indicates its requirements for ground-fault protection in terms of 1200-A pickup and 1-s delay at 3000 A of ground-fault current (refer to Art. 230-95), the implication is that electrical people will have enough information to set up a sequence network to calculate the ground-fault current $3I_0$. Although setting up the series sequence network for calculating prospective ground-fault current is easy enough (as in Example 2.2), getting your hands on the zero sequence data is not that easy. Estimates of the zero sequence reactances of transformers and motors are available from IEEE and manufacturer literature, but the zero sequence reactances of, for example, medium-voltage cables, cannot be looked up in tables. It can only be measured, and making such a measurement requires complete deenergization of the cable. We can make some educated guesses with a sparsity of hard data, however.

### 4.3.1 Low-voltage circuit

Figure 4.3 illustrates a commonly occurring ground-fault current path. The fault current actually travels through the conduit that contains the phase conductors, and it travels through the enclosures. You can see why the NEC is very specific about the mechanical requirements for a low-impedance path through conduit and enclosures. One rusty bushing along this path could cause a ground fault to burn to destruction. There needs to be a match between the prospective ground-fault current and the current-carrying capability of these conducting elements of the system. Insufficient ampacity in this path will impede the flow of ground-fault current that we need to drive our protective devices.

There has been some considerable research into this subject by Dunki-Jacobs (1972, 1986). The reader is encouraged to obtain these references from the IEEE because the notion of using conduit for a

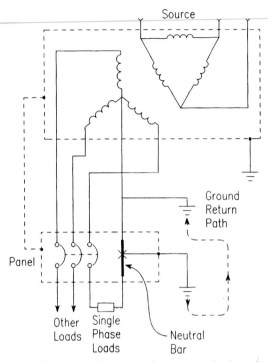

**Figure 4.3** Low-voltage ground current path—branch circuit fault. In a solidly grounded system, the fault current returns to the source primarily along the equipment grounding conductors, with a small proportion of this fault current flowing along a parallel path through building steel or water pipes. If the ground return impedance were as low as the impedance of the circuit conductors, ground-fault currents would be high enough for phase overcurrent protective devices to open the faulted circuit. But the impedance of the ground return path is usually higher, thereby throttling the ground-fault current we need to drive protective devices.

The grounding problem is particularly acute when emergency/standby generators are involved. Generators, as sources, actually define a separately derived service, but since they are only used in emergency/standby situations, they complicate ground-fault protection strategies. We want to avoid setting up multiple ground-fault current paths in which only some of the fault current can be seen. We want to see all of it; or as much as possible.

ground-fault current return path takes a little getting used to. This method works, of course, but the concept of an ampacity and an impedance of a conduit or bushing entering into our lumped parameter models of single-line-to-ground-fault sequence networks is an impedance that is frequently ignored.

## 4.3.2 Arcing faults

In low-voltage distribution circuits, arcing faults require special attention. Arcing faults are a common failure mode in 480-V circuits (and in systems with high X/R ratio, in particular), thus causing current to lag sufficiently to allow restriking of the arc at approximately the time that the ac current waveform passes through zero magnitude (Kaufman and Page, 1960).

Exact minimum values of arcing ground current are difficult to compute precisely for several reasons:

- Results are influenced by the geometry, spacing, environmental, and supply circuit characteristics.

- Current waveshape is generally irregular with a harmonic content.

- Current is frequently discontinuous.

The general expression for a fundamental frequency line-to-ground-fault current in a three-phase system is expressed in symmetrical component parameters on page 43.

Both positive and negative sequence impedances are associated only with the source and phase impedance of the equipment supplying the fault current since the currents of each of these two sequences combine to zero at the ground-fault location. Impedances $Z_1$ and $Z_2$ are equal for the circuit elements involved (transformers, buses, cables, and so on), and are the values we have studied in Chap. 1. The zero sequence impedance system, however, involves in-phase current in each of the three-phase circuits with each circuit consisting of the source and phase conductors of the equipment to the point of fault. The impedance to ground-fault currents for this network can be identified as the zero sequence impedance $Z_0$. The sum of the zero sequence currents in the phase conductors, $3I_0$ must then be returned to the power supply via the ground return path identified as $Z_g$. This path may consist of building steel, conduit, ground conductors, grounded neutral conductors, ground buses, bonding jumpers, grounding rods, earth, equipment grounded housings, and so on. In effect, an entire building can rise in potential momentarily while ground-fault current seeks zero potential. (This was an argument against solid grounding in the early days of power system history.)

This ground return circuit results in an additional impedance voltage drop of $3I_0Z_g$. By considering the voltage drop term $3I_0Z_g$ to be the product of $3Z_g$ and $I_0$, it becomes evident that it can be correctly accounted for by adding the impedance $3Z_g$ to the zero sequence impedance network. Thus the total zero sequence impedance network is

$$Z_0^{\text{total}} = (Z_0 + 3Z_g)$$

Each term need not be measured independently, but rather we may work with a value for the *total term* in our longhand short-circuit calculations when we need a value for zero sequence impedance to compute bolted single-line-to-ground fault current. It is important to recognize that both terms are present, however. Also, when minimum fault current is desired, any system component that would introduce additional impedance should be included in the foregoing equation as well.

Our expression for a bolted single-line-to-ground thus far does not consider the effects of the voltage drop due to the arc in an arcing condition. Because of the voltage drop across the arc, the resultant ground-fault current may be considerably lower than the bolted ground-fault current. This reduction can be accounted for by the multiplier K, which relates the arcing-to-bolted to ground-fault current as follows.

$$I_f^{\text{arcing}} = K \times \frac{3E_{\text{ln}}}{Z_1 + Z_2 + Z_0 + 3Z_g}$$

The values for K are given in Table 4.1 and are applied only in low-voltage systems since the effect of arc voltage is significant in comparison with the driving voltage. Note that K approaches zero for a 208-V system. It is important to remember that this calculation procedure for determining the ground-fault current is only an approximation. The minimum fault current value is dependent on actual system conditions at the time of the fault. Typical conditions that would increase the system impedance and thereby cause a lower ground-fault current than that calculated would be:

- Installation changes that depart from design, such as greater conductor spacings (phase-to-phase and/or phase-to-ground) or ground return path alterations (ground conductors, bonding jumpers, and so on)

- Operating conditions such as opening of one phase to the transformer primary, changes in the ground return path because of loose connections, open ground conductors, and the like

**TABLE 4.1   Approximate Minimum Values of Arcing Fault Currents in Per Unit of Bolted Values\***

| Type of fault | Nominal system voltage | | |
| --- | --- | --- | --- |
| | 600 V | 480 V | 208 V |
| Three-phase | 0.94 | 0.89 | 0.12 |
| Single-phase, line-to-line | 0.85 | 0.74 | 0.02 |
| Single-phase, line-to-ground | 0.40 | 0.38 | 0 |
| Three-phase, one transformer primary fuse open | 0.88 | 0.80 | 0 |

It is important to realize that these factors are *not* normalized upon the three-phase bolted fault. These factors may be applied only to (essentially) derate a known fault current value. For example, once you know what the bolted (zero impedance) three-phase fault current value is at 480 V, then the arcing fault current value is 89 percent of that. Similarly, once you have queued up your zero sequence networks to compute a single-line-to-ground fault current, then the arcing fault is 38 percent of that.

\* Adapted from IEEE Gray Book.

It is noteworthy that when a line-to-ground arcing fault occurs at the secondary terminals of a delta-wye transformer, the approximate magnitude of ground-fault current will be K times the three-phase short-circuit current value at the transformer terminals (because in many cases single-line-to-ground-fault current approaches three-phase fault current as indicated in Chap. 2). Therefore, for a 480/277 system, the approximate transformer terminal arcing gf terminal arcing ground-fault current value would be 38 percent $\times$ $I_{3\phi}$. This 38 percent value comes from realizing in the basic $I_f$ equation that the ground return path impedance $Z_g$ from a transformer phase terminal to its neutral is, for all practical purposes, zero. Furthermore, the zero sequence impedance $Z_0$ approaches the values of positive $Z_1$ and negative $Z_2$ impedances.

It should be observed, however, that for line-to-ground arcing faults at location in the system other than at the source transformer, the ground return impedance $Z_g$ is not zero. The $Z_0 + 3Z_g$ value becomes increasingly greater than the positive $Z_1$ or negative sequence $Z_2$ values as one advances into the system away from the source transformer.

When the ohmic value of the resistor far exceeds the other system phase and ground return impedance values, it then becomes the controlling impedance element determining the line-to-ground fault current magnitude. It may cause the arcing line-to-ground-fault current to be self-extinguishing by limiting the voltage across the arc below the restrike voltage.

From a system point of view, however, insertion of a resistor in the neutral circuit precludes (on a low-voltage circuit) that no neutral loads are to be served.

A great deal of work on this subject has been done by Dunki-Jacobs, Love, Nash, Smith, and others, and the reader is encouraged to seek the references and order reprints on this important subject from the IEEE.

---

### The 3000-A Threshold

The 1200-A maximum pickup permitted by the NEC is frequently too low to allow the use of circuit breakers and fuses in the 200- to 400-A range. A typical 1000-A main switch or breaker will generally be served from a transformer rated 500 or 750 kVA. With a typical impedance of 5.75 percent, the bolted three-phase symmetrical fault currents will be 10,464 and 15,696 A, respectively. Taking service entrance cable into consideration, the probable minimum arcing fault value will be in the 3500- to 5500-A range. Conservatively, then, it does not make much sense to protect for anything less than 3000 A. A 3000-A minimum would permit excellent coordination with virtually all 225-A breakers and some fuses as large as 400 A. While it may seem illogical to provide a 3000-A maximum ground-fault protection setting for a 1000-A overcurrent device, a review of the curves will show that it is not. Below 100 A, the purpose of ground-fault protection is principally to provide selectivity, not protection. So the 3000-A ground-fault protection maximum should not be of great concern to those who stress protection (Love, 1991).

### 4.3.3  Medium-voltage circuits

Medium-voltage distribution circuits are constructed to carry ground-fault current through a raceway just as low-voltage systems are constructed to carry ground-fault current through a raceway within a building. The NEC is very specific about the requirements for providing a continuous, low-impedance path for low-voltage ground-fault current to flow. There are requirements for the cross section of metallic conduit or ground conductors through nonmetallic conduit, junction box bushings, and the like. Figure 4.4 is a schematic diagram of the somewhat less familiar requirements of grounded medium-voltage distribution circuits.

A continuous, low-impedance path is required through manholes and raceway to the protective device. In bulk distribution systems, the medium-voltage cable shield is the critical ground current path we use to drive protective devices. We shall dwell on this issue in Chap. 8.

## 4.4  Controlling Ground-Fault Current

Let us examine the different types of grounding from the case of infinite impedance (ungrounded) through high and low impedance to zero impedance (solidly grounded). We will avoid repeating the information that appears in a great deal of the existing literature on the subject of grounding by dwelling on a few numerical examples to give you some feeling for the distinction among grounding methods. Figure 4.5 will apply to all of the grounding configurations discussed in this section with only modifications to the impedance between neutral and ground.

### 4.4.1  Ungrounded (free neutral) systems

An ungrounded power system has an impedance large enough to limit all ground-fault currents to zero. As Example 4.1 will illustrate, however, there will always be charging current the moment ac potential is applied to any conducting object. When we speak of an ungrounded, free neutral system, we mean that ground-fault current is *nominally* (or ideally) zero.

Under normal conditions, an ungrounded system operates no differently than grounded systems. There may be little indication of what kind of system you really have until there is a fault. For this reason, the following observations are a fairly positive indication of the kind of system you are working with:

- The absence of ground or neutral relays in medium-voltage feeder circuits
- The presence of pilot lamps, indicating equal potential across all three lamps in a low-voltage circuit

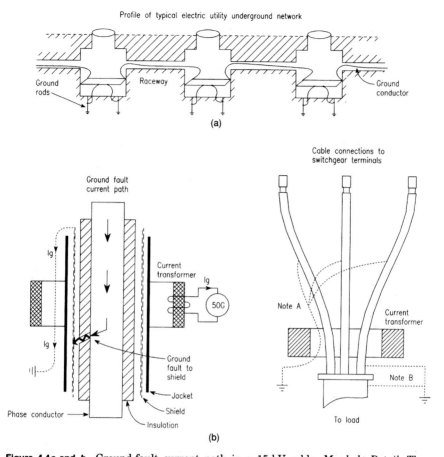

**Figure 4.4a and b** Ground-fault current path in a 15-kV cable. *Manhole Detail:* The equipment grounding strategy that applies to low-voltage circuit raceway applies to medium-voltage cable raceway—only over a much greater distance. There are two grounding methods involving the cable shield: multipoint (shown in the figure) and single-point. Both have implications for the amount of ground-fault current that we have to drive protective devices. Multipoint grounding decreases reactance to fault currents (due to the parallel impedance effect) but it also produces circulating currents in the shields. The amount of circulating current is determined by shield resistance, current flowing in the cable phases, and mutual inductance of other cables and is independent of the number of grounding points and the cable length. Single-point grounding eliminates circulating currents and the heating effect produced by them (this heating effect will reduce ampacity); however, when shields are bonded at only one end, a small voltage (on the order of 25 V) will be present in the shield. This voltage will rise with distance from the grounded point depending upon the mutual inductance to other cables.

*Cable Detail:* Most ground faults in multiconductor (three-phase) cables start as a ground fault between one conductor and the sheath or shield, usually due to the entrance of moisture into the cable. Appropriate applications of relays will open faulty circuits before the arc has spread to the other two conductors. Single conductor cables are subject only to phase-to-ground faults except at the terminals of the circuit.

*Note A:* Shields must be backfed through current transformer and grounded on the load side.

*Note B:* Lead, armor, conduit, interstice ground conductors, etc., must be terminated and solidly grounded on the load side of the current transformer.

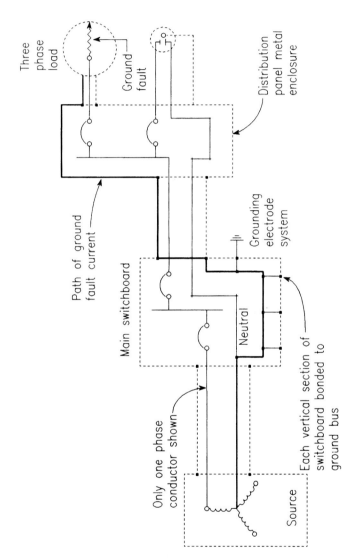

**Figure 4.5** Generalized source ground circuit. It is far easier to build a circuit with ground-fault protective devices than it is to maintain the continuity of the prospective ground-fault current path over the lifetime of a facility or a right-of-way.

When the pilot lamps burn with unequal brightness, the voltage difference indicates that there is an *unintentional* (usually accidental) path to ground. Many process-critical power delivery systems are ungrounded in order to maintain the flow of power to the load while investigation into the location of the unintended path to ground takes place. Many single-phase control systems are ungrounded in which case there are only two pilot lamps with which to be concerned.

### Ungrounded systems: pros and cons

- Not generally recommended but indicated for high service continuity
- Fault-current primary amperes very low so that equipment damage associated with current may be light
- Faults easy to detect but difficult to locate
- Fault current low, minimum damage
- High potential of transient overvoltages
- Arcing faults can be aggravated by repeated charging of line to ground capacitances on ungrounded systems
- Ferroresonance and neutral voltage transformer inversion possible

Another reason that ungrounded systems are actually grounded (just not in the intentional, conventional way) is that as soon as a fault detector is applied (such as two or three lamps or using one or three voltage transformers), the system is grounded through the high impedance of these devices. The resistance of the relays and associated ballast resistors helps limit the transient overvoltages so that very few cases of overvoltage actually exist.

### 4.4.2   High-impedance grounding

A high-impedance grounded power system has an impedance large enough to limit ground-fault currents to a very small value. That value cannot be ignored in our analytic models. The NEC permits high-resistance grounding in three-phase ac systems of 480 to 1000 V that do not serve line-to-neutral loads where certain conditions are met. One of the conditions is that a ground-fault detection system exist.

High-impedance grounded systems may be high reactance or high resistance, or both. Such systems will have a reactor near the service supply point. This reactor is frequently contained in a metal-clad housing about the size of a typical metal-clad switchgear unit, and it should have a nameplate identifying it as such.

## High-impedance grounding: pros and cons

- Recommended for industrial systems seeking high service continuity
- Fault current levels 1 to 10 A primary; therefore low damage
- Fault maintenance important
- Transient overvoltage limited to about 250 percent of line-to-neutral voltage

High-resistance grounded systems are commonly thought to be 10 A or less. High-resistance grounded systems are designed to meet the criterion of $R_0 \leq Xc_0$ to limit the transient overvoltages due to arcing ground faults. $Xc_0$ is the distributed per-phase capacitive reactance to ground the system, and $R_0$ is the per-phase zero sequence resistance of the system.

**Example 4.1**   High-Resistance Grounding

*Situation.*   An industrial plant 13.8-kV system with elements listed below. The actual circuit configuration is similar to the circuits that appear in Figs. 2.6a, 2.11, 2.12, and 3.2 with a surge capacitor connected to the 13.8-kV bus.

*Requirements.*   This system is to be grounded as shown in Fig. 4.6. Calculate what little ground-fault current there will be.

**solution**   From estimating data or specific test, we have the following capacitances to ground (microfarads per phase):

| | |
|---|---|
| Source transformer | 0.004 |
| Local generator | 0.11 |
| Motor | 0.06 |
| Power center transformer | 0.008 |
| Total connecting cables | 0.13 |
| Surge capacitor | 0.25 |
| Total capacitance to ground | 0.562 |

$$X_0^c = \frac{-j10^6}{2\pi fC} = -j\frac{10^6}{2(3.1416)(60)(0.0652)} = 4719.9 \ \Omega/\phi$$

Thus the charging current of this 13.8-kV system is

$$I^c = \frac{13,800}{\sqrt{3} \times 4719.9} = 1.69 \ A/\phi \text{ at } 13.8 \text{ kV}$$

The total capacitance per unit on a 20-MVA base is

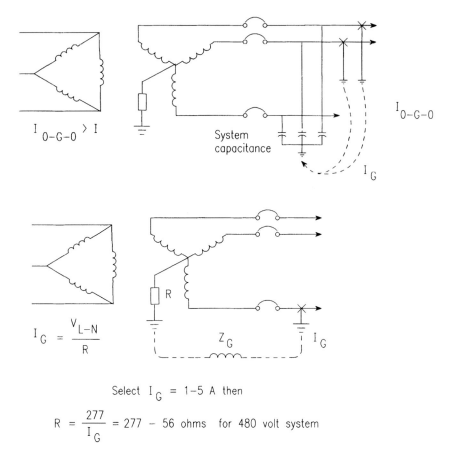

$$\text{Select } I_G = 1\text{--}5 \text{ A then}$$

$$R = \frac{277}{I_G} = 277 - 56 \text{ ohms } \text{ for 480 volt system}$$

**Figure 4.6**  High-resistance grounding. In a high-resistance grounded system the neutral is grounded through a predominantly resistive impedance whose resistance is selected to allow a ground-fault current through the resistor *equal to or somewhat more than* the capacitive charging current of the system. The resistor can be connected either directly from neutral to ground, or in the secondary circuit of one or more transformers. Typical ground-fault currents are 1 to 10 A on the primary system. At 1-5 A the circuit above falls within this range. (Westinghouse, 1986.)

$$X^c = \frac{20(4719.9)}{(13.8)^2} = 495.68 \text{ }\Omega \text{ pu}$$

For high-resistance grounding, $R = X_0^C$ so that R in the zero sequence network is 495.68 pu. For the system,

$$Z_0 = \frac{(495.7)(-j495.7)}{495.7 - j495.7} = 350.5 \angle -45° \text{ }\Omega$$

For a line-to-ground fault, the positive and negative sequence values of the system are very small and can be ignored. Thus for a line-to-ground fault on this 13.8-kV system

$$I_1 = I_2 = I_0 = \frac{1.0}{250.5 \angle -45^\circ} = 0.00285 \angle 45^\circ$$

The base per unit current is

$$I_b = 20{,}000/(\sqrt{3} \times 13.8) = 836.74 \text{ A}$$

Therefore the ground-fault current = $0.00285 \times 836.74 = 2.3847$ A

*Remarks.*    Various reference sources provide tables and curves for typical charging capacitances per phase of the power system components. In an existing system, the total capacitance can be determined by dividing the measured phase charging current into the line-to-neutral voltage.

High-resistance grounded systems are commonly found in industrial facilities supplying power to critical processes. Most typical low-voltage emergency standby systems are required to service line-to-neutral loads. The emergency generator windings are wye-connected, and the neutral is brought out for use as a circuit conductor. In this case, the generator would not be permitted to high-resistance grounded. However, where line-to-neutral loads need not be served (as with some 480-V motors) or where delta-wye isolation transformers are used to service a neutral for line-to-neutral loads, a 480-V 3-phase three-wire generator may be high-resistance grounded. In such applications, meeting the conditions established by the NEC would gain the advantages of high-resistance grounding in terms of continuity of service with a single-line-to-ground fault (Onan, 1991).

### 4.4.3   Low-impedance grounding

A low-impedance grounded power system has an impedance that allows substantial flow of ground-fault current. Where ground-fault current magnitude is determined primarily by resistance alone, the fault current is very close (on the order of 2°) to being in phase with system voltage.

Ground-fault current can be limited substantially by resistance with little compromise of advantages of the grounded system. Transitory overvoltage can be anticipated to be held within 2.5 times normal voltage, only slightly greater than the 1.8 value expected of solid grounding. Reactance grounding is generally limited to generators. Reduction of ground-fault current by reactors is kept to about 25 percent of three-phase current. Otherwise, there is risk of transitory overvoltage troubles because of repetitive restrike in an arc in the ground-fault systems. Resistance-grounded systems stay free of this trouble.

**Low-impedance grounding: pros and cons**

- Ground-fault current 50 to 600 A primary
- Recommended for industrial systems from 1000 V to 15 kV
- Easy to detect and locate faults selectively

**Example 4.2**   Low-Impedance Grounding

*Situation.*   The grounding reactor in the schematic of Fig. 4.6 is to be applied to limit the maximum line-to-ground-fault current in a system to 400 A primary.

*Requirements.*   Calculate the size of this reactor.

**solution**

Let $S_b = 20$ MVA. From the data in the Appendix, we determine "standard" impedances.

$$\text{Source } X_1 = X_2 = \text{MVA}_b/\text{MVA}_{sc} = 20/3200 = j0.00625 \ \Omega \text{ pu}$$

$$\text{Transformer } X_t = j0.052 \ \Omega \text{ pu}$$

$$\text{Total } X_1 = X_2 = j(0.0063 + 0.052) = j0.0583 \ \Omega \text{ pu}$$

$$\text{Total } X_0 = j(0.052 + 3X) \ \Omega \text{ pu}$$

For a 400-A primary fault:

$$I_1 = I_2 = I_0 = 400/3 = 133.33 \text{ A at } 13.8 \text{ kV}$$

$$I_b = 20,000/(\sqrt{3} \times 13.8) = 836.74 \text{ A}$$

$$I_1 = I_2 = I_0 = 133.33/836.74 = 0.159 \text{ A pu}$$

$$X_1 + X_2 + X_0 = j(0.1685 + 3X) \ \Omega \text{ pu}$$

Assuming $V = j1.0$ and solving for X, we get $X = 2.036 \ \Omega$ pu. Since $Z_b = (13.8)^2/20$, then reactor size would be $(13.8)^2/20 \times 2.036 = 19.38 \ \Omega$ at 13.8 kV.

Low-resistance grounding has not found wide acceptance in low-voltage systems. The need for a complete and separate series of coordinated ground responsive trips on the complex tangle of feeders, subfeeders, and branch circuits, which typically compromise a low-voltage distribution system, has made this grounding method less attractive than the others. Mining systems, however, have long been grounded through a high resistance because of the unique protection problems.

### 4.4.4   Solidly (zero impedance) grounded systems

The opposite of free neutral grounding is solid grounding. In this scheme, we do everything we can to secure all the ground-fault current into the sensing elements of our protective devices. Solid grounding permits the highest levels of current to flow in a faulted circuit. The higher the fault current the higher the probability (because of extreme phase current imbalance) that fuses and circuit breakers will operate in the instantaneous range. Save for a few exceptions allowed by the National Electric Code, most low-voltage power systems are solidly grounded, so that (with single-line-to-ground-fault magnitudes approaching three-phase bolted faults) the need for separate ground-fault protection is at least reduced. Article 250-5 requires ac power systems of 50 to 1000 V to be solidly grounded where the maximum voltage-to-ground on the line conductors will not exceed 150 V. Systems that supply phase-to-neutral loads are also required to be solidly grounded. As we are well aware, despite the advantages offered by neutral grounding, the NEC still requires separate ground-fault protection in the circuits that are the principal subject of this book.

The features of solidly grounded systems are the following:

- Recommended for industrial systems *up to* 1000 V and for systems *above* 15,000 V. (Middle-range voltages such as 2400 and 4800 V are commonly ungrounded.)

- Fault currents range from low to very high.

- Faults are easy to detect and selectively locate.

The IEEE Standard 142 has a specific definition for solid (or effective) grounding. When the power system constants are

$$X_0/X_1 \leq = 3.0 \text{ and } R_0/X_1 \leq = 1.0$$

then the system is said to be solidly grounded. From a practical standpoint, this means that there is no impedance between the system neutral and ground; hence this system is solidly grounded. We do it by connecting the neutral of the wye winding of the power transformers to the station ground mat and ground. In the diagrams, this would be shown as in Fig. 4.7 with $X_R$ omitted. The magnitudes depend on the power system configuration and constants, location of the fault, and the fault resistance that may or may not be significant. Since the current level can vary with the fault location, it becomes easier to locate the fault and selectively isolate the trouble area by protective relays. The various techniques used are covered in the various chapters on equipment protection. The CTs are applied to operate time-overcurrent relays set sensitively and with time to coordinate with the various line, feeder, and relays that they overreach. Hence this serves as backup last-resort protection for ground faults around the area that is not properly cleared by their primary and associated backup protection.

**Example 4.3**   Solidly Grounded System

*Situation.*   Assume that the system described in Example 4.2 is now solidly grounded. $X_g = R_g = 0$. Refer to Fig. 4.7.

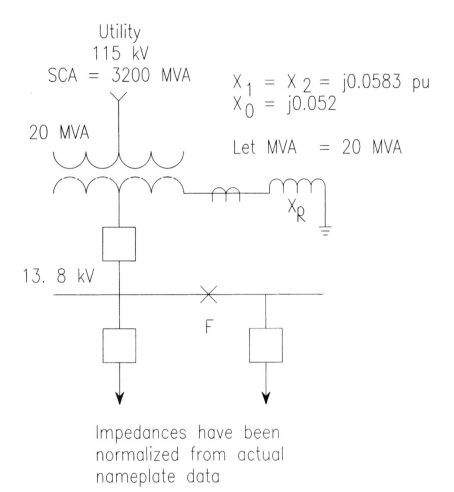

Utility
115 kV
SCA = 3200 MVA

$X_1 = X_2 = j0.0583$ pu
$X_0 = j0.052$

20 MVA

Let MVA = 20 MVA

13. 8 kV

F

$X_R$

Impedances have been
normalized from actual
nameplate data

**Figure 4.7** Schematic of circuit with three-phase ground-fault current less than single-phase. Phase faults usually have a lower power factor than ground faults because of the inductance of transformers and generators included in the circuit.

*Requirements.*    Calculate single-line-to-ground-fault current.

**solution**

For a fault at F, $X_1 = X_2 = j0.0583$ pu

$X_0 = j0.052$ all on a 20-MVA, 13.8-kV base

Thus $X_1 + X_2 + X_0 = j0.1685$ and

$$I_1 = I_2 = I_0 = \frac{j1.0}{j0.1685} = 5.934 \text{ pu}$$

$= 4965.8$ A at 13.8 kV with $I_b = 836.74$ A

$$\text{Then } I_a = 3I_0 = 3(5.934) = 17.8 \text{ pu}$$

$$= 14{,}897.5 \text{ A at } 13.8 \text{ kV}$$

For a three-phase fault at F and taking $V = j1.0$

$$I_1 = \frac{j1.0}{j0.0583} = 17.17 \text{ pu}$$

$$= 14{,}364.6 \text{ A at } 13.8 \text{ kV}$$

*Remarks.*   The difference between three-phase and single-line-to-ground-fault current in this example is small because the source is quite large compared to the supply transformer. If the source impedance were larger, the two fault currents would be lower, but the ground fault would be a larger percentage of the three-phase fault.

System designers should be aware that in all but solidly grounded systems, the interrupting capabilities of molded-case breakers are affected by the method of grounding.

---

### Summary of System Grounding Classifications

Where R is the system fault resistance, X the system fault reactance, subscripts 1, 2, and 0 are the positive, negative, and zero sequence impedances, respectively.
   *Effectively grounded:*   $R_0 \leq X_1$ and $X_0 \leq 3X_1$
   *Reactance grounded:*   $X_0 \leq 10X_1$
   *Resistance grounded:*   $R_0 \geq 2X_0$
   *High-resistance grounded:*   $R_0 \leq X_0^c/3$, where $X_0^c$ is the capacitive zero-sequence reactance
   Grounded for serving line-to-neutral loads: $Z \leq Z_1$, where Z is the system fault impedance.

---

## 4.5   Methods of Sensing Ground-Fault Current

If we are going to have coordinated ground-fault protection, then we must be able to sense ground-fault currents at as many locations on a circuit as we can afford. The usual locations on a circuit where we place devices to sense ground-fault current are:

- *Branch circuit receptacles.*   This is ground-fault protection closest to the electrical end user, and it must be very sensitive protection to pick up ground-fault current of 5.0 mA or less. The 1993 NEC extends ground-fault protection requirements to more facilities than ever before.

- *Power distribution panels.*   If there is a 480 delta to 208 wye distribution.

- *Unit substation feeder breakers.* Must have ground-fault sensors per NEC Art. 517.

- *Unit substation main breakers.* Where we can see ground-fault currents in the 1000- to 3000-A range.

- *Medium-voltage distribution feeders.* The cable has shielding through which ground current can flow.

- *Medium-voltage distribution bus.* Optionally protected.

The *time* of operation of the device as well as the ampere setting of the ground-fault protection device must be considered carefully to ensure that the continuity of the electrical service is maintained. The time of operation of the device includes

- the sensing of the ground fault by the ground-fault protection monitor

- the monitor signaling the disconnect switch to open

- the actual opening of the contacts of the disconnect device (either a switch or a circuit breaker)

The total time of operation may result in a time lapse of several cycles or more.

Large (high-magnitude) ground-fault currents can cause destructive damage even though a ground-fault protection is installed. The amount of arcing damage depends on how much current flows and the length of time that current exists. For example, if a ground-fault protection device is set for a ground fault of 500 A and the time setting is six cycles, then the device will need six cycles to signal the switch or circuit breaker to open the circuit wherever the ground fault is slightly more than 500 A or as large as 20,000 A. The six cycles needed to signal the circuit breaker plus the operation time of the switch or breaker may be long enough to result in damage to the switchgear.

### 4.5.1 Low-voltage distribution systems

For low-voltage systems, in general, ground-fault current can be monitored either as it flows out to the fault or on its return to the neutral point of the source transformer or generator. When monitoring the *outgoing* fault current, the currents in all power conductors are monitored either individually or collectively. When monitoring the *return* fault current, only the ground-fault return conductor is monitored. You need to make sure that whatever ground-fault current you capture on the return bypasses the *outgoing* monitoring current transformer. You do this by following NEC requirements.

Arcing faults, while not unique to low-voltage systems, present a special problem because of the dominance of overcurrent protection on low-voltage systems, in particular, because the amount of current that flows in an arcing phase to ground fault is frequently lower when compared to the rating or setting of the overcurrent device. For example, an arcing fault can generate a current flow of 600 A and a main breaker rated at 1600 sees this as load current, indifferent to the fault-current component.

The operation of an NEC-required ground-fault protection device assumes that under normal conditions total instantaneous current in all of the conductors of a circuit will exactly balance—our old friend Kirchoff, again. Thus, if a current coil is installed so that all of the circuit conductors run through it, the normal current measured by the coil will be zero. If a ground fault occurs, some current will return through the grounding system, and an imbalance will result in the conductors.

The NEC requires the use of ground-fault protection devices on services that meet the conditions outlined in NEC Sec. 230-95. An alternative to installing ground-fault protection may be to provide multiple disconnects rated less than 1000 A. For example, six 800-A disconnecting means may be used, and in this case ground-fault protection would not be necessary. The second fine-print note in 230-95(b) recognizes that ground-fault protection may be desirable at lesser amperes on solidly grounded systems for voltages exceeding 150 V to ground but not exceeding 600 V phase-to-phase. The code does not discourage the use of ground-fault protection on 208/120 circuits less than 1000 A.

The NEC merely establishes minimum requirements, and system designers should not be constrained by it. If your instincts tell you that more ground-fault protection is better than less and the economics of the project allow you to do so, consider any of the following:

- Ground-fault protection on unit substation main breakers that operate at 208/120.

- Ground-fault protection on all unit substation feeder breakers.

- Design independent ground-fault protection for the most critical feeders.

- Group loads so that emergency systems are unlikely to be taken out by ground faults on equipment connected to the same ground-fault protection device.

- Ground-fault protection in power panels downstream from unit substation feeder breakers. If you have specified ZSI on the substation, you will need to include a communication cable between the devices in their respective zones.

- Differential bus protection for main switchboard ground-fault protection. This will cause some difficulty with respect to the requirement for separately derived system in the NEC, but the difficulty may be overcome with the installation of current transformers on the neutral of the utility's service transformer as shown in Fig. 4.8.

Ground-fault relays that work at a *definite current pickup* are preferable to ground-fault relays that work as a percentage of the current transformer rating. Ground-fault relays require correct wiring and calibration. If the system neutral is incorrectly or accidentally grounded on the load side of the sensor, a ground-fault current will have a return path over the neutral and never trip the relay.

An expensive but effective way of detecting and clearing ground faults in customer secondary-unit substations will result with the application of the differential principle. Phase-differential bus protection would detect the low-level arcing ground faults that so frequently elude overcurrent schemes. The differential protection would be permitted to be set between, for instance, 200 and 1200 A with a time delay of up to 1.0 s. Such an arrangement would only trip for a main bus fault and would be very unlikely to experience a nuisance trip because of feeder or breaker circuit faults. With differential bus protection, it would not be necessary for anyone to provide downstream protection for the purpose of providing selective tripping (Nash, 1990).

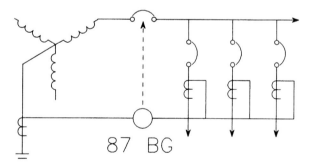

**Figure 4.8** Bus differential protection for main switchboard ground-fault protection. Some electrical people have suggested that the NEC recognize bus differential protection for main switchboard ground-fault protection. Differential protection would detect low-level arcing faults. The differential protection would be permitted to be set between, say, 200 and 1200 A with a time delay of up to 1 s. Such an arrangement would only trip for a main bus fault and would be very unlikely to experience a nuisance trip because the feeder or branch circuit fails. With differential bus protection, it would not be necessary for anyone to provide downstream protection for the purpose of providing selective tripping.

### 4.5.2  Medium-voltage distribution systems

The several methods of sensing ground-fault current on medium-voltage systems are voltage, residual, zero sequence, and ground return methods.

**Voltage detection.**    Voltage provides the best detection of a ground fault since the current is very low and basically does not change with the fault location. Voltage transducers may be applied on low-voltage systems, and voltage transformers may be applied on medium-voltage systems. The connection is shown in Fig. 4.9.

This method indicates that a ground fault exists but not where it is in the primary system. Wye-grounded, broken delta voltage transformer connections are preferred. A ballast resistor is applied to reduce the shift of the neutral from either unbalanced excitation path of the voltage transformer or from ferroresonance between the inductive reactance of the voltage transformers and relays and the capacitive system.

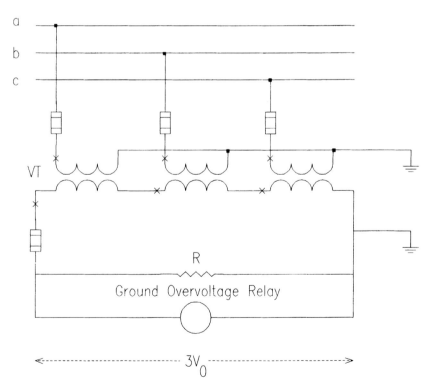

**Figure 4.9**   Voltage ground-fault detection method for ungrounded system.

The voltage available to the relay for a phase-to-ground fault on the ungrounded system is three times the normal line-to-neutral voltage. Usually, a VT ratio of primary $V_{ln} = 69.3$ V is used so that the maximum relay voltage for a *solid ground* (recall that not all ground faults are solid) would be $3 \times 69.3 = 208$ V. Since the relay will be used to alarm, its continuous voltage rating should be greater than or equal to this 208 value. Lamps or transducers can be connected, with each broken delta secondary winding to provide visual or audio alarm to the ground-fault condition. A more complete discussion of this topic, including particulars regarding neutral inversion and sizing the ballast resistor, appears in Blackburn (1987).

### Residual connection

**Low-voltage systems.** The operation is based on the concept that the phase currents in a balanced three-phase system add vectorially to zero. If the current transformers correctly transform phase currents to secondary currents, these secondary quantities will also add up to zero. As a consequence, a residually connected ground-fault relay will sense zero current during normal, balanced, three-phase operation.

When using this scheme, two limitations should be observed:

- The sensitivity is influenced to a large extent by the phase-current transformer ratio, which is selected on the basis of relatively large phase currents. Hence the ground-fault sensitivity suffers as the current transformer ratio increases.

- Transformation inaccuracies caused by slight differences in characteristics of the phase-current transformer may not cause the secondary currents to add up to zero, even though the primary currents do so. This characteristic may become a problem during inrush currents or through faults that contain a dc component of subtransient current. These current transformer error currents usually decay rapidly in a matter of cycles but sometimes not quickly enough to avoid false operation of a residually connected instantaneous type relay. Hence, only time-overcurrent relays should be applied. Note that these limitations are avoided in the design and construction of protection programs that are an integral part of low-voltage circuit breakers.

For the three-phase, three-wire system, only three-current transformers are required. The three-phase, four-wire system required four current transformers to blind the residually connected relay to any unbalanced line-to-neutral loading current. The fourth current transformer makes it possible to set the relay at a sensitive pickup level, regardless of the anticipated imbalanced load current magnitude. If the anticipated worst case imbalanced line-to-neutral load current is lower than the pickup setting of the ground relay, the neutral current transformer shown can be omitted.

A residually connected ground relay is widely applied to protect medium-voltage systems.

Overcurrent relays used for ground-fault protection are generally the same as those used for phase-fault protection, except that a more sensitive range of minimum operating current values is possible since they see only fault currents. This application is subject to nuisance operation because of error currents arising from current transformer saturation and unmatched characteristics as in differential relays. Often, the optimum speed and sensitivity of a residual ground relay must be compromised because of this.

**Core balance.** This method is based on primary current vector addition or flux summation. The remaining zero sequence component, if any, is then transferred to the secondary. The core balance current transformer or sensor is the basis of several low-voltage ground-fault protective systems introduced in recent years. The core balance current transformer is frequently called a zero sequence sensor or window current transformer, but the term *core balance* is preferable since it more specifically describes the function of the current transformer. The principle of the core balance current transformer circuit is shown in Fig. 4.10.

The main conductors pass through the same opening in the current transformer and are surrounded by the same magnetic core. Under normal conditions, all current flows out and returns through the current transformer. The net flux produced in the current transformer core will be zero, and no current will flow into the ground relay. When a ground fault occurs, the ground-fault current returns through the equipment-grounding circuit conductor (and possibly other ground paths), bypassing the current transformer. The flux produced in the current transformer core is proportional to the ground-fault current, and a proportional current flows in the relay circuit. Relays connected to core balance current transformer can be made quite sensitive; however, care is necessary to prevent false tripping from unbalanced inrush currents that may saturate the current transformer core or through fault not involving ground. If only phase conductors are enclosed and neutral current is not zero, the transferred current will be proportional to the load zero sequence or neutral current. Systems with grounded conductors, such as cable shielding, should have the current transformer surround only the phase conductors and not the grounded conductor.

By properly matching the current transformer and relay, ground-fault detection can be made as sensitive as the application requires.

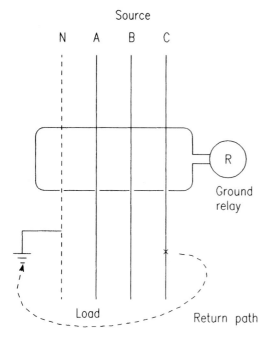

**Figure 4.10** Core balance current transformer. In normal, healthy power systems, there is no significant zero-sequence current flow. In abnormal conditions, a window-type current transformer will produce a current in its secondary that is proportional to the presence of zero-sequence current. The current transformer secondary current can be fed through an overcurrent relay which can programmed to open an interrupting device.

Under other circuit conditions—balanced, unbalanced, or single-phase load conditions—the net flux produced in the current transformer core will be nearly zero. Because of conductor spacing and geometry, some net flux will exist which represents an error in the zero-sequence summing of currents. The error can be minimized by centrally locating and/or bundling conductors. The error can also be minimized by applying current transformer with heavy cores.

The relay is fast to limit damage and may be adjustable (for current, time, or both) in order to obtain selectivity. Many ground protection systems now have solid-state relays specially designed to operate with core balance current transformers.

When terminating medium-voltage shielded cable, the cable is pulled through a core balance current transformer, and the cable jacket is removed to expose the shielding tape or braid. Connecting the shields together, the connection to ground is made after this shield lead is brought back through the current transformer. This precaution would have been necessary only if the shield had been pulled through the current transformer. Between the multiple shield ground connection on a single conductor cable, a potential exists that drives a circulating current, often of such magnitude as to require derating of the cable ampacity. When applying a core balance current transformer, the effects of this circulating current should be subtracted from the measuring circuit.

### 4.5.3   Zero sequence relay

A single window type current transformer is mounted and encircles all of the three-phase conductors. In many applications, the physical size of this current transformer may preclude the application of this method. On four-wire systems with possible imbalanced line-to-neutral loads, the neutral conductor must also pass through the current transformer window. Only circuit faults involving ground will produce a current (because of magnetic flux differences) in the current transformer secondary to operate this relay. Since only one current transformer is employed in this method of sensing ground faults, the relaying is not subject to current transformer errors due to ratio mismatch or dc saturation effects; however, ac saturation can cause appreciable error.

**Ground return.**   Ground return sensing is only applicable at the source transformer or generator because of the problems associated with multiple grounding points we discussed earlier in this chapter. This strategy involves sensing the transformer ground for current flow. Since normal load current should not return to the source through the ground on this conductor, any current sense will be fault current.

In this scheme, ground-fault current returns through the current transformer in the neutral bus to ground bus connection. For feeder circuits protected with this scheme, an insulating segment may be introduced in busway or conduit, and a bonding jumper connected across the insulate to carry the ground-fault current. A current transformer enclosing this jumper will then detect a ground fault. This method is not recommended simply because of the practical difficulties in maintaining an insulated joint.

**Application of the differential principle to sensing ground-fault currents.** As indicated in Chap. 3, differential protection is a generic term applied to a variety of protection schemes that utilize vector or algebraic subtraction or addition of signals. Ground differential relaying is effective for main bus protection since it has inherent selectivity. With the differential scheme in Fig. 4.9, core balance current transformers are installed on each of the outgoing feeders, and another smaller current transformer is placed in the transformer neutral connection to ground. This arrangement can be made sensitive to low ground-fault currents without incurring tripping for ground faults beyond the feeder current transformer. All current transformers must be very carefully matched to prevent improper tripping for high-magnitude faults occurring outside the differential zone.

---

**Factors That Affect the Sensitivity of Ground-Fault Sensing**

- Circuit charging current drawn by surge arrestors, shielded cables, and motor windings
- The number of coordination steps between the branch circuit and the supply
- Primary rating and accuracy of the largest current transformer used to supply residually connected relay in the coordination
- How well matched the current transformers used for residually connected relays are
- Burden on the current transformers—in particular, that of the residually connected relay; solid-state and some induction disk have burdens of 40 ohms for a 0.1 tap
- Maximum through-fault current and its effect upon the current transformers, with selected relays for phase and residual connections
- Fault contact resistance
- Location of conductors within core balance transformers.

Reference: IEEE Std. 242 (Buff Book, 1986).

---

**Neutral relaying.** A time-overcurrent relay connected to a current transformer located in the grounded neutral of a transformer or generator, provides a convenient, low-cost method of detecting ground fault. Since only ground-fault currents will flow in this relay, it can be set to operate on very low values of current. This scheme is widely applied on 5-kV and 15-kV systems where low-resistance grounding is frequently used and where the fault current may be as low as 200 A. The relay can be set to minimum values of current pickup and time delay, which will be selective with the feeder ground-fault relays.

## 4.6   Typical Ground-Fault Protection Schemes

Economic considerations will always figure into your decisions regarding the extent to which you apply the various ground-fault protection methods. Ideally, of course, ground-fault protection should be applied at each protective device, but the expense, particularly in retrofit situations, is frequently prohibitive. You may discover that reliance on phase overcurrent devices at the branch circuit and subfeeder level is sufficient ground-fault protection if it reduces budget constraints in other more critical parts of the distribution circuit.

## A Noteworthy Formulation of the Solution Methodology for the Determination of Single-Line-to-Ground-Fault Currents

Given the classical sequence component expression for bolted single-line-to-ground-fault current

$$I_{slg} = 3E/(Z_1 + Z_2 + Z_0 + 3R_0)$$

Given that $3R_0 = 0$ for a solidly grounded system and that $Z_1 = Z_2$ for passive elements on a power distribution system, the classical sequence component for single-line-to-ground current expression can be rearranged thus:

$$I_{slg} = 3E/(2Z_1 + Z_0)$$

Further rearrangement allows us to derive the following:

$$I_{slg} = E/Z_1[3/(Z_0/Z_1 + 2)]$$

which essentially expresses the single-line-to-ground-fault current as a function of the three-phase bolted fault current we normally compute with the infinite bus method multiplied by (ultimately empirical) ratio of the zero-to-positive sequence impedance. An effective overall $Z_0/Z_1$ ratio may be tabulated from the known positive sequence impedances of the distribution circuit elements (multiplied by the empirical $Z/Z_1$ ratio) and substituted into the expression above.

Practical circuit values of $Z_0/Z_1$ may range from 1 to 50 depending upon the construction of the ground return circuit. Some typical values of the $Z_0/Z_1$ ratio are 2 for aluminum conduit (with or without internal ground conductor), 4 to 14 for steel conduit (with internal ground conductor), and 15 to 30 for cable in magnetic armor.

A complete treatment of this subject appears in Gienger (1960) and in Kaufman (1972), and a solved problem based upon this method is detailed in the IEEE Std. 241 (Gray Book, 1990), Chap. 9.

### 4.6.1 Phase overcurrent ground-fault protection

We need to remember that simple phase protection offers a certain level of ground-fault protection. Fuses and circuit breakers with series trips will certainly do the job for a large share of ground faults without the need for protective arrangements that respond only to ground-fault current. We may discover difficulties in coordinating phase protection for ground faults, but circuits can certainly be made to open in fault conditions.

A common circuit configuration is shown in Fig. 4.11. A 350-A thermal-magnetic circuit breaker supplies a panelboard with a 20-A thermal-magnetic molded-case branch circuit breaker and 100-A thermal-magnetic subfeeder breaker. There may be other circuits in the panel, but we shall focus on these two devices, both of which may be retrofitted with ground-fault relays if we choose to solve the coordination problem that way.

You can see from the log-log plot that at high short-circuit currents, above 3500 A, the instantaneous trip characteristic of the feeder breaker overlaps that of both branch circuit and the subfeeder break-

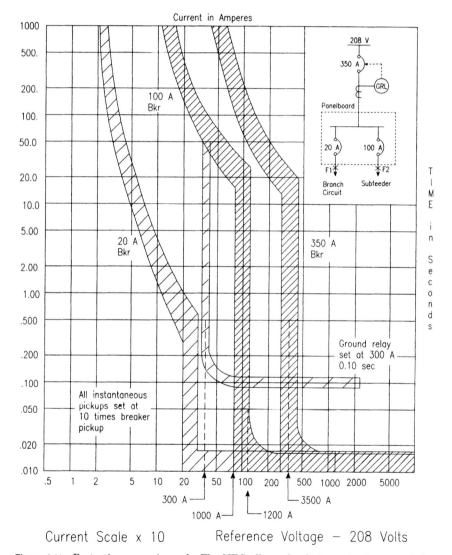

**Figure 4.11** Protection on mains only. The NEC allows the designer to circumvent the requirement for ground-fault protection on all service mains of 1000 A or greater by permitting the application of multiple mains. Electrical people should be aware, however, that using multiple mains may increase the amount of exposed unprotected bus on the line or utility side of the mains.

ers. For short circuits at F1 and F2, the feeder breaker may be tripped unnecessarily. Without ground-fault protection on the feeder breaker, arcing faults of 3500 A or less in the panelboard or closer to the feeder breaker will be removed only after a considerable time delay by the feeder breaker.

A low-set short-time delay rather than an instantaneous element on the feeder breaker would avoid this nuisance tripping problem and in many cases would also significantly improve, without supplemental ground-fault relaying, the protection provided by the feeder breaker on the occurrence of a ground fault. When a ground-fault relay is applied, the combined characteristic (instantaneous + definite time pickup set at 300 A and 0.1 s) is as shown in the shaded area of Fig. 4.11.

With a relay pickup setting of 300 A, less than the continuous rating of the feeder breaker, selectivity with the 20-A branch circuit breaker is secured for arcing single-line-to-ground faults from 300 to 3500 A, above which level the feeder breaker instantaneous trip takes over. But most important, for arcing ground faults in this range, the fault clearing time of the feeder breaker is reduced from minutes to cycles, tremendously diminishing the arcing damage that would be incurred for such faults.

The application of the ground-fault relay will require a decision as to how sensitive the relay pickup setting shall be, since maximum sensitivity may make it nonselective with downstream phase overcurrent device on low-level ground faults. The low-set feeder breaker will not be selective with the 100-A circuit breaker for ground-fault currents between 300 and 1200 A, for example. Ground-fault current of this magnitude beyond the 100-A branch circuit will cause the feeder breaker to trip via a signal from the ground-fault relay. Adding ground-fault sensing on the branch circuit would eliminate the problem but may not be economically feasible. Then you may just have to live with the nonselectivity or raise ground-fault relay pickup values.

Raising of the ground-fault relay pickup is shown in Fig. 4.12. You can see that the decreased sensitivity of the ground-fault relay makes it completely selective with the phase overcurrent trip devices on the branch circuits. Now, however, in contrast to the situation in Fig. 4.12, the ground-fault currents between 300 and 1200 A occurring beyond the 100-A branch circuit will not be quickly removed but must wait for the operation of the long time delay (thermal element of subfeeder breaker), thus allowing severe damage to occur.

The usual compromise in this situation, particularly at the outer fringes of a distribution system where circuit ratings and protective devices are usually small and where continuity of service is much less vital than at main switchboards and substations, is to risk an occasional burndown. If the budget is tight, you may have no choice but to equip only the most vital circuits' instantaneous ground-fault protec-

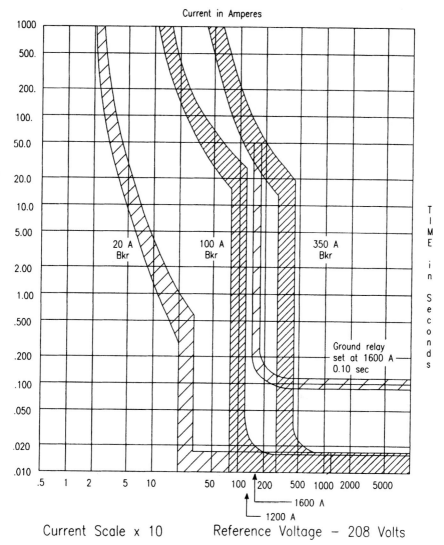

**Figure 4.12** Protection on mains and feeders. Single-line-to-ground faults are driven by line-to-neutral voltages such as 277, or 120 V. Because of phase unbalance during high-magnitude ground faults, conventional overcurrent protection device fuses or circuit breakers cannot differentiate between a high-magnitude ground fault or a high-magnitude phase-to-phase fault. You may see two phase devices (fuses) plotted on the same log-log paper as a ground-fault relay (single-line-to-ground device).

tion and allow the remaining branch circuits to rely on their phase overcurrent devices. The 1993 NEC broadened the scope of ground-fault protection for branch circuits. It is the matter of ground-fault protection for subfeeders that pose the most questions for system designers.

## Where Ground-Fault Protection IS Required

- On solidly grounded wye services above 150 V to ground, but not over 600 V between phases (for example, on 277/480- or 600/347-V systems).
- On service disconnects rated 1000 A or more.
- On service disconnects, the maximum setting is 1200 A; however, there is no minimum, and it should be noted that lower settings increase the likelihood of nuisance tripping.
- So that the maximum time of opening the service switch or circuit breaker does not exceed on 1 s for ground-fault currents of 3000 A or more. The requirements provide a maximum delay of 1 s for ground-fault currents equal to or greater than 3000 A in order to minimize the amount of damage done by an arcing fault, which is directly proportional to the time it is allowed to burn.
- To limit damage to equipment and conductors on the load side of the service disconnecting means. GFP will not protect against damage caused by faults occurring on the line side of the service disconnect.

These ground fault protection requirements do not apply on services for a continuous process where a nonorderly shutdown will introduce additional or increased hazards, Secs. 230-95 and 240-12, 517.

## Where Ground-Fault Protection Is NOT Required

- Delta-connected three-phase systems
- Ungrounded wye-connected three-phase systems
- Single-phase systems
- 120/240-V single-phase systems
- 120/208 three-phase systems
- Systems over 600 V; for example, 4160/2400 V
- Service disconnecting means rated at less than 1000 A
- Systems where the service is subdivided (for example, a 1600-A service may be divided between two 800-A switches)

### 4.6.2  Systems with an alternate power source

We began this chapter with a discussion about the need for single-point grounding. In the case of double-ended substations, emergency, or standby power sources, however, we may need to ground the neutral terminal of an alternate power source at its location, thus contradicting everything we have said thus far about the need to avoid stray neutral currents.

Solutions to this problem involve single-point grounding (again), four-pole transfer switches, overlapping neutral contacts, and transformer isolation.

*Single-point grounding.*  Single-point grounding eliminates the above identified problems and permits simple relaying methods. We will discuss these at length in the section on double-ended substations in Chap. 7.

*Four-pole transfer switches.* Using four-pole transfer switches throughout the system may allow complete isolation of service and emergency generator neutral conductors. This eliminates possible improper ground-fault sensing and nuisance tripping caused by multiple neutral-to-ground connections. When this is done, the generator will comply with the NEC definition of a separately derived system. However, momentary opening of the neutral conductor may cause voltage surges.

*Automatic transfer switches.* A variation of the method of isolating the normal and emergency source neutrals is for the automatic transfer switch to include overlapping neutral transfer contacts. This provides the necessary isolation between neutrals and at the same time minimizes abnormal switching voltages. With overlapping contacts, the only time the neutrals of the normal and emergency power sources are connected is during transfer and retransfer. With a conventional double-throw transfer switch, this duration can be less than the operating time of the ground-fault sensor, which is usually set anywhere from 6 to 24 cycles (100 to 400 ms).

*Isolation transformer.* Where a three-phase, four-wire critical load is relatively small compared to the rest of the load, an isolating transformer is sometimes used. This requires both power sources connected to the transfer switch to be three-phase, three-wire, and the delta-wye isolating transformer must be inserted between the transfer switch and the four-wire load. An imbalance of the critical load would have no effect on the ground-fault protector at the incoming service.

The issue of ground-fault coordination with emergency and/or standby power sources is particularly important in health care facilities where at least one additional level of ground-fault protection is required. This additional level of ground-fault protection is typically located on the feeders downstream from the main service. A coordinating time interval of not less than 0.1 s (six cycles) must be provided between the main and the feeders. Even if the feeder ground-fault devices are set for instantaneous operation, the device on the service ground-fault device must have at least a 0.1-s delay. A zone-selective ground-fault protection system with a feedback lockout signal to an instantaneous relay could satisfy the rule on selectivity.

There is an ongoing debate among protection specialists about the NEC requirements for ground-fault protection and coordination. While the debate continues, we need to know something about how we might go about coordinating ground-fault protection in critical feeder circuits now. Table 4.2 is adapted from Nash (1990) and is a good starting point for a set of coordination guidelines.

**TABLE 4.2   GFP Arrangements for Critical Applications**

| GFP arrangement | Main GFP settings | Branch GFP settings | Main bus protection | GFP selectivity[a] | Downstream selectivity[b] | GFP backup[c] |
|---|---|---|---|---|---|---|
| Time delay coordinated | 1200/max | 1000/Int | fair[d] | good | fair | yes |
| Zone selective with delay | 1200/max | 1000/Int | excellent | good[e] | fair | yes |
| Zone selective with blocking | 1200/max[f] | 1200/Int | excellent[f] | best[e] | best | no |

[a] Coordination between two levels of GFP.

[b] Coordination between branch (second-level) GFP and downstream fuse or circuit breaker.

[c] GFP backup is provided by GFP on the main in the event the branch GFP fails.

[d] The degree of protection will vary depending on the bus size and the corresponding NEMA tolerable damage level for that bus. We consider protection fair for any bus when a 3000-A fault is interrupted in less than 1 s, because a serious burndown has been prevented.

[e] Any zone-selective system has some risk that the feedback signal will not reach the main, causing a nuisance trip of the main.

[f] Lower settings provide better protection. The maximum settings may be preferable in case the blocking signal is not received. Some units may not have adjustable time. In general, we found manufacturers' product information on zone-selective systems to be inadequate. This leads the author to wonder if inadequate or confusing product data lead to some of the misapplications we see in the field.

## 4.7   Solved Problem

The following problem is an adaptation of an application situation that appears in ABB, *System Neutral Grounding and Ground Fault Protection Guide*. It illustrates the difficulties of protection against arcing ground faults on, for example, a unit substation secondary, with only primary fuses and/or phase-tripping devices.

**Example 4.4**   The Case for Secondary Main Breakers

*Situation.*   The customer secondary unit substation is shown in Fig. 4.13. Assume a bolted single-line-to-ground fault occurs at F.

*Requirements.*   Calculate arcing fault current and determine how long it will take a primary fuse to clear the fault.

**solution**   A bolted single-line-to-ground-fault current is determined using the equation on p. 43. In per-unit on a 750-kVA base:

$$\text{Source impedance, } Z_{1s} = Z_{2s} = 750/250,000 = j0.003 \text{ pu}$$

$$\text{Transformer, } Z_{1t} = Z_{2t} = Z_{0t} = j0.0575 \text{ pu}$$

Assuming no motor contribution at the secondary bus, the total sequence impedances to F are

$$Z_1 = j0.003 + j0.0575 = j0.0605 \text{ pu}$$

$$Z_0 = Z_{0t} = j0.0575 \text{ pu}$$

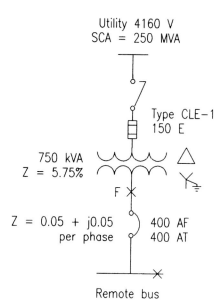

Utility 4160 V
SCA = 250 MVA

Type CLE−1
150 E

750 kVA
Z = 5.75%

F

Z = 0.05 + j0.05
per phase

400 AF
400 AT

Remote bus

**Figure 4.13** Schematic for the case for secondary main breakers.

$$I_f = \frac{j3}{j0.0605 + j0.0605 + j0.575} = \frac{j3}{j0.1785} = j16.81 \text{ pu}$$

The actual fault current at 480 V is

$$16.81[750/(\sqrt{3} \times 480)] = 16.81 \,(902.1) = 15{,}164 \text{ A}$$

The effect of an arcing fault is to reduce the current significantly at this voltage level. A typical arc voltage for arcs in switchboard-type enclosure is about 150 V, essentially independent of the current magnitude. Thus for an arcing fault in the secondary switchgear,

$$I_f = (15{,}164) \,[277 - 150/277] = 6952 \text{ A}$$

The primary current flowing through the fuses will be

$$6952[480/(\sqrt{3} \times 4160)] = 463 \text{ A at } 4160 \text{ V}$$

If you were to consult with the time-current characteristic of a typical current-limiting fuse applied at this voltage (for example, a 150E CLE-1 fuse), you would see that the *total* clearing time would be something on the order of 200 s for 463 A.

*Remarks.*  The energy released during this delay would be $E = V_{arc} \times I_f \times \text{time} = 150 \times 6952 \times 200 = 2.09 \times 10^8$ joules. This is enough energy to melt 1151 lb of copper. Similar calculations, including the impedance of the cable to a remote bus, would reduce the level of ground-fault current, but the energy released would still be very destructive. A main secondary breaker with ground trips is recommended.

# Bibliography

Blackburn, J. L., *Protective Relaying: Principles and Applications,* Marcel Dekker, Inc., New York, 1987.

Dunki-Jacobs, J. R., "The Effects of Arcing Ground Faults on Low Voltage System Design," *IEEE Transactions on Industry Applications,* May/June 1972.

Dunki-Jacobs, J. R., "The Escalating Arcing Ground Fault Phenomenon," *IEEE IAS,* Nov./Dec. 1986.

Gienger, J. A., O. C. Davidson, and R. A. Brendel, "Systems in Standard Steel or Aluminum Conduit," *AIEEE Transactions,* May 1960, pp. 84–90.

Kaufman, R. H., and J. C. Page, "Arcing Fault Protection for Low Voltage Power Distribution Systems—Nature of the Problem," *AIEE,* June 1960.

Kaufman, R. H., "Let's Be More Specific about Equipment Grounding," *Proceedings of the American Power Conference,* 1972.

Love, Daniel J., and Nasrollah Hashemi, "Failure Analysis of Components Due to 480 Volt Ground Faults," *IEEE IAS,* vol. 1A-22, July/Aug. 1986.

Nash, Jr., Hugh O., "Ground-Fault Protection and the Problem of Nuisance Tripping of Critical Feeders," *IEEE Transactions on Industry Applications,* vol. 26, no. 3, May/June 1990.

Vey, Larry, and Jim Iverson, "Grounding of AC Generators and Switching the Neutral in Emergency and Standby Power Systems," Publication no. 900-0262, Onan Corporation, Minneapolis, Minn., May 1991.

West, Robert B., "Equipment Grounding for Reliable Ground-Fault Protection in Electrical Systems Below 600 Volts," *IEEE IAS,* March/April 1974.

### General references

"ANSI/IEEE Recommended Practice for Grounding of Industrial and Commercial Power Systems," *ANSI/IEEE Std. 142-1982* (IEEE Green Book).

GE Electrical Distribution and Control, "Ground-Fault Protection for Solidly Grounded Low-Voltage Systems," Application Engineering Information, GET-6533A-0691BLE.

"IEEE Guide for Safety in AC Substation Grounding," *ANSI/IEEE Std. 80-1986.*

"Grounding," Chap. 7, *Recommended Practice for the Design of Reliable Industrial and Commercial Power Systems, ANSI/IEEE Std. 446-1987* (Orange Book).

Westinghouse Electric Corporation, "Power Distribution System Design," *Westinghouse Consulting Application Guide,* July 1991.

Westinghouse Relay and Telecommunications Division, "System Neutral Grounding and Ground Fault Protection Guide," PRSE-4E, Feb. 1986. [N.B. Asea-Brown-Boveri acquired the relay division of Westinghouse Electric Corp. in the recent past. Some technical literature that originated with Westinghouse is now distributed by Asea-Brown-Boveri, Coral Springs, Florida.]

### Further reading

Doughty, Richard L., et al., "Optimum Use of Oil-Filled Distribution Transformers to Design Resistance Ground Sources for Medium-Voltage Delta-Connected Power Sources," Mar/April 1985.

Dwight, H. B., "Calculations of Resistances to Ground," *AIEE,* 1936. This paper features formulas for practical use in calculation of the resistances of grounding conductors of varying configurations.

Hamer, Paul, and Barry Wood, "Are Cable Shields Being Damaged During Ground Faults?" *IEEE IAS,* Nov./Dec. 1986.

Morley, Lloyd A., et al., "Coordination-free Ground Fault Detection for Mine Distribution Systems," Jan./Feb. 1985.

Nichols, Neil, "The Electrical Considerations in Cogeneration," *IEEE,* May/June 1985.

Smith, R. L., "Neutral-deriving transformers for grounding low voltage systems with delta-connected source transformers," *IEEE Transactions on Industry Applications,* March/April 1982.

Trutt, Frederick C., et al., "A Coordination-Free Ground Fault Relay for AC Mine Distribution Systems," *IEEE Transactions on Industry Applications,* Sept./Oct. 1989.

Wang, Gary N., et al., "High Resistance Grounding and Selective Ground Fault Protection for a Major Industrial Facility," *IEEE Transactions on Industry Applications,* July/Aug. 1984.

West, Robert B., "Compliance Guide: OSHA and the National Electric Code Requirements for Grounding and Ground Fault Protection on Construction Sites," *IEEE IAS,* May/June 1979.

Woodbury, Frank, "Grounding Considerations in Cogeneration," *IEEE IAS,* Nov./Dec. 1985.

# 5

# Protection and Coordination
# in Power Panels

## 5.1 Foreword

We revisit the load aspect of overcurrent and short-circuit protection
with a discussion of feeder, subfeeder, and branch circuit design. The
bulk of the rules for the foregoing are indicated in the following pas-
sages of the NEC:

Art. 210  Branch Circuits

Art. 215  Feeders

Art. 220  Branch Circuit, Feeder, and Service Calculations

Art. 225  Outside Branch Circuits and Feeders

Art. 240  Overcurrent Protection

Assuming that the issue of voltage drop and circuit makeup has been
dealt with appropriately, we will focus on the relational aspects of low-
voltage branch and feeder circuit overcurrent protection one and two
devices upstream from the load. As we shall see, the coordination relationships are easier to establish at low voltage than at medium voltage
(or between low- and medium-voltage devices) because in many cases
we may apply simple coordination ratios between fuses or circuit
breakers in series with the flow of fault current.

The statement in the NEC that makes overcurrent coordination virtually the law in many jurisdictions is the following from Art. 240-12:

> Where an orderly shutdown is required to minimize hazard(s) to person-
> nel and equipment, a system of coordination based on the following two
> conditions shall be permitted:

1. Coordinated short-circuit protection
2. Overload indication based on monitoring systems or devices

(FPN): Coordination is defined as properly localizing a fault condition to restrict outages to the equipment affected, accomplished by choice of selective fault-protective devices. The monitoring system may cause the condition to go to alarm, allowing corrective action or an orderly shutdown, thereby minimizing personnel hazard and equipment damage.

It is important to distinguish between the use of the word overcurrent in the context of NEC requirements versus its use as a term used in the context of a textbook such as this book that discusses protective devices that operate on *overcurrent principles*. You could say that a short circuit *is* an overcurrent—but a very fast overcurrent—and one that requires a different sensing and clearing strategy than the relatively slower overcurrent.

## 5.2 Low-Voltage Distribution Circuits

Electrical people usually regard circuits in terms of the voltage and the current rating the protective devices that protect and control them. For example:

$$\text{load current} = 80\% \times \text{current rating of protective device}$$

You may think of this equation as one of the first principles of protection design. Since the size of a conductor and the device that protects it are a matched pair, cable size must be equal to or greater than that specified in the appropriate tables of the NEC. Any insulation type may be selected, but the cross section of the current path must remain constant. An electrical person new to protection design practice should go to Chap. 9 of the NEC which contains practical examples of conductor-overcurrent device calculations.

Table 5.1, taken directly from the 1993 NEC, is one of many useful tables you should have in your bag of tricks.

Another one of the more frequently used sections of the NEC is Art. 240. If you have used it in the past you will find that in the 1993 version of the code, it has been completely rewritten. In previous editions of the NEC, the protection design rules were stated as exceptions to the rule. Now all the rules for overcurrent protection are stated in positive language. Among the most frequently used among these are the rules concerning

- circuits above 800 amps
- motor circuits
- transformer secondary conductors

**TABLE 5.1  Summary of Branch-Circuit Requirements**

| Circuit rating | 15 amp | 20 amp | 30 amp | 40 amp | 50 amp |
|---|---|---|---|---|---|
| CONDUCTORS: (min. size) | | | | | |
| Circuit wires* | 14 | 12 | 10 | 8 | 6 |
| Taps | 14 | 14 | 14 | 12 | 12 |
| Fixture Wires and Cords | | | Refer to Section 240-4 | | |
| Overcurrent protection | 15 amp | 20 amp | 30 amp | 40 amp | 50 amp |
| OUTLET DEVICES: | | | | | |
| Lampholders Permitted | Any type | Any type | Heavy duty | Heavy duty | Heavy duty |
| Receptacle Rating† | 15 max. amp | 15 or 20 amp | 30 amp | 40 or 50 amp | 50 amp |
| Maximum load | 15 amp | 20 amp | 30 amp | 40 amp | 50 amp |
| PERMISSIBLE LOAD | Refer to Section 210-23(a) | Refer to Section 210-23(a) | Refer to Section 210-23(b) | Refer to Section 210-23(c) | Refer to Section 210-23(c) |

\* These gauges are for copper conductors.
† For receptacle rating of cord-connected electric-discharge lighting fixtures, see Section 410-30(c).
From *1993 National Electric Code Handbook,* used with permission.

In Chap. 1 we indicated that it took some considerable experience to feel comfortable with the NEC rules for locating a protective device in a circuit. Our comfort may be hastened by some familiarity with the situations in which protective devices are *not* required (though sometimes desirable). Smaller conductors tapped to larger conductors or to buses are a particular hazard unless the cable is protected by fuses or circuit breakers.

Lighting panels must be individually protected on their supply side by an overcurrent device having a rating not more than that of the lighting panel itself. If a panel is supplied through its own individual feeder or subfeeder, as shown in Fig. 5.1a, then a main overcurrent device is *not* required at the panel *if* the feeder overcurrent protection is not greater than the rating of the panel. A main breaker is required for a lighting panel that is supplied directly from the secondary of its own step-down transformer. If the panel is tapped off a feeder that also supplies other panels as shown in Fig. 5.1c, then a main breaker is required at each panel to provide individual protection to the panel itself and to enable the panel to be shut off without the necessity of affecting the power to the other panels in the feeder.

It is frequently desirable to feed motors from branch circuits tapped off the main branch circuit conductors. Rather than require that the tap conductors be the same size as the main conductors, the size of the tap conductors down to the motor controller may be reduced without requiring additional overcurrent protection at the point of the tap provided that:

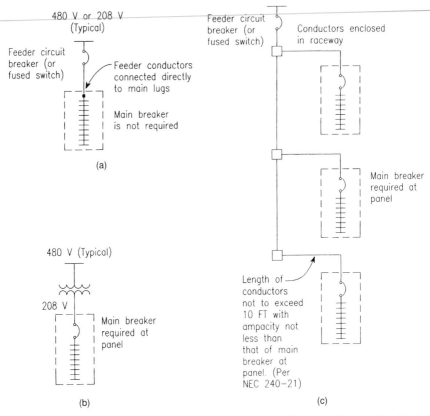

**Figure 5.1a** Lighting panel rules. Distance from the transformer to the panel is limited to 10 or 25 ft, subject to the requirements of (newly rewritten) 1993 National Electric Code Article 240-21. If overcurrent protection is placed at the transformer secondary connection to protect secondary conductors, the circuit can run any distance to the panel. If the panel fed by the transformer secondary is a lighting panel and requires main protection, the protection must be on the secondary.

- The ampacity of the tap conductors to the motor is a minimum of one-third the ampacity of the main branch circuit conductors.

- The distance from the tap to the motor controller with overload devices is a maximum of 25 ft.

- The tap conductors are adequately protected from physical damage.

- The motor controller and overload devices are each listed for group installation with the size of the branch circuit overcurrent protection provided.

The tap conductors must also follow the usual rules regarding 125 percent of the full-load current of the motor as required of any motor circuit (NEC Art. 430 and 240).

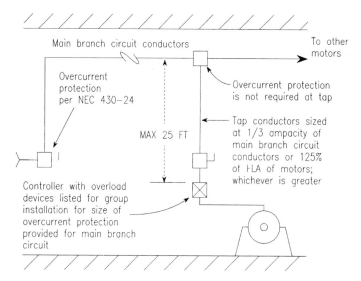

**Figure 5.1b**  Single motor circuit tap. The rules for tapping a main branch circuit to supply power to a single motor are indicated in NEC 430-53(d). The size of the tap conductors down to the motor controller may be reduced without requiring additional overcurrent protection at the point of the tap provided that:

- The tap conductors must be a minimum of 125 percent of the full-load current of the motor.
- The ampacity of the tap conductors to the motor is a minimum of *one-third* the ampacity of the main branch circuit conductors.
- The distance from the tap to the motor controller with overload devices is a maximum of 25 ft.
- The tap conductors are adequately protected from physical damage.
- The motor controller and overload devices are each listed for group installation with the size of the branch circuit overcurrent protection provided.

We mention in passing here, and then in more detail in Chap. 7, that branch and feeder circuits may be interlocked with upstream devices using zone interlocking. Many zone interlocking schemes have a minimum of three levels of communication built into the standard base unit. Two of the communication levels exist between, for example, the building substation main breaker and its feeder breakers, and yet another (frequently unwired and ignored) third level may be brought out to power panels, motor control centers, and the like—anything protected by a similar breaker to the first two breakers. The application would require that communication wiring be installed between the power panels (with the smart breaker) and the unit substation, and this would incur costs. But if the arrangement provides coordinated ground-fault protection where coordination would otherwise be difficult to obtain, then, especially in the case of hospitals, the cost must be paid.

## 5.3    Application of Low-Voltage Fuses

As we indicated, it is natural to start with fuses since fuses were the first protective device invented. It is also natural to begin with the device classified in the category named after the inventor—the common Edison plug fuse.

### 5.3.1    Common plug fuse

The common plug fuse is seen in older residences, though considerably less so in commercial and industrial system branch circuits. Plug fuses protect single-phase lighting and receptacle power circuits and are noteworthy for the light bulb type screw-in base. They are rated 125 V or less to ground and up to 30 A maximum. Nominally, they have no interrupting rating, and they are subjected to one ac short-circuit test with an available current of 10,000 A. The Edison base type may be specified with or without a time delay according to the inductive characteristic of the branch circuit. The time delays are on the order of 12 s at 200 percent of their rating.

### 5.3.2    Non-current-limiting fuses (class H)

These fuses interrupt overcurrents up to 10,000 A but do not limit the current that flows in the circuit to the same extent as do recognized current-limiting fuses. As a general rule, they should be applied only where the maximum available current is 10,000 A and all conducting elements in the power panel are fully rated to withstand the fault duty.

### 5.3.3    Current-limiting fuses

These fuses are widely applied in motor starters, fused circuit breakers, and fused switches of motors and feeder circuit for protection of busway and cable. As a matter of definition, an alternating current-limiting fuse is a fuse that safely interrupts all available currents within its interrupting rating and within its current-limiting range, limits the clearing time at rated voltage to an interval equal to or less than the first major or symmetrical current loop duration, and limits peak let-through current to a value less than the peak current that would be possible with the fuse replaced with a solid conductor of the same impedance.

### 5.3.4    Dual-element or time-delay fuses

Because of inherent limitations in various types of overcurrent devices for motor application, two or more different devices are applied. An example of this is the practice of protecting motor with a combination of a general purpose fuse to clear short circuits and a motor circuit protector to clear overloads. In place of this combination, you may apply a single dual-element fuse. Dual-element, time-delay fuses are able to withstand normal motor starting current and can be sized closer to the motor rating. The time-delay element permits short-duration overloads but melts if these overloads are sustained. When properly applied, dual-element fuses offer economic advantages because fuse sizing closer to the motor starting characteristics permits a smaller motor switch size. Refer to NEC Table 430-152 (also adapted in Table 6.3 of this textbook).

### 5.3.5  Cartridge fuses

Cartridge fuses may be either renewable or nonrenewable. Nonrenewable fuses are factory assembled and should be replaced after operating. Renewable fuses can be disassembled and the fusible element replaced. Renewable elements are usually designed to give a greater time delay than ordinary nonrenewable fuses, and in some designs the delay on moderate overcurrents is considerable. The renewable fuse is not available in the higher interrupting ratings.

Cartridge fuses differ in dimensions according to voltage and current ratings. They have ferrule contacts in ratings of 60 A or less and knife-blade contacts in larger ratings. Cartridge fuses of varying types and characteristics have been classified by the ANSI-UL 198 series:

1. Miscellaneous cartridge fuses

2. Class H fuses

3. Class K high-interrupting-capacity fuses

4. Class R current-limiting fuses

5. Class J current-limiting fuses

6. Class L current-limiting fuses

Many fuses have a size-limiting feature that prevents overfusing.

### 5.3.6  Fuse selectivity ratio tables

One manufacturer (see Cooper-Bussman) has put together a simple checklist for selectivity (Table 5.2). It is the best tool for quick verification of overcurrent coordination among fuses that you will find. To use it, you look at the line side fuses on the left vertical axis and match the load side fuse along the upper horizontal. Coordination ratios vary from 2:1 to 5:1 regardless of the level of short-circuit current. When closer fuse sizing is desired, check with the fuse manufacturers because the ratios may be reduced for lower values of short-circuit current.

**TABLE 5.2    Fuse Selectivity Ratio Tables***

| | Load Side | | | | |
| Line side | Class L time delay fuse 601–6000A | Class L fuse 601–6000A | Class K1 fuse 0–600A | Class J fuse 0–600A | Class K5 dual-element fuse 0–600A |
|---|---|---|---|---|---|
| Class L time delay fuse 601–6000A | 2:1 | 2.5:1 | 2:1 | 2:1 | 4:1 |
| Class L fuse 601–6000A | 2:1 | 2:1 | 2:1 | 2:1 | 4:1 |
| Class K1 fuse 0–600A | | | 2:1 | 2:1 | 8:1 |
| Class J fuse 0–600A | | | 2:1 | 2:1 | 8:1 |
| Class K5 dual-element fuse 0–600A | | | 1.5:1 | 1.5:1 | 2:1 |

* General application principles for branch circuit fuses and fittings are covered in Sections 240-50 and 240-60 of the National Electric Code. Time-current characteristics of fuses do not need ampere scale correction when plotted against ground-fault relays with neutral sensors. Single-line-to-ground faults are driven by line-to-neutral voltages such as 7620, 277, or 120 volts.

Fuse manufacturers point out that circuit breakers with low interrupting capacity can be applied where high short-circuit current levels exist *if they are protected by current-limiting fuses.* Properly chosen fuses placed on the line side of the breaker will limit fault currents to levels that do not exceed the breaker's capability. To do this, however, you should refer to UL's *Recognized Component Directory.* This publication lists actual fuse-circuit breaker combinations that have series ratings.

Low-voltage fuses in feeder and branch circuits are sometimes applied in combination with circuit breakers. Fuse performance is well documented in the form of peak let-through current curves, but information about the ultimate current withstand capability of a circuit breaker may be known only from laboratory tests. These test data are seldom available to people when they need to make comparisons during the design of a project. However, it is possible to establish a conservative value of circuit breaker withstand capability by analyzing UL Standard 489.

An example of the "up-over-and-down" method of applying fuses ahead of circuit breakers in order to supplement their withstand capability is provided at the end of this chapter. This is sometimes called a series or integrated rating. The resulting interrupting rating of the combination is higher than the marked interrupting rating of the lowest rated breaker when applied alone. The NEC states that series-combination short-circuit ratings may now be met by equipment so identified.

Although this scheme is consistent with parts of Arts. 110 and 240, there is some controversy over the issue in the industry. The discussion centers around the fact that the dynamic nature of circuit breakers actually changes the total circuit impedance downstream from a fuse to such a degree that the up-over-and-down method could be invalid. It appears to be an issue over which good people disagree. This example is provided to you so that you might be better prepared to participate in the debate.

---

### Protection for Lighting Circuits— Fusing Individual Fixtures

Lighting circuits where P-rated ballasts are applied require supplemental short-circuit protection. The sections of the NEC which advance the requirements for ballasts (which is essentially a transformer and a capacitor) are NEC 410-73e (which states that ballasts for indoor fluorescent fixtures must have integral thermal protection) and NEC 450 (which states the requirements for transformers). NEC 450-3b1 requires 300 percent maximum primary, short-circuit protection for transformers with less than 2 A primary. On the other hand, a 1-A rated ballast can be protected by a 20-A branch circuit overcurrent protective device. This is a 2000 percent rating or 20 times the 1-A primary rating of the ballast. The thermal protective device in the P-rated ballast is for overload protection only. It removes the ballast from the faulted circuit when the ballast temperature approaches its insulation limitations. See Fig. 5.A.

To limit fault current you should fuse each fluorescent ballast individually with a dual-element, time-delay fuse, which is designed specifically for individual ballast protection as shown in the figure. The application for time-delay fuses will assure coordination with upstream devices as required by NEC 240-12 and will ride through the transformer inrush. Without individually fused fixtures in the circuit, above a 975-A fault in the unfused circuit would trip the breaker, cutting off all power to the lighting branch circuit which may well cause panic among occupants (*Consulting-Specifying Engineer*, June 1990).

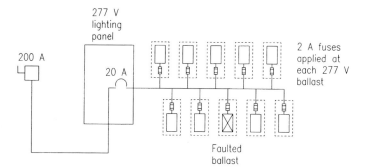

**Figure 5.A**  Ballast protection. Without individually fused ballasts, the 20-A circuit breaker at the panel opens and possibly even the 200-A fuse. A non-time-delay fluorescent ballast fuse or dual-element fluorescent ballast fuse opens the faulted circuit and all upstream breakers and/or fuses are unaffected.

## 5.4    Application of Low-Voltage Circuit Breakers

One of the first decisions an electrical designer has to make when laying out branch circuits from panelboards or laying out feeders from a secondary unit substation is the choice between molded case and power circuit breakers. By power circuit breakers, we mean the heavy duty breakers that are generally rack mounted, applied at voltages up to 600 V, and break fault current in air. Power circuit breakers (obviously) cannot and are not applied in tiers of 42 in power distribution panels for the protection of branch and feeder circuits, but a comparison between the two will help us to understand important application principles related to overcurrent protection design. Some history may help.

Molded case and power circuit breakers originated from opposite ends of the ratings spectrum but now converge into an almost bewildering array of choices, given recent developments in current-limiting and insulated case circuit breakers with any number of integral or detachable trip units available. Since power circuit breakers were always used within enclosures in heavy industrial power distribution circuits, they were designed for a 100 percent continuous rating within metal cladding. Molded case breakers were designed for use in continuous operations. When applied in an enclosure, molded case breakers were derated to 80 percent of their continuous current rating. In recent years, however, many molded case breakers have been designed with a 100 percent rating when used within an enclosure.

For economic reasons, molded case circuit breakers are used in lighting circuits or other branch circuit loads that are considered nonessential. When it is economical, power circuit breakers are applied on mission critical circuits where selectivity is important. This being the case, power circuit breakers need the high short-time ratings to allow a backup circuit breaker to remain closed during the length of time that it takes to clear the fault on its circuit.

Since high short-time ratings and selectivity were not the principal advantage in a molded case breaker, they could be designed for extremely fast interruption by means of quick operating contacts. In fact, if you compare the time-current characteristics of molded case breakers with the time-current characteristics of the power breakers, you will see that the time scale goes down an extra log-log decade to 0.001 s. The rapid opening of the contacts under high short-circuit conditions allows the molded case circuit breaker to have higher interrupting ratings than the power breaker because the power breaker's massive construction is intended to allow it to ride through fault currents while a selectively programmed protective device downstream clears the fault. In addition to withstanding large fault currents, most power circuit breakers can close and latch against their high short-time ratings. The rapid opening of the molded case circuit breaker provides clearing action on the order of current-limiting fuses.

### 5.4.1 Comparison of molded case and power circuit breakers

Electrical industry steering organizations establish testing and rating standards. Knowledge about the details of how these devices are tested, rated, and ranked is worth having but beyond the scope of this book. It is worthwhile knowing something about how we might apply some of the principles we discussed in Chap. 3 to each of these kinds of breakers.

The power factor for the power circuit breaker interrupting test is 15 percent or less, which is an X/R ratio of 6.6 or greater. The molded case standard requires a power factor between 15 and 20 percent. Therefore 20 percent must be used as the basis of rating with asymmetry factors in Table A.2. For example, at 15 percent power factor, the molded case circuit breaker must have short-circuit ratings (1.171-1.127 = 4.4 percent) about 5 percent or greater than a power circuit breaker in order to be applied on an equivalent basis (confirm with each manufacturer).

The short-time ratings of power circuit breakers are specified in C37.13 as being equal to the 600-V interrupting ratings. The short-time current duty cycle is specified as two periods of one-half-s current flow separated by a 15-s interval of zero current (a total of 1 s). Molded case breakers do not, essentially need not, have similar requirements. Because of the reduced short-time capability of the molded case breakers, they are always equipped with instantaneous trip functions to protect the circuit breaker from damage during large fault-current flow. The various trip elements may allow us to set the instantaneous pickup levels high, but the fact remains that *selectivity is not possible among molded case breakers at short-circuit currents greater than the instantaneous or short-time pickup ratings.* It is tempting to disable instantaneous elements in trip units that allow you to do so, but you must realize that this may subvert the manufacturer's intention to protect the breaker within its rating.

Comparing ratings leads to a number of considerations when evaluating the use of molded case, power, or insulated case circuit breakers. These are summarized in Table 5.3. In general, then:

- If very high interrupting ratings are required and instantaneous opening of the circuit breaker is permissible, the molded case circuit breaker may have advantages over the power circuit breaker.
- Where continuity of service is mandatory, the short-time capability of the power circuit breaker is required.

TABLE 5.3    Application Considerations of Molded-Case v. Power Circuit Breakers*

| | Advantage to: | |
|---|---|---|
| Characteristic | Low-voltage power circuit breaker | Molded-case circuit breaker/ insulated case circuit breaker |
| Critical loads (i.e., process industry) | X | |
| Noncritical loads (i.e., commercial building) | | X |
| Selectivity critical at all interrupting levels | X | |
| Loss of selectivity at higher short-circuit current levels not critical | | X |
| Repetitive duty | X | |
| Infrequent operation | | X |
| Maintainable to extend life | X | |
| Extended life not critical | | X |
| Interrupting rating at 480 v | | |
|    Up to 65 kA without fuses | X | X |
|    Up to 150 kA without fuses | | X |
|    Up to 200 kA with integral fuses | X | |
| Application on corner grounded systems | X | |
| Large single pole faults possible on ungrounded systems | X | |
| Large X/R (low power factor) systems | X | |
| High short-time capability | X | |
| Low operating temperatures for extended insulation life and low losses | X | |
| High current inrush applications (motors, etc.) | X | |
| Closed door racking | X | |

\* This table may be used as a checklist for general application considerations for low-voltage breakers. You should remember that trip settings may vary among various frame sizes of a breaker of a given manufacturer. For example, a static trip breaker which has instantaneous pickup values of 4 to 10 times for frames 250 to 2000 amperes. The same manufacturer may offer for frames 2500-A and above instantaneous trip settings of only 4 to 8 (*Consulting-Specifying Engineer*, 1987).

- If the interrupting capability of the power circuit breaker is not high enough, this can be achieved by means of an integral fuse.
- If circuit breakers are operated relatively infrequently where selectivity is not important, the molded case breaker provides the most economical solution.

### 5.4.2  Electromechanical (thermal-magnetic) breakers

Thermal-magnetic (or electromechanical) breakers are the warhorses of the electrical protection industry, and it is fair to say that the reliability and economy of these devices have been, at least in part, responsible for the existence of improved industrial, commercial, and institutional facilities throughout many nations. When project budgets were tight, and the choice was between a building with an electrical system and a building with no electrical system at all (tantamount to no building at all), old-fashioned thermal-magnetic devices, based on the immutable laws of thermodynamics and electromagnetism, brought the project under budget with only a few people noticing the difference. Tight coordination was not always possible, especially in circuit retrofit situations in which there were many different circuit breakers from many different manufacturers, but a breaker was put in where it might not have otherwise been put in, which counts as a net improvement. As of 1980, about half of all solid-state molded case breakers produced in the United States today with continuous current ratings about 600 A have solid-state trip units (Wafer, 1980).

This is the part of the book where we stand back, take a breath, and make sure that we do not go overboard extolling the virtues of microprocessor technology. Sure, coordination of overcurrent devices is important, but if the choice is between circuit safety and a new circuit breaker that does everything but tap dance, take safety. Over the lifetime of a building, for instance, a college dormitory with no critical kitchen or life-support circuits involved, the occupants ought to be able to suffer through an outage (due to miscoordination in the short-time region of the log-log plot) once or twice every 50 years.

The nature of a thermal-magnetic circuit breaker is revealed in its time-current characteristic, as shown in Fig. 5.2 and also App. item A.3. You see the wide tolerance thermal bands in the overload zone of the log-log paper and the (virtual) impulse trip region in the short-circuit zone of the time-current characteristic, which is due to the magnetic action. There are usually only three settings: low, medium, and high. The thermal elements are calibrated in the factory and are not adjustable after the breaker has been assembled. A specific thermal element must be supplied for each trip rating. The thermal time-delayed tripping is achieved through use of a bimetal element that is heated directly by the passage of the circuit current. The bimetal element has two bonded strips of metal with different rates of thermal expansion. The heat from an overload current causes the element to deflect at a rate that is dependent on the amount of current. Ultimately, the element deflects far enough to physically push the trip bar and unlatch the breaker contacts. Unlatching time is the point beyond which the opening action of the breaker is irreversible. In older power circuit breakers, it is common to see a thermal-magnetic device installed for each phase. Time-delay action is produced with a dashpot.

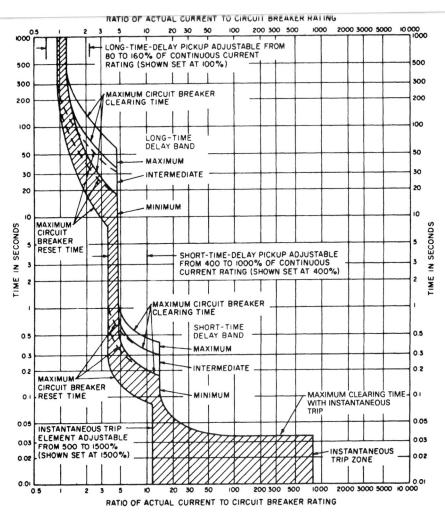

**Figure 5.2** Electromechanical breaker. The long time pickup tends to be the first segment of a low-voltage circuit breaker time-current characteristic that is applied because it helps orient the designer to the continuous current relationships of the devices. It is also recognized by the NEC as the indicator of the breaker's continuous current rating. You should confirm whether or not changing the amp tap adjustment has the same effect as changing the value of the current sensor. In other words, confirm whether or not changing the long time pickup changes the settings of all other functions. Confirm with the manufacturer whether the trip unit long delay pickup on the low-voltage breaker may be set above 100 percent when the sensor rating is equal to the frame size. In many cases it is not. (*From* IEEE Red Book, 1986, *used with permission.*)

The magnetic instantaneous action is achieved through the use of an electromagnet in series with the load current. The passage of a short-circuit current through the coil of the electromagnet creates sufficient force to attract the armature, thus moving the trip bar and unlatching the breaker contacts. The only delaying factor is the fraction of time (one cycle or less) that it takes for the unlatching to take place. Thus the action is said to be instantaneous. This is considerably faster than medium-voltage breakers because there are not the large angular time constants associated with the inertial elements in the larger breakers.

Molded case circuit breakers with more complex characteristics and most low-voltage power circuit breakers are equipped with solid-state electronic trip units. The continuous-current rating may be adjustable, and long-time and short-time functions may be adjustable for current pickup and time delay. The instantaneous response may also be adjustable. Figures A.8 and A.9 illustrate an overcurrent time-current characteristic curve for a solid-state electronic trip circuit breaker with all of these adjustments.

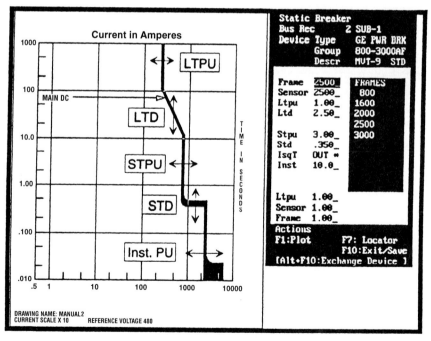

**Figure 5.3**   Generalized solid-state breaker trip curves as shown on coordination software screen (*courtesy of SKM Analysis*). Note the option for $i^2t$ OUT (or IN—not shown) under short time delay. With short time $i^2t$ OUT, the length of the delay is constant and independent of the overcurrent level. It permits better coordination with other solid-state trip breakers. With short time $i^2t$ IN, a sloping curve permits easier coordination with thermal magnetic circuit breaker or fuses.

### 5.4.3  Classical solid-state trip unit

A distinction can and should be made between solid-state trip units and trip units that are built around a microprocessor. The term *static* might even be confused with a microprocessor-based trip unit. In the era after the dominance of thermal-magnetic breakers but before the era of the microprocessor was the era of the solid-state, static, or electronic trip unit. The solid-state or electronic trip units did not employ integrated circuitry, if at all. Now it is difficult not to make an electronic trip unit without an integrated circuit of some kind. Figure 5.3 indicates how a solid-state circuit breaker appears on the computer screen in an overcurrent coordination program (SKM Analysis, 1994).

Figure 5.4 is the time-current characteristic of what we might call a classical solid-state trip unit of the kind that (though electronic) does not apply microprocessors but still represents a large and very reliable number of applications. The following discussion concerns the various setpoints on the tripping curve.

*Current in multiples of sensor rating.*   Let us base our example on a 1000-A sensor. The sensor itself may be adjustable from 80 to 120 percent of its rating. In the case of a 1000-A sensor, we will have 800 to 1200 sensing. If the sensor was 800 A, adjustable with the same, we would have 640 to 960. This allows a global adjustment so that by changing this one variable, we can change all the other settings without changing the relationship among them.

*Long-delay pickup calibrated at 0.5. through 1.25 times sensor rating.*   This is fairly straightforward. For example, take our example sensor rating and multiply it by the calibration setting, and we will have 500- through 1250-A pickup. This means that a fault, usually an overload, that develops beyond 1000 s (16.67 minutes) will trip the breaker.

*Long-delay time calibrated at 4 to 36 s (at 6 times sensor rating).* This one is a little more difficult to understand. If you multiply our 1000-A sensor times 6 and find the 6000-A mark and follow this vertical line up to 4 through 36 s, you define a slanted line that intercepts the vertical line established by the long-delay pickup.

*Short-delay pickup calibrated at 4 to 10 times sensor rating.*   These curves allow much more current but for a much shorter period of time: 4000 through 10,000 A. As you do more coordination studies, you will begin to see that the squeeze for "daylight" for selective tripping frequently involves the short-time pickup adjustment. The short-time adjustment is very handy, however, when you need to hold a breaker closed long enough for downstream devices to clear an even farther downstream fault. Some units come with a built-in instantaneous override at, for instance, 12.5 × continuous amp setting. This is handy when (in the case of a power circuit breaker) you need to trip the breaker on instantaneous when the fault current flowing through it exceeds its short-time rating.

*Short-delay time calibrated at 0.5, 0.33 and 0.18 times (at 2.5 times short-delay pickup).* Same slope as long-delay time—this time keyed to the short-delay pickup described above. In microprocessor-based trip units, there is an option for a flat $I^2t$ segment associated with short-time pickup and delay. This is discussed in detail in Chap. 7.

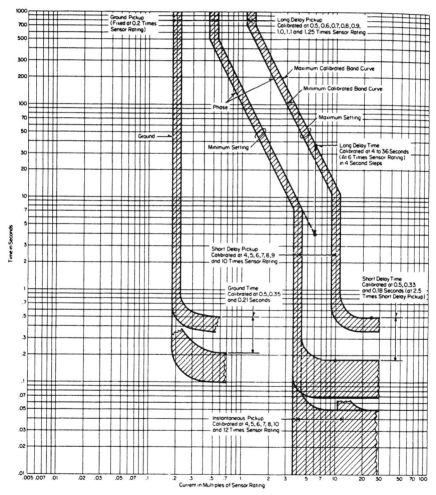

**Figure 5.4**    TCC of solid-state trip unit. The 1990 National Electric Code added an exception to the rules of Article 240-6 so that the *long time* pickup rating of an adjustable trip circuit breaker could be considered the circuit breaker rating if access to the adjustment means was limited due to location of the adjustment means behind sealable covers or locked doors accessible only to qualified personnel. Fuses have the advantage that once installed, no controls can be tampered with.

## Overrides in Trip Functions

*Instantaneous Override.*   An instantaneous override is provided on breakers with short-time delay functions. It is an instantaneous trip function with a fixed pickup value of 1.414 times the rms value of the short-time rating. It ensures that the breaker trips rapidly on high short circuit currents within the breaker interruption capacity.

*Selective Override.*   Selective override provides a higher level of selectivity than instantaneous override. It is used in conjunction with short-time delay and provides an instantaneous trip level set at 2.3 times the rms value of the short time rating of the breaker. This allows for full asymmetry at the short-time rating that is possible on a system, with a power factor as low as 15 percent. It is not just a higher override value, as it monitors the peak current value. Figure 5.B indicates a comparison between the instantaneous and selective override options.

*Discriminators.*   The discriminator is often referred to as the making current release. The close and latch current level of a circuit breaker is generally lower than its short-time rating because of the dynamics in closing a breaker. The discriminator ensures that the breaker closes and latches within its capability and is required when a short-time function is provided without an instantaneous trip function. The discriminator provides an instantaneous trip at approximately 10 times the breaker current rating during the first 0.1 s when the breaker is closed. After this time has elapsed, the discriminator is disabled.

("The Impact of Solid State Technology on Molded Case Circuit Breakers," John A. Wafer, *IEEE IAS,* Sep/Oct 1980.)

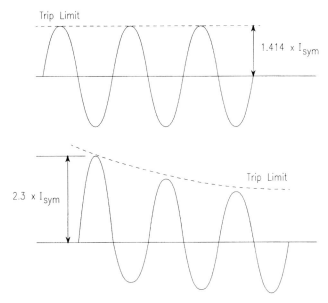

**Figure 5.B**   Instantaneous vs. selective override fault current waveforms.

*Instantaneous pickup calibrated at 4,6,8,10, and 12 times sensor rating.* Instantaneous tripping is required in high-fault-current conditions. You can see the inverse or staircase of increasing levels of current for shorter periods of time.

*Ground-fault pickup and delay.* Many manufacturers prefer to print the ground-fault time-current characteristics on a different sheet of log-log than the phase-tripping curves so that you do not confuse phase and phase-to-ground-fault-current levels. Also, manufacturer time-current characteristic curves for low-voltage protective devices are not always printed with the NEC 1200-A limitation burned into the tripping characteristic. Be careful. Your ground-fault pickup can be set no higher than 1200 A, and the ground-fault time-*delay* setting must not exceed 1 s at 3000 A. You might even mark the NEC rule (from Art. 230-95) on your log-log paper as just another fixed constraint.

Further refinement of the electronic trip unit short-time delay characteristic for overcurrent protection of the ground-fault time-delay characteristic may be obtained by shaping part of the response curve as an inverse function of the product of time and current, $It$, or ampere-squared seconds, $I^2t$ illustrated by the sloping portion of Figs. A.8 and A.9. The $I^2t$ tripping curve has, by definition, slope of minus 2 (made possible through the magic of logarithms). Do not assume that the lower and upper tolerances of the $I^2t$ curves will be exactly parallel, though rare are the circumstances when this has any bearing on coordination. The $I^2t$ response curves more readily coordinate with downstream thermal-magnetic circuit breakers or fuses that have a similarly sloping response curve.

The time-current characteristic curves of low-voltage power circuit breakers of the simplest type, combining long-time delay and instantaneous characteristics, are similar to those of molded case circuit breakers. Even the simplest low-voltage power circuit breakers include adjustments for long-time current pickup, long-time delay, and instantaneous pickup.

## 5.5   Conductor Protection

The reader is referred to Art. 310 of the NEC, "Wiring Methods and Materials." The selection of the correct size of the conductors and raceway for feeders and branch circuit depends on the following:

- Continuous current rating
- Short-circuit rating
- Maximum allowable voltage drop

Although our discussion is limited to the issues that pertain to overcurrent protection, the designer will need to deal with the related matter of voltage drop. The NEC does not have an explicit requirement for maximum allowable voltage drop (the voltage drop rules are established by ANSI), but as a general rule, you should not allow more than a maximum of 5 percent voltage drop on a feeder + branch circuit to the most distant point of power use.

The physical principle involved in conductor protection is that in alternating current circuits the current-carrying capacity decreases with the size of the conductor because of skin effect. It is also because it is harder to dissipate heat within large conductors and difficult to pull through conduit; therefore, it is preferable to parallel smaller conductors.

### 5.5.1   Short-circuit protection of cables

Feeder conductors must be sized to carry fault current long enough for the protective devices to clear the fault without damaging the insulation. How much time does the typical low-voltage circuit breaker need?

Refer to Table 5.4 where correction factors $K_1$ and $K_0$ for initial and maximum short-circuit temperatures, the clearing times, and $K_0$ factors are indicated.

$$I_{asy} = K_0 \times I_{sym}$$

where   $I_{asy}$ = asymmetrical short-circuit current
$I_{sym}$ = available short-circuit symmetrical current

The maximum short-circuit temperature rating depends on the type of insulation material used for the cable.

The precise calculation to determine the short-circuit current ratings of a cable is rather time consuming. The precise formula is

$$\left[\frac{I}{A}\right]^2 t = 0.0297 \log \frac{(T_2 + 234)}{(T_1 + 234)}$$

**TABLE 5.4   Cable $K_0$ Factors**

| System voltage | Feeder overcurrent device | Total clearing time (cycles) | $K_0$ factor |
|---|---|---|---|
| Up to 1000 V | Circuit breaker* | 2 | 1.3 |
| | Current-limiting fuse | ½ | 1.4 |
| Above 1000 V | Air circuit breaker | 5 | 1.15 |
| | Oil circuit breaker | 8 | 1.1 |
| | Power fuse | 1 | 1.6 |
| | Current-limiting fuse | ½ | 1.6 |

\* Non-current-limiting type.

where   I = short-circuit current in amperes
       A = conductor area in circular mils
       t = time of short-circuit in seconds
       $T_1$ = maximum operating temperature 75°C
       $T_2$ = maximum short-circuit temperature 150°C

There are tables you can use for this calculation. These graphs show short-circuit current on the vertical axis and the conductor size on the horizontal axis with a series of diagonal lines indicating the duration of the fault (the total clearing time of the overcurrent device protecting the conductors). These graphs are available from manufacturers for every conductor and insulation type.

The chart in Fig. 5.5 is an example of one cable manufacturer's data about the maximum currents to which various size copper conductors can be subjected for various times without injuring the insulation. It is based on a 90°C conductor operating temperature. The maximum current for short-circuit ratings for 75°C conductor temperatures and for other than 250°C may be obtained by multiplying the value obtained for $T_1 = 90$°C and $T_2 = 250$°C from the chart by an appropriate correction factor for other values of $T_1$ and $T_2$.

**Example 5.1   Determine Short-Circuit Current Rating of a Low-Voltage Conductor**

*Situation.*   Various 600-V class cable systems are being evaluated for protection by a circuit breaker.

*Requirements.*   Determine the symmetrical short-circuit current rating of a 2/0-kcmil copper conductor in order to specify overcurrent protection.

**solution**   From Table 5.4, the clearing time for a circuit breaker is 2 cycles and the cable $K_0$ factor is 1.3. From Fig. 5.5, we read about 50,000 A at the point of intersection of the 2/0-kcmil conductor line with the 2-cycle line. The symmetrical rating is therefore 50,000/1.3 = 38,461 A.

*Remarks.*   In addition to the characteristics of copper versus aluminum cables each cable *insulation type* will have a short-circuit characteristic similar to that shown in Fig. 5.5. These cable short-circuit characteristics are available from cable manufacturers and are generally available in the libraries of overcurrent coordination software.

**Example 5.2   Overcurrent Protection of Cables**

*Situation.*   An electrical load estimate reveals the need to feed 134 A at 480 V. Available short-circuit on the line side of a prospective circuit breaker is 53,000 A.

*Requirements.*   Select the size of the conductor and specify overcurrent protection.

**solution**   The minimum trip rating for the breaker is 125 percent of 134 = 167.5 A. From the manufacturer's application literature, we find that the next highest

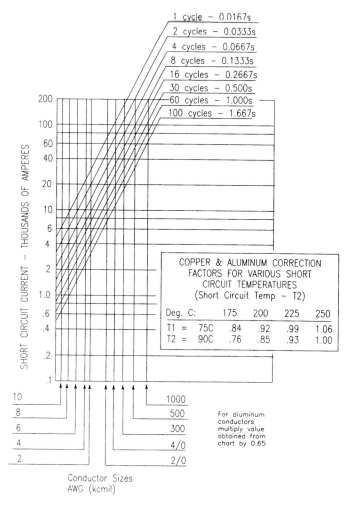

**Figure 5.5** Cable short-circuit withstand curves. The allowable short-circuit time-current characteristic for insulated copper or aluminum conductors can be determined from formulas or curves (in IPCEA) based on the maximum continuous operating temperature of the insulation. These curves are of the $I^2t$ type and will be parallel to the short-circuit withstand current curve for the oil-immersed transformer. The slope of these curves is $-2.0$ on log-log paper intercepting the current axis at an angle of 63.4 degrees. If only one point on both of these curves is plotted, the remaining portion of the curves can be quickly drawn through these points parallel to a line whose slope is two cycles along the time axis and one cycle on the current axis. The practical limits for plotting these curves are between 10 s and the maximum three-phase symmetrical fault current to which the primary cables and transformer are exposed (Okonite).

standard trip rating is 175 A. The ampacity of the four #3/0 XHHW in conduit is $0.80 \times 225 = 180$ A.

The frame size required for the 175-A trip is 225 A, which has an interrupting rating of 22,000 symmetrical at 480 V, well above the available short-circuit level at that application point.

*Remarks.*   We have assumed that voltage drop is less than 2 percent with this design.

Figure 5.6 indicates overcurrent devices protecting three cables in series. The circuit is a practical circuit, but the intention is to give you

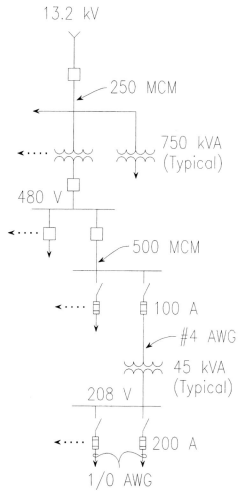

**Figure 5.6**   Three conductors in series. This is a generalized schematic of a typical building electrical distribution system.

the sense of the daylight between protective devices and the cable dam age curves. You do not need to work up a coordination study every time you specify a feeder cable, but you should do it the first time you work with a new device application or new insulation type.

Cable protection strategies cannot be applied without consideration for the other aspects of branch circuit and feeder design either, namely, voltage drop associated with a given conductor and the cost of raceway that complies with NEC construction requirements that are intended to ensure safety (Fig. 5.7). Effective circuit design is essentially a multivariable optimization problem within which overcurrent protection is only one component.

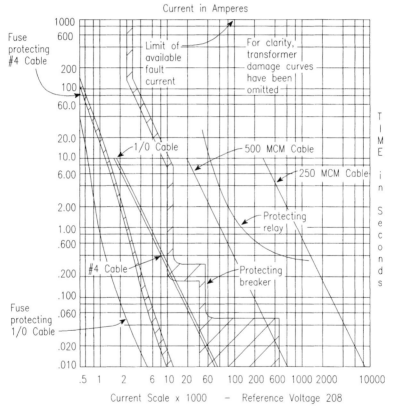

**Figure 5.7** Cable Coordination Study. This simplified study shows only circuit breakers and fuses. Cable limiters may also be applied in place of other protective devices for short-circuit protection. The current-carrying capacity of cable limiters is indicated in terms of cable size rather than amperes. Thus a #2 cable limiter will carry the current of a #2 cable. Cable limiters generally confine damage to the point of the short-circuit fault. They are effective in stopping long-length cable burn back and the striking of multiple arcs when faults occur.

## 5.6  Transformer Protection

Art. 450 of the NEC provides us with protection design rules for transformers. We discuss transformer protection rules for transformers applied at less than 600 V in this chapter (see Fig. 5.8) and continue our discussion of transformers applied at more than 600 V in Chap. 7.

The type of transformers that typically feed (or are fed from) power panels are classified as Category I transformers. By ANSI-IEEE C37.91 definition, a Category I transformer is 5 to 500 kVA single-phase, 15 to 500 kVA three-phase. These transformers typically have 480 V on the primary and 208 V on the secondary and are used to feed small motors, lighting, and receptacle panels. We shall deal with Category II transformers (single-phase 501 to 1667 and three-phase 501 to 5000 kVA) in the chapter on unit substations (Chap. 7).

The basic rules are as follows:

- Each transformer 600 V, nominal, or less shall be protected by an individual overcurrent device on the primary side, rated or set at not more than 125 percent of the rated primary current of the transformer. This does not mean that the setting cannot be 80 or 110 percent, just that the setting of the overcurrent device, a device

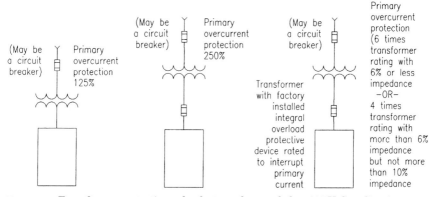

**Figure 5.8**  Transformer protection rules for transformers below 600 V. Coordination may be compromised when the National Electric Code requires that you choose a lower (or higher) rated device in order to apply a device with a standard rating. (National Electric Code Article 240-6 deals with the issue of standard ampere ratings.) For example, the rules regarding protection of the primary of a 600-V transformer may allow a designer to specify the next higher standard rating fuse or circuit breaker (where the primary current of a transformer is 9 A or more), while it may require the next lower standard ampere rating (where the primary current of the transformer is less than 9 A). In either case you may find that there will be miscoordination between, say, a panel main and the transformer overcurrent device, or between, say, the substation feeder breaker and the transformer overcurrent device. As a general rule, whenever you notice coordination ratios falling below 2:1 you will need to look into the particulars about how the feeder and/or breaker circuit is designed.

responding to sustained current in excess of rated capacity, may be no larger than 125 percent.

- A transformer 600 V, nominal, or less having an overcurrent device on the secondary side rated or set at not more than 125 percent of the rated secondary current of the transformer shall not be required to have an individual overcurrent device on the primary side if the primary feeder overcurrent device is rated or set at a current value not more than 250 percent of the rated primary current of the transformer.

- A transformer equipped with coordinated thermal overload protection by the manufacturer and arranged to interrupt the primary current shall not be required to have an individual overcurrent device on the primary side if the primary feeder overcurrent is rated or set at a current value not more than six times the rated current of the transformer or transformers having not more than 6 percent impedance and not more than four times the rated current of the transformer for transformers having more than 6 but not more than 10 percent impedance.

It is important to note that transformer primary protection is not acceptable as suitable protection for the secondary-circuit conductors, even if the secondary conductors are adequately sized according to the current transformation ratio. On three and four wire transformer secondaries, it is possible that an unbalanced load may exceed the secondary conductor ampacity that is normally specified, assuming balanced conditions (McPartland, 1986).

Coordination may be compromised when the NEC requires that you choose a lower (or higher) rated device in order to apply a device with a standard rating. NEC Art. 240-6 deals with the issue of standard ampere ratings. For example, the rules regarding protection of the primary of a 600-V transformer may allow a designer to specify the next higher standard rating fuse or circuit breaker (where the primary current of a transformer is 9 A or more), while it may require the next lower standard ampere rating (where the primary current of the transformer is less than 9 A). In either case, you may find that there will be miscoordination between, for example, a panel main and the transformer overcurrent device, or between the substation feeder breaker and the transformer overcurrent device. As a general rule, somewhat implied in Table 5.2, whenever you notice coordination ratios falling below 2:1, you will need to look into the particulars about how the feeder and/or breaker circuit is designed.

The 1990 NEC added an exception to the rules of Art. 240-6 so that the long-time pickup rating (as opposed to the instantaneous trip setting) of an adjustable trip circuit breaker could be considered the circuit breaker rating if access to the adjustment means was limited because of location of the adjustment means behind sealable covers or locked doors accessible only to qualified personnel.

Assuming all the rules have been followed, the tool we use to ensure protection of the transformer is ANSI C37.91. Reference to Fig. A.13, the Category I transformer damage curve, indicates a simple curve (one line actually) that covers both thermal and mechanical limits, as well as frequent and infrequent faults. Properly applied fuses and circuit breakers at 480 V almost always clear this curve (fall to the left of it).

### 5.6.1  Transformer inrush and instantaneous trips

Small 480- and 208-V primary transformers up to about 300 kVA are commonly protected by direct-acting trips on molded case and steel frame power breakers that provide time delay or instantaneous tripping when required. In practice, circuit breaker instantaneous trips must be set above the offset value of the transformer or motor inrush currents to avoid unnecessary tripping. As a result, it has become a widespread practice to set breaker instantaneous trips as high as their range permits, perhaps checking only that the setting does not exceed the maximum fault current available. But high instantaneous trip settings do not assure detection and interruption of low-level fault currents. A substantial overall improvement in system protection can be secured by simply setting instantaneous trips no higher than required to avoid nuisance tripping under normal conditions. In some situations, the instantaneous trip pickup may be no higher than two times the continuous current rating; in others, it may be 12. Setting instantaneous trip pickups on this basis should become a general practice in distribution systems. You might supplement this protection strategy with the application of short-time trip functions where possible.

### 5.6.2  Ferroresonance

Sometimes small 480/277- or 208/120-V transformers are protected with fuses only. A problem that can arise with transformers that are single phased is a phenomenon known as ferroresonance. It can happen when an unloaded or lightly loaded transformer sustains an open conductor at its primary circuit. Ferroresonance causes system overvoltage as a result of the transformer core inductance forming a tuned circuit with the system distributed capacitance. To avoid ferroresonance, all three lines must be switched simultaneously (as with a

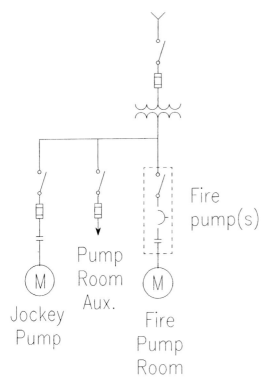

**Figure 5.9** Fire pump overcurrent protection requirements. The overcurrent device for a transformer supplying a fire pump installation is required to be sized to carry indefinitely the locked rotor current of the fire pump motors and associated fire pump accessory equipment. This may require that the transformer be increased in size. (*From* 1993 National Electric Code Handbook. *Used with permission.*)

medium-voltage breaker). The same result can be accomplished with primary fuses if a contactor tripping mechanism that operates from a striker pin is located in the fuse. When the fuse element burns in two, the spring-loaded striker pin is released, and it projects upward and operates a contact that trips the contactor.

### 5.6.3   Transformers for fire pumps

The 1993 NEC Art. 450-3 contains a noteworthy change to the overcurrent protection requirements for fire pump circuits that are fed by transformers (NFPA, 1993; ECEM, 1992; *Consulting-Specifying Engineer,* 1993).

(d) Fire pump installations. Where the transformer is dedicated to supplying power to a fire pump installation, it shall not require secondary overcurrent protection. Primary overcurrent protection shall be provided in accordance with Section 450-3(a) or 450-3(b). The primary rating or setting shall be sufficient to carry the equivalent of the transformer secondary current sum of the locked-rotor currents of the fire pump motor(s) and associated fire pump accessory equipment indefinitely.

In view of the fact that we choose to allow fire pump circuits to operate to destruction if necessary, the requirement makes sense. The next upstream device needs to be able to carry the locked rotor currents, as reflected through the transformer winding ratio, of the fire pump system indefinitely. (See Fig. 5.9.)

We will deal with the related issue of coordinating overcurrent protection for emergency or standby circuits when such circuits are fed from unit substations. We will want to make sure that standby circuits do not cause cascade tripping of protective devices from remote sources.

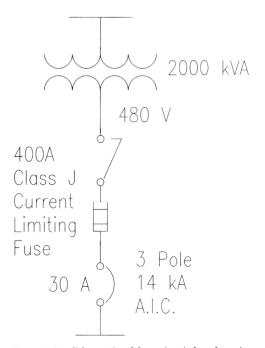

**Figure 5.10** Schematic of fuse-circuit breaker circuit.

## 5.7  Solved Problems

### Example 5.3  Up-Over-and-Down Method

*Situation.*   Your utility circuit neighbor has just installed a small cogeneration unit, thus increasing the fault availability to 50,000 A at your service drop. You have a small, 30-A circuit breaker with a 14,000-A interrupting rating that will not withstand the 50,000 A available on the line side of the breaker.

*Requirement.*   Select a fuse to protect the circuit breaker. Compare fuse peak let-through current to the circuit breaker-tested peak-current withstand capability. See Fig. 5.10.

**solution**   Remember the distinction we made in Chap. 3 regarding the difference between withstand and interrupting ratings. From the circuit breaker manufacturer (the catalog or the sales representative), we learn that the circuit breaker will withstand 24,000 A before destruction. From the fuse manufacturer, we obtain a diagram such as Fig. 5.11. This particular diagram is the let-through time-current characteristic for a Class J fuse (Bussman, 1990).

On the horizontal axis we read 50,000 A; on the vertical axis, we read 24,000 A. We must try to find a fuse size with an instantaneous peak let-through current less than 24,000 A. We find that the 400-A fuse satisfies this condition, and therefore the circuit breaker will be protected.

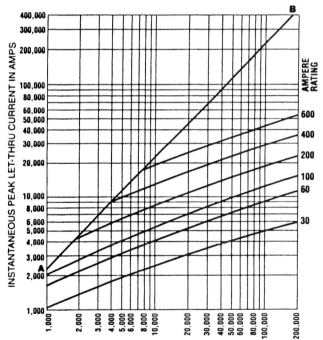

**Figure 5.11**  Typical Class J peak let-through current data at 600 V. (*Cooper-Bussman*)

*Remarks.* This approach has proven to be the conservative approach. A fuse with a rating higher than 400 A may well protect a given circuit breaker, but higher rated fuses should not be applied without series test data to prove their suitability (EC&M, 1987).

## Bibliography

Box, Ken, "Do/P-Rated Ballasts Offer Adequate Component Protection?" *Consulting-Specifying Engineer,* June 1990.

Bussman, *SPD—Electrical Protection Handbook,* Cooper Industries, Jan. 1990.

*DAPPER and CAPTOR User Manual,* SKM Analysis, Manhattan Beach, Calif.

*Engineering Data for Copper and Aluminum Conductor Electrical Cables,* Bulletin, EHB-88, The Okonite Company.

Hansen, Steven, "Protecting Molded-Case Circuit Breakers," *EC&M,* March 1987.

Hartwell, Fred, "Illustrated Changes to the 1993 National Electric Code," *EC&M,* Sept. 1992.

McPartland, J. F., *Practical Electrical Design,* McGraw-Hill, New York, 1986.

Telander, S. H., "Circuit Breakers—Choosing the Right Type for Specific Applications," *Consulting-Specifying Engineer,* July 1987.

Valvoda, Frank R., "Changes to the 1993 Affect Engineering Design," *Consulting-Specifying Engineer,* Feb. 1993.

Wafer, *IEEE Transactions on Industry Applications,* Sept./Oct. 1980.

### General references

"Applying Short Circuit Current and Series Connected Ratings," *Circuit Breaker Application Guide SD401,* 8/88, Square D Company.

Beck, Paul E., "Untangling the 1993 NEC," *Consulting-Specifying Engineer,* Oct. 1991.

Bussman, NE93, *Overcurrent Protection and the 1993 National Electric Code—Questions and Answers to Help You Comply,* Cooper Industries.

Chen, Kao, *Industrial Power Distribution and Illuminating Systems,* Marcel Dekker, Inc., 1989.

"Determining Current Carrying Capacity in Special Applications," *Circuit Breaker Application Guide SD261 R1,* 7/88, Square D Company.

Distribution and Control Business Unit, *A Working Manual on Molded Case Circuit Breakers,* Westinghouse Electric Corporation, BB4, File 29-000, 1992.

"Electronic Trip Molded Case Circuit Breaker Basics," *SD378,* Square D Company, 1989.

"Engineering Data for Copper and Aluminum Conductor Electrical Cables," Bulletin EHB-88, The Okonite Company.

Farrell, George W., and Frank R. Valvoda, "Protecting Wires and Cables," *Consulting-Specifying Engineer,* March 1993.

General Electric Company, "Application and Selection of Spectra RMS Molded Case Circuit Breakers," GET-7002B 0491 BLK, 1991.

Hughes, S. D., *Electrical Systems in Buildings,* PWS-Kent Publishers, 1988.

Kussey, Frank W., and Jack L. Warren, *Design Fundamentals for Low-Voltage Distribution and Control,* Marcel Dekker, Inc., 1987.

Love, Daniel, "Molded-case Circuit Breakers—Is There Danger in the Present Rating Methodology?" *IEEE IAS,* Sept./Oct. 1991.

McPartland, J. F., *Practical Electrical Design,* McGraw-Hill, New York, 1987.

Raff, Will, "Specifying Switchboards and Panelboards," *Consulting-Specifying Engineer,* Nov. 1989.

Rosenberg, Paul, *Installation Requirements of the 1990 National Electric Code,* "An Audel Book," Macmillan Publishing Company, 1991.

"Selection and Application Guide, Sentron Panelboards," Siemens Bulletin, 4.5-2A.

Titus, R., and T. Mills, "Accurate Voltage Drop Calculations Can Save Money," *Consulting-Specifying Engineer,* Sept. 1993.

## Further reading

"Branch Circuit and Service Circuit Breakers," UL 489. Order from UL Publications Stock, 333 Pfingsten, Road, Northbrook, IL 60062.

Freund, Arthur, "Replacement Circuit Breakers—Boon or Bomb?" *EC&M,* June 1989.

Gearhart, Gary L., "Limit Fault Current, End Costly Nuisance Shutdowns," *Specifying Engineer,* June 1984.

IEEE Standard for Metal-Enclosed Low Voltage Power Circuit Breaker Switchgear, ANSI/IEEE C37.20.1-1987. This is the mother standard which contains general information about ratings and testing requirements for this class of equipment. References to switchgear components are listed. You may find the Transformer Through-Fault Protection Curves in ANSI/IEEE Standard C37.91, *IEEE Guide for Protective Relay Applications to Power Transformers.* This is the principal standard in transformer protection. The Appendix to this standard contains a few solved coordination problems involving use of the through-fault curves.

*Molded Case Circuit Breakers,* AB-1 Standards Publication. Order from NEMA Publications, 155 East 44th St., New York, NY 10017.

Saporta, Vincent J., "Simplified Motor Control Conductor Protection Based Upon the 1984 National Electric Code," *IEEE IAS,* vol. 1A-22, May/June 1986.

Standard for Trip Devices for AC and General Purpose DC Low-Voltage Power Circuit Breakers, ANSI C37.17. This standard contains information about how the circuit breaker manufacturers establish the ranges and tolerances for short, long, and instantaneous trip curves.

WC-375 Circuit Breaker, Molded Case; Branch Circuit and Service.

# Protection and Coordination for Motors and Motor Control Centers

## 6.1 Foreword

The applications of motors to industrial processes have come a long way since the early days of electricity when one motor supplied rotational power to an entire plant by a long shaft. Motor control was accomplished by using extension rods to change the belts around overhead pulleys. Now we have an almost dizzying variety of choices with respect to motor control and protection. What used to be simply protection devices are now control devices and vice versa. It takes a considerable amount of contact with motor control and protection devices offered by all manufacturers to feel comfortable within this equipment class.

The time you spend in motor circuit design, however, is time well spent. Most of the elements of power circuit design are concentrated in the NEC requirements for motor circuits. In the interest of keeping our focus on overcurrent protection, we will not dwell on the related issues of voltage drop and raceway design. Furthermore, we will restrict our treatment to low-voltage motors up to about 500 hp—the bulk of circuits at work in industrial, commercial, and institutional facilities.

## 6.2 Relevant Theory of Induction Motors

It is worthwhile undertaking a brief review of the classical lumped parameter model of an induction motor circuit in order to understand where some of the numbers we shall use in constructing starting curves come from.

A simplified lumped parameter induction motor equivalent circuit is shown in Fig. 6.1 (Blackburn, 1987). Typical values for induction motors in per unit on the motor kVA or kV as shown in Fig. 6.1 are

$$R_s \text{ and } R_r = 0.01 \text{ per unit}$$

$$jX_m = j3.0 \text{ per unit}$$

$$jX = jX_d'' = 0.15 \text{ per unit}$$

From these the typical locked rotor or starting is

$$I_{starting} = 1/jX_d'' = 1/0.15 = 6.67 \text{ pu}$$

Thus it can be seen where the six times motor full-load current = inrush comes from. There are some refinements, however. First, this is the symmetrical value that we show in segment A in Fig. 1.2; the asymmetrical current is higher as shown with segment C in Fig. 1.2.

Since the shunt $jX_m$ is high relative to the other impedances, the equivalent at the motor input reduces with the typical values above to

$$Z_{m1} = z_{m2} = 0.144 \angle 82.39°$$

or practically equal to $jX_d'' = 0.15$ per unit as commonly applied for a stalled motor (S = 1.0). If the motor is running (S = 0.01), the values above give

$$Z_{m1} = 0.927 \angle 25.87°$$

$$\text{and } Z_{m2} = 0.144 \angle 84.19°$$

Thus, for practical purposes

$$Z_{m1} = 0.9 \text{ to } 1.0 \text{ and } Z_{m2} = 0.15 \text{ per unit}$$

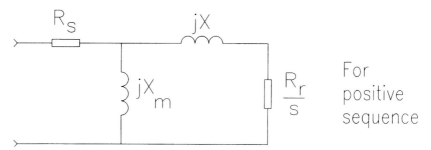

**Figure 6.1**  Typical induction motor equivalent circuit.

$R_s$ = stator resistance
$jX_s$ = stator leakage reactance at rated frequency
$R_r$ = rotor resistance
$jX_r$ = rotor leakage reactance at rated frequency
$jX_m$ = Shunt exciting reactance
$jX == jX_s + jX_r == jX_d''$

S (slip) = synchronous RPM—rotor RPM / (synchronous RPM) = 1.0 stalled = 0 + running.

From stalled to running, the positive sequence impedance changes from approximately 0.15 to 0.9 or 1.0 per unit, while negative sequence impedance remains essentially the same at approximately 0.15 per unit. Again, these are on the base of the rated motor kVA, which is roughly equal to the motor horsepower. These values will vary with each individual motor and at different voltages, but these typical values are close and quite useful in the absence of other data.

The maximum starting current curve is at rated voltage. Currents for lower voltages exist to the left, with the knee at a higher time level.

With respect to the information in Table 6.1, it is noteworthy that these faults occurred in spite of the use of normal protection. Thermal overloads and single phasing make up 44 percent of malfunction causes. Approximately 80 percent of these problems occurred in motors rated 50 hp or larger. This study indicates the relative importance of the individual causes of damage.

*Motor characteristics.* These include type, speed, voltage, horsepower rating, service factor, power factor rating, type of motor enclosure, lubrication arrangement of winding and their temperature limits, thermal capabilities of rotor and stator during starting, running, and stall conditions.

*Starting conditions.* Full voltage or reduced voltage, voltage drop and degree of inrush during starting, repetitive starts, frequency, and total number of starts, and others.

*Ambient conditions.* Temperature maxima and minima, elevation, adjacent heat sources, ventilation arrangement, exposure to water, chemicals, exposure to rodents, and various weather and flood conditions.

*Driven equipment.* Characteristics will influence chances of locked rotor, failure to reach normal speed, excessive heating during acceleration, overloading, and stalling.

TABLE 6.1    Major Causes of Motor Problems*

| Causes of motor malfunction | Percent |
| --- | --- |
| Overload | 30 |
| Single-phasing | 14 |
| Contaminants | 19 |
| Old age | 10 |
| Bearing failures | 13 |
| Rotor failures | 5 |
| Miscellaneous | 9 |

*Base:* 9000 failure events (study by Electrical Research Assn., Leatherhead, England).

* SOURCE: Laurie, 1987.

Motor voltages below nameplate rating result in reduced starting torque and increased full-load temperature rise. Motor voltages above nameplate rating result in increased starting torque, increased starting current, and decreased power factor. The increased starting torque will increase the accelerating forces on couplings and driven equipment. Increased starting current causes greater voltage drop in the supply circuit and increases the voltage dip on lamps and other equipment. In general, voltages slightly above nameplate rating have less detrimental effect on motor performance than voltages slightly below nameplate rating.

## 6.3 Overcurrent Protection Strategies

The fundamental and basic aim should be to permit the motor to operate up to but not to exceed its thermal and mechanical limits for overload and abnormal operation conditions and to provide maximum sensitivity for faults.

One common protection configuration for low-voltage motors is the fuse + thermal overload combination in which time-delay fuses provide short-circuit protection and overload "heaters" provide overload protection. The time-delay fuses are designed to allow normal motor inrush current to flow without opening the circuit but are designed to open at abnormal (short-circuit) levels of current. The nature of time-delay fuses, however, makes them unable to open motor circuits undergoing sustained overloads, thus the combination.

Typically, the overloads are contained within the motor, and the fuses are located in the equipment immediately upstream from the motor terminals.

The UL definition for time delay means having a 10-s operating delay at 500 percent of the fuse label rating.

Combination fused motor starters that employ overload relays sized for motor running overcurrent protection ($\leq$115 percent for 1.0 service factor and $\leq$125 percent for $\geq$1.15 service factor) should incorporate time delay fuses sized at 115 percent for 1.0 service factor and 125 percent for $\geq$1.15 service factor or the next larger standard size to serve as a backup protection. A combination motor starter with backup fuses will provided comprehensive protection.

When applying bolted pressure contact switches, there is a possibility of blowing the fuse in only one phase during a ground fault. This problem is called single phasing, and it can be injurious to motors because many older motor overload protection devices do not react in time to protect the motor for this condition. In addition, when a single fuse isolates a ground fault, the fault can still be fed from the other phases through the motor windings, even though the current magnitude has been greatly reduced. Thus, the switch should be purchased with the anti-single-phasing option and an electrical shunt trip. At the same time, a ground-fault trip unit can be purchased to trip the switch.

Three-phase motor, single-phasing protection may be provided by time-delay fuses that are sized at approximately 125 percent of the motor running current. Loss of one phase will result in an increase to 173 to 200 percent of the line current to the motor. This will be sensed by the motor fuses because they are sized at 125 percent. Provided the fuses are sized to the actual motor running current, the single-phasing current will open the fuses before damage to the windings occurs. When the motors are running well under load, anti-single-phasing may be provided by sensitive anti-single-phasing type motor overload relays.

### 6.3.1   Summary of 1993 NEC requirements

As can be seen in Fig. 6.2, the essential components of a motor branch circuit are as follows:

- Branch circuit, short-circuit, and ground-fault protection

- Breaker circuit conductors

- Motor controller with overload protection

- Disconnecting means

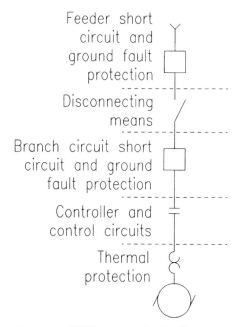

**Figure 6.2** NEC motor circuit diagram—
Guideline to Article 430.

Refer also to Tables 6.2 and 6.3.

Article 430 of the NEC represents over 100 years of experience working with motor circuits. Although all of the information in the article will be used by the protection specialist, Tables 430-150, 151, and 152 that appear at the end of the article will be used most frequently.

The NEC requires that where the current rating of a motor is applied to determine the ampacity of the conductors, the ampere ratings of switches, branch circuit protective devices, and so on, the values listed in NEC Tables 430-17 through 430-150 (including notes) be applied, instead of the actual current rating marked on the motor nameplate. This helps to standardize the design process on which other parts of the NEC depend. You might think of the NEC motor tables as establishing *nominal* values of full-load current in the same way that we use nominal voltage levels such as 120 or 460 V. It is noteworthy that in Table 430-159 the full-load amperage of 460-V motors roughly follows the horsepower rating. The correspondence is hardly exact, but if you are in a pinch and you did not have a code book nearby, you would not be far off in guessing that the full-load amperes of a 100-hp motor is about 100 A (it is actually 109). Of course, at higher voltages, the full-load amperes would be lower.

The NEC requires that continuous duty motors above 1 hp with a service factor of 1.0 require overload protection no greater than 115 percent of motor full-load current, for example. Similar motors with a service factor 1.15 and greater require overload protection no greater than 125 percent of motor full-load current. As you can see, the selection of these protective devices depends on how large the motor is and how it will be used (continuous or intermittent duty). The reader should be familiar with the section of the NEC.

It should be remembered that these motor curves are approximate representations of thermal damage zones for normal operation. The relays should operate just before the limits are reached or exceeded. Microprocessor-based motor protective devices permit excellent coordination and flexibility.

Over many years overload protection has been accomplished by thermal relays or heaters to match the thermal limit curves, the inverse time-overcurrent relays for locked rotor protection. All manufacturer application catalogs contain a page or two with charts and tables and guidelines for selecting a heater. When selecting a heater to match a particular motor, use the actual motor nameplate rating for full-load current. You should never select a starter for a motor that has a higher horsepower rating than that shown on the starter nameplate, even though the normal motor current is within range of heaters listed for the starter.

### 6.3.2 Example motor circuit

The best way to learn motor circuit protection design is to simply do it. Let us begin with the circuits in Fig. 6.3:

**TABLE 6.2    Full-Load Current* Three-Phase Alternating-Current Motors (NEC Table 430-150)**

| HP | 115V | 200V | 208V | 230V | 460V | 575V | 2300V | 230V | 460V | 575V | 2300V |
|---|---|---|---|---|---|---|---|---|---|---|---|
| | | Induction-type squirrel-cage and wound-rotor amperes | | | | | | Synchronous-type unity power factor[†] amperes | | | |
| ½ | 4 | 2.3 | 2.2 | 2 | 1 | .8 | | | | | |
| ¾ | 5.6 | 3.2 | 3.1 | 2.8 | 1.4 | 1.1 | | | | | |
| 1 | 7.2 | 4.1 | 4.0 | 3.6 | 1.8 | 1.4 | | | | | |
| 1½ | 10.4 | 6.0 | 5.7 | 5.2 | 2.6 | 2.1 | | | | | |
| 2 | 13.6 | 7.8 | 7.5 | 6.8 | 3.4 | 2.7 | | | | | |
| 3 | | 11.0 | 10.6 | 9.6 | 4.8 | 3.9 | | | | | |
| 5 | | 17.5 | 16.7 | 15.2 | 7.6 | 6.1 | | | | | |
| 7½ | | 25.3 | 24.2 | 22 | 11 | 9 | | | | | |
| 10 | | 32.2 | 30.8 | 28 | 14 | 11 | | | | | |
| 15 | | 48.3 | 46.2 | 42 | 21 | 17 | | | | | |
| 20 | | 62.1 | 59.4 | 54 | 27 | 22 | | | | | |
| 25 | | 78.2 | 74.8 | 68 | 34 | 27 | | 53 | 26 | 21 | |
| 30 | | 92 | 88 | 80 | 40 | 32 | | 63 | 32 | 26 | |
| 40 | | 119.6 | 114.4 | 104 | 52 | 41 | | 83 | 41 | 33 | |
| 50 | | 149.5 | 143.0 | 130 | 65 | 52 | | 104 | 52 | 42 | |
| 60 | | 177.1 | 169.4 | 154 | 77 | 62 | 16 | 123 | 61 | 49 | 12 |
| 75 | | 220.8 | 211.2 | 192 | 96 | 77 | 20 | 155 | 78 | 62 | 15 |
| 100 | | 285.2 | 272.8 | 248 | 124 | 99 | 26 | 202 | 101 | 81 | 20 |
| 125 | | 358.8 | 343.2 | 312 | 156 | 125 | 31 | 253 | 126 | 101 | 25 |
| 150 | | 414 | 396.0 | 360 | 180 | 144 | 37 | 302 | 151 | 121 | 30 |
| 200 | | 552 | 528.0 | 480 | 240 | 192 | 49 | 400 | 201 | 161 | 40 |

* These values of full-load current are for motors running at speeds usual for belted motors and motors with normal torque characteristics. Motors built for especially low speeds or high torques may require more running current, and multispeed motors will have full-load current varying with speed, in which case the nameplate current rating shall be used.

[†] For 90 and 80 percent power factor, the above figures shall be multiplied by 1.1 and 1.25 respectively.

The voltages listed are rated motor voltages. The currents listed shall be permitted for system voltage ranges of 110 to 120, 220 to 240, 440 to 480, and 550 to 600 volts.

Adapted from 1993 NEC (used with permission).

Consider one 40-hp, 460-V, three-phase squirrel cage induction motor

- Service factor 1.15
- Nameplate rating of 50 A
- Full voltage starting
- Nontime-delay fuses

Observations:

- Current rating: From NEC Table 430-150, the rated current of a 40-hp motor is 52 A. This is the value that must be applied except for overload protection.

TABLE 6.3    Maximum Rating or Setting of Motor Branch-Circuit, Short-Circuit, and Ground Fault Protective Devices (NEC Table 430-152)

| | Percent of full-load current | | | |
|---|---|---|---|---|
| Type of motor | Non-time delay fuse | Dual element (time delay) fuse | Instan- taneous trip breaker | Inverse time breaker* |
| Single-phase, all types | | | | |
| No code letter | 300 | 175 | 700 | 250 |
| All ac single-phase and polyphase squirrel-cage and syn- chronous motors† with full- voltage, resistor or reactor starting: | | | | |
| No code letter | 300 | 175 | 700 | 250 |
| Code letters F to V | 300 | 175 | 700 | 250 |
| Code letters B to E | 250 | 175 | 700 | 200 |
| Code letter A | 150 | 150 | 700 | 150 |
| All ac squirrel-cage and synchro- nous motors† with autotrans- former starting: | | | | |
| Not more than 30 amps | | | | |
| No code letter | 250 | 175 | 700 | 200 |
| More than 30 amps | | | | |
| No code letter | 200 | 175 | 700 | 200 |
| Code letters F to V | 250 | 175 | 700 | 200 |
| Code letters B to E | 200 | 175 | 700 | 200 |
| Code letter A | 150 | 150 | 700 | 150 |
| High reactance squirrel-cage | | | | |
| Not more than 30 amps | | | | |
| No code letter | 250 | 175 | 700 | 250 |
| More than 30 amps | | | | |
| No code letter | 200 | 175 | 700 | 200 |
| Wound-rotor— | | | | |
| No code letter | 150 | 150 | 700 | 150 |
| Direct-current (constant voltage) | | | | |
| No more than 50 hp | | | | |
| No code letter | 150 | 150 | 250 | 150 |
| More than 50 hp | | | | |
| No code letter | 150 | 150 | 175 | 150 |

For explanation of code letter marking, see Table 430-7(b).

For certain exceptions to the values specified, see Sections 430-52 through 430-54.

* The values given in the last column also cover the ratings of nonadjustable inverse time types of circuit breakers that may be modified as in Section 430-52.

† Synchronous motors of the low-torque, low-speed type (usually 450 rpm or lower), such as are used to drive reciprocating compressors, pumps, etc., that start unloaded, do not require a fuse rating or circuit-breaker setting in excess of 200 percent of full-load current.

Adapted from 1993 NEC (used with permission).

# Specifying Motor Overloads

Motor overloads are sized according to the actual full-load current stamped on the motor nameplate. When you have this data you need to obtain an electrical equipment manufacturer's catalog with a schedule that correlates the overload (or heater) with the motor full-load current. A typical manufacturer schedule appears below.

| Motor full-load current (amp) | Thermal unit no. | Maximum fuse rating (amp) | Motor full-load current (amp) | Thermal unit no. | Maximum fuse rating (amp) |
|---|---|---|---|---|---|
| 0.28–0.30 | JR 0.44 | 0.6 | 2.33–2.51 | JR 3.70 | 5 |
| 0.31–0.34 | JR 0.51 | 0.6 | 2.52–2.99 | JR 4.15 | 5.6 |
| 0.35–0.37 | JR 0.57 | 0.6 | 3.00–3.42 | JR 4.85 | 6.25 |
| 0.38–0.44 | JR 0.63 | 0.8 | 3.43–3.75 | JR 5.50 | 7 |
| 0.45–0.53 | JR 0.71 | 1.0 | 3.76–3.98 | JR 6.25 | 8 |
| 0.54–0.59 | JR 0.81 | 1.125 | 3.99–4.48 | JR 6.90 | 8 |
| 0.60–0.64 | JR 0.92 | 1.25 | 4.49–4.93 | JR 7.70 | 10 |
| 0.65–0.72 | JR 1.03 | 1.4 | 4.94–5.21 | JR 8.20 | 10 |
| 0.73–0.80 | JR 1.16 | 1.6 | 5.22–5.84 | JR 9.10 | 10 |
| 0.81–0.90 | JR 1.30 | 1.8 | 5.85–6.67 | JR 10.2 | 12 |
| 0.91–1.03 | JR 1.45 | 2.0 | 6.68–7.54 | JR 11.5 | 15 |
| 1.04–1.14 | JR 1.67 | 2.25 | 7.55–8.14 | JR 12.8 | 15 |
| 1.15–1.27 | JR 1.88 | 2.5 | 8.15–8.72 | JR 14.0 | 17.5 |
| 1.28–1.43 | JR 2.10 | 2.8 | 8.73–9.66 | JR 15.5 | 17.5 |
| 1.44–1.62 | JR 2.40 | 3.2 | 9.67–10.5 | JR 17.5 | 20 |
| 1.63–1.77 | JR 2.65 | 3.5 | 10.6–11.3 | JR 19.5 | 20 |
| 1.78–1.97 | JR 3.00 | 4.0 | 11.4–12.7 | JR 22 | 25 |
| 1.98–2.32 | JR 3.30 | 4.0 | 12.8–14.1 | JR 25 | 25 |

Suppose you need to provide protection for a 240-V motor with a 1.5-A full-load amps stamped on the nameplate. According to the schedule the appropriate overload (heater) to apply is a number JR 2.40. The NEC allows this heater to be applied at 125 percent of the motor nameplate full-load current provided that (1) the service factor is 1.15 or larger, and (2) the temperature rise is not greater than 40°C. The manufacturer has already taken this into consideration when setting up the schedule. If the service factor is less than 1.15 or the temperature rise is greater than 40°C, then the heater will be 10 percent oversized, thus making the motor vulnerable to burnout. If the motor service factor is less than 1.15, multiply the motor full-load current by 0.9 and use this new value to size the overload. In our example, multiplying 1.5 A by 0.9 results in 1.35 A. The overload corresponding to 1.35 A is the JR 2.10 unit.

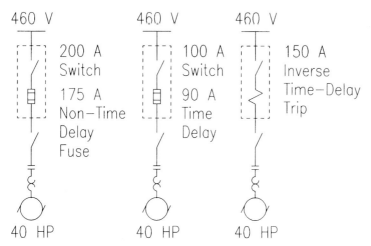

**Figure 6.3**  Three low-voltage motor circuits compared. These three circuits indicate the tradeoffs among fuse and circuit breaker applications in terms of protection, coordination, and economy.

- Branch circuit protective device and disconnecting means: From Table 430-152, the maximum fuse size = 300 percent of 52 = 156. Reference to typical fuse manufacturer application literature reveals that the next largest standard size is 175 A. The same literature indicates a switch size of 200 A for motors up to 50 hp.

- Overload protection: From NEC the maximum allowed = 125 percent of 50 = 62.5 A. (Note the use of actual nameplate full-load current). See box, "Motors with Low Full-Load Currents," for an example of sizing motor overloads.

---

### Motors with Low Full-Load Currents

When 15-A inverse time circuit breakers are applied to protect motor branch circuits for full-load current of 1 A or less, the overload heater elements are apt to explode under short-circuit conditions because the high resistance of the heater element limits the fault current to something less than the tripping current of the circuit breaker. Yet this small fault current is beyond the limit of self-protection of the overload relay element so it burns open before it can cause the overload relay to operate. Strict compliance with the NEC prohibits the use of inverse time circuit breakers with motors having full-load currents less than 3.75 A because control manufacturers have marked their equipment to specify small fuse sizes for this range of motor currents (Paape, 1976).

---

- Time-delay fuses: Maximum fuse = 175 percent of 52 = 91 A. From manufacturer literature the nearest standard size is 90 A (note that the size could be increased to 100 A). This example shows the advantages in using time-delay (dual-element) fuses in reducing the size and cost of the fused switch.

- Molded case circuit breaker: From Table 430-152 the maximum breaker = 250 percent of 52 = 130 A. From typical manufacturer literature, the next highest standard trip rating is 150 A. The frame size of the breaker is 225 A.

The reader is encouraged to read fuse and circuit-breaker literature available from the manufacturers.

### 6.3.3   Thermal-magnetic breakers

In motor circuits, thermal-magnetic breakers have limitations because coordination of their characteristics with those of the thermal-overload relay of *lower* horsepower starters is sometimes a challenge. This problem is most apparent in the analysis of high-impedance faults. During high-impedance faults, the thermal capacity $I^2t$ of the thermal-overload relay heating element is less than the minimum reaction time of the thermal-magnetic breaker. Thus, magnetic trip only breakers may be preferred for the protection of lower horsepower motors. It must be recognized, however, that this type of breaker will never provide overload protection to the motor and its conductors; it provides only fault protection. However, such breakers are significantly better in the fault protection of smaller sized motors when subjected to high-impedance faults. The combination of magnetic only or thermal-magnetic breaker with current-limiting fuses provides the ultimate in protection for users who prefer the convenience of reestablishing the circuit after minor faults merely by closing the handle without fuse replacement.

A problem has developed because the NEC permits a 15-A thermal-magnetic breaker to protect all motors of 3 hp or less at 460 V. A 20-A breaker may be selected to protect a 5-hp motor. Many heater elements, whether a separate entity or integral with a temperature-sensing element such as a bimetal or solder pot, will be destroyed before the thermal-magnetic relay can respond and open its contacts to disconnect the motor from the power source. A thermal-magnetic breaker in this current range will not open before the heater element disintegrates and arcing occurs across the heater element, which is not designed to be a circuit interrupter. The end result may well be a phase-to-phase arcing fault at the line terminals of a motor starter that could result in the complete destruction of the combination motor starter.

In the above case, a current above 20 times motor full-load current will cause the breaker to open and thus will protect all elements of the combination motor starter. It is not too unusual to see a high-impedance fault of 9 A on a motor drawing 1 A full-load current. At 9 A, most thermal-overload relays will open and protect the circuit. However, at higher currents in motors of 3 to 5 hp, the fault currents may well be more than 10 times full-load current, and the heater element of the thermal-overload relay may open and form an arc. A properly selected and adjusted magnetic-trip breaker or fusible combination starter will prevent the destruction of thermal-overload heater elements at currents above 10 times full-load current and thus will prevent any damage to the motor control center. Proper adjustment of a magnetic trip breaker is to set the trip unit at maximum trip current and then start the motor. The breaker should not trip at this setting. The trip current is then reduced to the allowable increments, and the motor is started in each position. When the breaker trips, the currents should be set back one notch. If no tripping occurs when the motor is started again, the breaker should be sealed in this position. Care must be exercised so that the motor is not overheated during this process.

### 6.3.4  Fused combination starters

The NEC requires at least 10,000-A interruption capacity and 400 percent of full-load current. Under these conditions, this fuse will provide little if any overload protection to the cables between the starter and the motor itself. Dual-element current-limiting fuses are rated on the order of 100,000 and 200,000-A symmetrical interruption capacity and allow the current rating of the fuse to be approximately 20 percent above the full-load current. These fuses consist of a time-delay thermal element and high-interrupting capacity element. There are current-limiting fuses designed for the specific purpose of minimizing fault currents. These fuses as well as the dual-element types are available in the quick trip variety that require application between 300 and 400 percent of motor full-load current as well as delayed trip types with characteristics of time-delay type fuse.

### 6.3.5  Simple motor circuit protection
### with thermal elements (heaters)

Overload relays are usually connected to the load side of the motor starter of the magnetic contactor style. These thermal-sensing elements, often called heaters, use the heat generated by line current to trip the relay. If the motor load current exceeds the rated value of the thermal element for a specified length of time, the relay reacts to open the overload contacts, which in turn breaks the control circuit to the starter coil of the controller.

Industry standards designate an overload relay by a class number indicating the maximum time in seconds at which it will trip when carrying 600 percent of its rated current. A class 10 relay will trip in 10 s or less, a class 20 relay in 20 s or less, and so on. The class 20 relay is applied for general applications in which the accelerating time of the motor is normal.

All of the application guides provided to electrical designers by electrical equipment manufacturers have time-current characteristic curves for their line of thermal overloads. The curves are plotted with the time

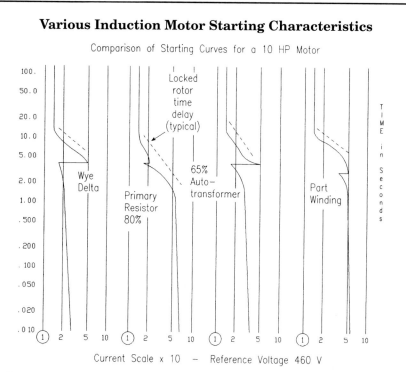

## Various Induction Motor Starting Characteristics

Comparison of Starting Curves for a 10 HP Motor

Computer representation of three different induction motor starting characteristics: wye-delta, primary resistor 80 percent, 65 percent autotransformer, and part winding. Note the variety in slopes of the locked rotor time delay segment. A well-coordinated thermal overload (Device 46) will lie just above these slopes for conventional induction motors.

High inrush current *preceding* the locked rotor current will flow into premium efficiency motors during full-voltage starting. These currents may be very high and persist for less than one cycle—enough to open the instantaneous magnetic element or clear a fast fuse. Premium efficiency motors will generally have a higher locked rotor current and a longer starting time. Starting currents of 840 percent in for 10 sec are not unusual. Confirm with coordination software manufacturers if their starting curves have been updated.

in seconds on a log scale against the percentage of current of the relay on a linear scale. The heater type number is selected using the full-load current nearest to the actual full-load current shown on the nameplate of the motor. The rated current of the relay in amperes at 40°C is 115 percent of the full-load current listed for the heater type number. Note that the heater type numbers shown in the left column are the manufacturers' designation. It is necessary to follow the manufacturers' complete set of recommendations before the final selection is made.

### 6.3.6   Arcing faults in small induction motor circuits

We continue the discussion of arcing faults begun in Chap. 4. Love illustrated that for specific ground-fault levels for motors 15 hp and below that the thermal limits of overload heaters for small motor protection coincidentally remains below the 10,000 kW/cycle arcing fault-damage curves. Small induction motors 1.5 hp and below had overload relay elements that tripped below the 1,600 kW/cycle damage curve.

This research indicates that it is safe to omit ground-fault protection for small branch circuits and that overload relay failures will not cause any adverse effects without ground-fault protection. This would include branch circuits for motors up to 15 hp because

- Arcing ground faults are less likely because X/R ratios of branch circuits of this size are less than 1.0.

- Even if arcing did exist, the small motor overload relay would operate before permanent damage could occur.

- Even if the overload relay failed to clear the fault, the phase overload heaters would open before sufficient energy.

## 6.4   Protection for Groups of Induction Motors

A motor control center is a special kind of power panel. It is a free-standing switchboard and, as such, must follow NEC requirements stated in Art. 384 as well as the requirements in Art. 430.

Motor control centers have continuous, withstand, and interrupting ratings of their own. They are rated for use on systems up to 600 V nominal, and they can be specified with horizontal buses with nominal ampacitive of 600, 1000, 1200, and 2000 A. You should specify your upstream protective device settings accordingly.

When a group of motors in a motor control center are supplied by one circuit breaker or fuse, it is necessary to develop a combined motor characteristic curve. One rule of thumb is to *assume that the largest motor in the motor control center is starting, and the remaining motors are running at full load.* The individual curves can then be superposed to create a combined motor characteristic curve. Using the four squirrel-cage motors of Fig. 6.4, for example, we would have (with reference to NEC 430-150)

$$14 + 14 + 40 + [6 \times 65] \times \frac{460}{480} = 439 \text{ A}$$

You may need to use your judgment in each situation. NEC 430-24, 25, and 26 deal with the requirements of group motor installations which recognize special situations in which a group of motors operates at current levels greater or less than the foregoing rule of thumb.

Some computer software manufacturers will allow you to adjust the motor starting curve to suit your situation and judgment. The motor starting curve in Fig. 6.4 shows LRA = 798 (six times the sum of the FLAs) to indicate how much daylight there is between the feeder fuse and worst-case starting current.

### 6.4.1 Withstand and interrupting ratings

NEMA ICS-1975 and ICS-2-322 established the short-circuit ratings of motor control centers at the incoming line terminals. These values, including any motor contributions, are 10,000, 14,000, 22,000, 30,000, and 42,000 A. Although many applications require interrupting capacities on the order of 65,000, 85,000, and 100,000 A, there are no industry standards for motor control center interrupting capacity testing for vertical and horizontal bus bracing above 42,000 A.

It should be noted that NEMA standards specify that the combination starter be tested with its output terminal shorted with minimum length connectors. Thus, the impedance of the breaker, the starter, thermal-overload relay elements, and internal wiring are in series during this test. The combined impedance of these elements of the combination starter will reduce the magnitude of the short-circuit current. These standards are based on field experience that has shown that the probability of a fault occurring between the starter terminals and the terminals of its thermal-overload relay or at the load terminals of the combination starter's circuit breaker or fused disconnect is remote. However, the user needs to consider this against the increased cost of the motor control center to prevent them, the cost of downtime, and safety hazards. Motor control centers typically carry mission critical loads. If the circuit breaker or fused disconnect interrupting capability is inadequate for this increased fault current, total destruction of the combination starter may occur, and the fault may spread to the vertical and then to the horizontal bus structure. If it spreads to the bus, the main breaker will be required to clear it, or the entire motor control center will be destroyed.

All manufacturers offer higher interrupting capacity breakers with a 30,000 to 40,000 rating. While the user of breakers with a 22,000-A fault capacity system can be assured that they will not require maintenance or replacement under fault conditions, the possibility of repair or replacement of the starter of the combination motor control center unit remains unchanged. A user may choose a circuit breaker with current-limiting fuses for his combination starter application. This selection may result in an increase in unit cost over the cost of the higher interruption capacity breakers. However, the user can be assured that after fuse replacements, required only when faults exceed the current interruption capacity of the breaker, both starter and breaker will need no repair or replacement. By proper selection of the type of fuse and disconnect, the user can also be assured of no damage to any component in the combination motor starter when subjected to a bolted fault condition.

A feeder tap must be selected to interrupt a bolted fault at its load terminal. Here again the user has an option of determining the class of protective equipment involved. The user may select a breaker that has the capacity to interrupt but may require repair or replacement after it has cleared a bolted fault. The selection of proper fuse and disconnect will ensure that the maximum fault is cleared with nothing more than the fuses requiring replacement. For systems of 30,000- and 42,000-A symmetrical short-circuit capacity, the basic criteria of component selection remains the same as the considerations given for a 22,000-A system. If a user selects a combination starter for a system with this potential magnitude of fault current, he or she must select the components of the motor control center unit and feeder taps with considerably more care than for a system of less capacity. The circuit breaker available will have a maximum interruption capacity at 460 V between 30,000 and 40,000 A symmetrical. The interruption capacity available is determined by the frame ampere rating chosen. The 100-A frames have less interruption capacity than the larger ampere rated frames.

The manufacturer supplying a combination motor controller of this class is required by industry standards to have tested these units with the criterion that when a bolted fault occurs at the terminal of the motor starter, the breaker or fused disconnect must interrupt the short circuit, and any damage must be confined to the unit. However, as with equipment rated 22,000 A, the breaker fuses, disconnect, and/or starter may require maintenance or replacement. Proper selection of fuses will ensure that no damage due to overload or fault will occur to the components of the system, other than the fuses. The fuses, however, must be replaced after a fault or overload regardless of the magnitude, whereas when circuit breakers with current-limiting fuses are applied, fault of less than maximum may result in the fault being cleared by the breaker without damage to the fuse and without the fuses requiring replacement.

The short-circuit current available at the incoming terminal of a motor control center can be limited by various means. The most logical method is based on selecting a proper size of incoming transformer to allow for a practical and economical selection of motor control center components. The transformer impedance may be specified to limit fault current without reducing voltage. Current-limiting fuses can be applied in incoming line section; however, their effectiveness is limited to motor control center loading of 600 A and less. Most current-limiting fuses of higher sizes will pass significant short-circuit currents and thus are relatively ineffective in limiting fault currents within a motor control center (Smeaton, 1987).

### 6.4.2 Coordinating interrupting capacities of motor control center components

**Example 6.1** Four Induction Motors

*Situation.* Four induction motors as indicated in Fig. 6.4

1  50-hp squirrel-cage induction motor with full voltage starting
1  30-hp wound-rotor induction motor
2  10-hp squirrel-cage induction motors

The source is 440 V, three-phase, 60 Hz.

*Requirements.* Determine the feeder size and specify its protection.

**solution**

■ From NEC Table 430-150, the motors have full-load current as follows:

$$50 \text{ hp} = 65 \text{ A}$$

$$30 \text{ hp} = 40 \text{ A}$$

$$10 \text{ hp} = 14 \text{ A}$$

The combined motor-starting characteristic is plotted on the basis of these data, assuming the worst case situation in which they all start at the same moment.

■ From NEC 430-24 the feeder conductors must carry

$$(1.25 \times 65) = 81 \text{ A} + 40 \text{ A} + (2 \times 14 \text{ A}) = 149 \text{ A}$$

From NEC 310-16, select 3/0 THW.

■ From NEC 430-52 and 62, overcurrent protection for each of the motors should be as follows:

$$50 \text{ hp} \rightarrow 65 \text{ A} \times 300\% \rightarrow \text{not more than 200-A fuse}$$

$$30 \text{ hp motor} \rightarrow 40 \text{ A} \times 150\% \rightarrow \text{not more than 60-A fuse}$$

$$10 \text{ hp motors} \rightarrow 14 \times 300\% \rightarrow \text{not more than 45-A fuses}$$

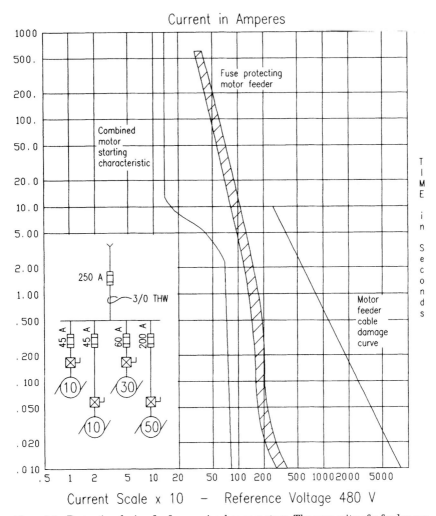

**Figure 6.4**   Protection design for four squirrel-cage motors. The ampacity of a feeder supplying a group of two or more motors must be equal to the sum of 125 percent of the rated full-load current of the largest motor plus the sum of the rated full-load currents of all the remaining motors in the group. It is not necessary to provide for simultaneous overloads on all motors. Where there are two or more motors, all the same rating, then only one of the motors need be treated as the largest.

- From NEC 430-62, the motor feeder overcurrent protection can have a maximum rating or setting equal to the rating or setting of the largest of the branch circuit protective devices plus the sum of the full-load currents of the other motors. Then the feeder fuse size may be

$$200 + 40 + 14 + 14 = 268 \text{ A maximum}$$

The nearest standard fuse rating that does not exceed 268 is 250 A. The fuse protecting the THW feeder is plotted in Fig. 6.4 along with the cable thermal damage curve for 600-V THW cable. As you can see, there is quite a bit of daylight in the coordination curves. In some applications, there is not enough fault current available to damage feeder cables.

*Remarks.* Unlike other areas of the NEC there is no provision in the NEC that permits the use of the next higher size, rating, or setting of the protective devices for a motor feeder when the calculated maximum rating does not correspond to a standard size (McPartland, 1986).

**Motor protection elements.** The protective devices for motors cannot be rated to match the ampacity of motor branch circuits because of the high starting current of all motors. If the rating of the fuse is too low, then the large starting current of the motor will open the fuse before the motor can accelerate to rated speed. Even with a time-delay fuse, a fuse can be specified at a lower rating yet still not open during starting.

Another approach to motor circuit protection is to use a circuit breaker with adjustable magnetic trip action, thus providing instantaneous protection only. The trip unit is set to exceed the locked rotor current of the motor. Therefore, the breaker will only be tripped if there is a short circuit on the motor branch circuit or within the motor. This device is widely applied and goes by the trade name of *motor circuit protector* (MCP). An MCP can only be applied as part of a complete combination starter unit that provides coordinated motor branch circuit overload and short-circuit and ground-fault protection and that has been approved for such applications.

The setting of the motor circuit branch circuit device cannot exceed the value calculated using the percentage values shown in Table 430-152. Where the calculated value does not correspond to a standard rating of fuse or circuit-breaker trip unit, then the next higher rating is permitted.

---

### What About Variable Frequency Drives?

Typical VFDs consist of three sections: a rectifier, a dc link, and an inverter. Three-phase ac power is applied to the terminals of a VFD just like any other motor controller, but special consideration should be given to protection of the solid-state components therein. Among the protection considerations specific to the VFD and/or the reactor or isolation transformer upstream from the motor terminals:

- Incoming line transient protection.
- Surge suppression with power device snubbers. Power devices in the VFD should be rated on the order of 2.5 times the line voltage.
- Power device overtemperature.
- Control logic circuit malfunction.

In addition to the usual consideration for adjustable overvoltage or undervoltage trip, you should look for auto restart which will ride through a momentary dip and through at least a one-cycle power loss. Since most VFDs have a "bypass mode" of operation in which VFD control of starting current is disabled, you should coordinate your protective devices with respect to the classical time-current characteristics discussed in Chap. 1 and elsewhere in this chapter.

## 6.5   Protecting Larger Motors

### 6.5.1   Special problems associated
### with the protection of large induction motors

- Large motors have a higher relative transient inrush than smaller machines even though they meet NEMA maximum steady-state requirements.

- Thermal type current sensors must be used since higher settings for the electronic controls would violate the NEC.

The phase-fault current at the terminals of a motor is usually considerably larger than any normal current, such as starting current or the motor contribution to a fault. For this reason, a high-set instantaneous trip unit is recommended for fast, reliable, inexpensive, simple protection. Where the starting current value approaches the fault current, however, some form of differential relaying becomes necessary. The sen-

---

### IEC Type 1 and 2 Coordination

Motor control and fuse manufacturers have introduced a new term to the North American electrical equipment market that describes the level of short-circuit protection provided to the motor starter in a motor branch circuit. That new term is *Type 2 Coordination*. It has nothing to do with time-current characteristics of protective devices or the time and current margins between them. It refers to the degree to which a motor starter will survive a short-circuit. The following are excerpts from the IEC 947-1 definition:

*Type 1 Coordination* . . . "under short-circuit conditions, the contactor or starter shall cause no danger to persons or installation and *may not be suitable for further service* [emphasis added] without repair and replacement of parts . . ."

*Type 2 Coordination* . . . "under short-circuit conditions, the contactor or starter shall cause no danger to persons or installation and *shall be suitable for further use* [emphasis added]. The risk of contact welding is recognized, in which case the manufacturer shall indicate the measures to be taken in regards to the maintenance of the equipment . . ."

The use of the term "coordination" refers to the manner in which the various components of a motor starter (contactor, overload relay, and fuse) will perform as a working whole with respect to UL, IEC, and NEMA testing standards for withstand and let-through energies. The existing UL standard (508) for motor starters allows for significantly more damage to the motor starter when it is protected by a circuit breaker than when it is protected by a fuse. When fuses are used for short-circuit protection no damage is allowed to the overload relay. When a circuit breaker is used for short-circuit protection, complete burnout of the overload relay is allowed and this damage is equivalent to IEC Type 1 Coordination. Among other criteria indicated to meet Type 2 Coordination requirements is that the overload relay in the motor starter shall not be damaged by a short-circuit and that the short-circuit not alter the time-current tripping characteristics of the overload relay.

sitivity of the differential relay is independent of starting current, while instantaneous trip units, which respond only to phase current, must be set above the starting current (including dc offset).

To allow for fault resistance and different types of faults and to ensure twice pickup on the unit for minimum fault, the instantaneous phase relay pickup should be set at less than one third of $I_{3\phi}$ where $I_{3\phi}$ is the systems contribution, excluding the motor contribution, to a symmetrical, three-phase fault on the motor feeder. Also, pickup should be set at 1.6 times $I_{lr}$ or more, where $I_{lr}$ is the actual symmetrical starting current, as limited by source impedance. The ratio $I_{3\phi}/I_{lr}$ should thus be greater than about 5.0.

In general then, instantaneous trip units can be applied for phase protection if the motor kVA (or approximately the horsepower) is less than one half the supply transformer kVA. If not, differential relays are required for sensitive motor fault detection. If he or she has not done so already, the reader is encouraged to investigate the feasibility of protecting larger motors with a microprocessor-based protective device that combines protective functions 49, 50, and 51.

The evolution of motor control since the belt and pully methods (or even dual-element fuse protection) is probably no better demonstrated than in the number of choices you have in programming a motor starter. Table 6.4 is adapted from a diagram in the programming manual of a solid-state motor control (and protection) unit.

**Example 6.2**   Single 50-hp Motor Protection Design

*Situation.*   The circuit of Fig. 6.5 fed at 440 V.

*Requirements.*   Size feeder conductors, select overcurrent and short-circuit protection, and plot time-current characteristic curves of each device. Show motor starting and cable thermal limit curves.

**solution**   We use the FLA of 65 A because the footnote to NEC Table 430-150 accommodates an operating voltage range of 440–480 V. For LRA: $65 \times 6 = 390$ A. The motor starting curve is shown thus. #2 THW is selected from NEC 310-6. The fuse is selected from NEC 430-152 and the overload is selected by the method discussed in the box appearing previously in this chapter.

**Example 6.3**   Group Motor Protection Design

*Situation.*   Given the circuit in Fig. 6.6 where the following data applies to three motors operating at 460 V:

1. One 25-hp squirrel-cage induction motor, full voltage starting nameplate current of 31.6 A, service factor 1.15, Code letter F
2. Two 30-hp wound rotor induction motors, nameplate primary current 36.4 A, nameplate secondary current 65 A, 40°C rise

Determine the following:

- Branch circuit and feeder conductor sizes
- Motor overload protection
- Branch circuit short-circuit and ground-fault protection

**TABLE 6.4  Motor Control Programming Chart**

| | Input | | |
|---|---|---|---|
| Address | Data | Setpoint range | Units |
| I1 | Motor HP: | 0–1000 | hp |
| I2 | Volts: | 100–1000 | V |
| I3 | FLA: | 0.0–1000.0 | A |
| I4 | Freq: | 50/60 | Hz |
| I5 | Accel time: | 0–240 | Sec |
| I6 | CT Ratio: | 1–1000 | Ratio |
| I7 | Service factor: | 1.00–1.40 | Decimal |
| I8 | Winding RTD type and qty: | 1–50 | Number |
| I9 | Motor bearing RTD type and qty: | 1–50 | Number |
| I10 | Load bearing RTD type and qty: | 1–50 | Number |
| I11 | Load case RTD type and qty: | 1–50 | Number |

| | Output | | |
|---|---|---|---|
| | Data | Setpoint range | Units |
| O1 | Locked rotor current | 300–1200 | % FLA |
| O2 | Stall time in sec | 1–60 | sec |
| O3 | Ultimate trip current | 50–150 | % FLA |
| O4 | Jam trip level | 100–1200 | % FLA |
| O5 | Underload trip level | 0–90 | % FLA |
| O6 | Winding temperature alarm | 0–199 | °C |
| O7 | Motor bearing trip alarm | 0–199 | °C |
| O8 | Load bearing trip alarm | 0–199 | °C |
| O9 | Load case trip alarm | | °C |
| O10 | Winding temperature trip | 0–199 | °C |
| O11 | Motor bearing trip temp | 0–199 | °C |
| O12 | Load bearing trip temp | 0–199 | °C |
| O13 | Load case trip temp | 0–199 | °C |
| O14 | Ground-fault trip level | 0.1–10.0 | A |
| O15 | Ground-fault start delay | 0–1000 | cycles |
| O16 | Ground-fault run delay | 0–1000 | cycles |
| O17 | Instantaneous overcurrent | 200–2000 | % FLA |
| O18 | Phase unbalance alarm level | 10–50 | % |
| O19 | Phase unbalance trip | 10–50 | % |
| O20 | Phase unbalance alarm run delay | 0–240 | sec |
| O21 | Starts per time allowed | 1–10 | Number/min |
| O22 | Time allowed for starts count | 1–10 | Number/h |
| O23 | Motor start transition current level | 50–150 | % FLA |
| O24 | Motor start transition time | 0–240 | sec |
| O25 | Reversing or nonreversing starter | Non/Rev | Toggle |

\* A sample programming schedule adapted from two manufacturers' motor protection units. It is remarkable how many functions (49/50/51) can be derived from a current transformer, a resistance thermal device, and a real-time clock.

Overload function 49 is programmed to match closely the allowable heating times of the motors. This allows use of the full overload capability of the machine without the risk of damage or reduced life due to the continuous or repetitive overloads. In microprocessor-based units the device has memory of previous overloads with long reset time—long enough to ensure proper protection in applications involving repetitive overloads and hard starts.

For phase fault functions 50 and 51 characteristic curves should be programmed when microprocessor-based units are applied in series with fused motor starters. A minimum time delay on a definite time characteristic will permit the fuse to beat the contactor for high-level faults beyond the rating of the starters but will allow the relay to beat the fuse for low-level faults, thus saving fuse replacement.

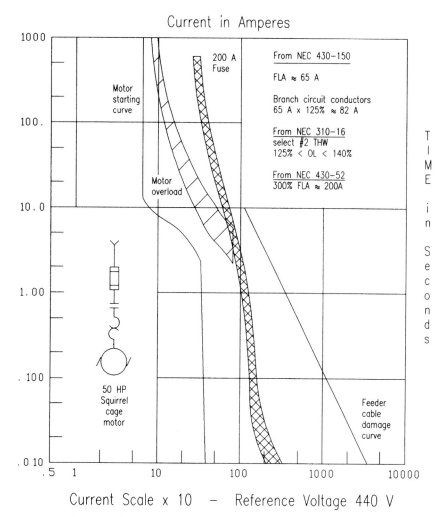

Current Scale x 10   –   Reference Voltage 440 V

**Figure 6.5**  Single 50-hp motor protection design.

**solution:**

*Branch and feeder conductors. For the 25-hp motor branch conductor:* From Section 430-6(a) and Table 430-150. A full-load current of 34 A × 1.25 = 42.5 A (NEC 430-22). You may refer to NEC Table 310-16 to specify the branch circuit conductor. One acceptable choice would be AWG #8 copper, 90°C THHN.

*For the two 30-hp motor branch conductors:* The full-load current value used to determine the ampacity of primary conductors for each 30-hp motor is 40 A. A full-load *primary* current of 40 A × 1.25 = 50 A. A full-load *secondary* current of 65 A × 1.25 = 81.25 [Section 430-23(a)]. You may refer to NEC Table 310-16 to specify the branch circuit conductor. One acceptable choice would be AWG #4 copper, 90°C THHN.

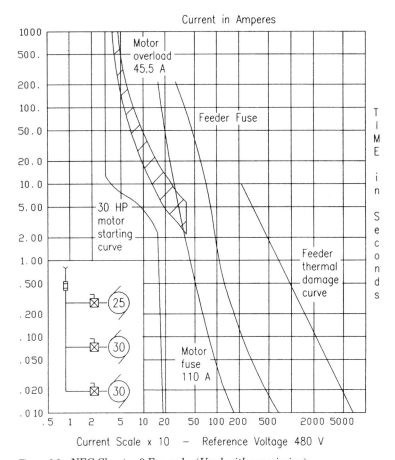

Figure 6.6 NEC Chapter 9 Example. (*Used with permission*)

*For the feeder:* The feeder ampacity must be 125 percent of the sum of the motor full-load currents or, (from Section 430-24)

$$1.25 \times (40 + 40 + 34) = 124 \text{ A}$$

*Overload protection.* Where protected by a separate overload device, the 25-hp motor will have overload protection of not over 39.5 A. Where protected by a separate overload device, the 30-hp motor will have overload protection of not over 45.5 A [NEC 430-6(a) and 430-32(a)(1)].

If the overload protection is not sufficient to start the motor or to carry the load, it may be increased according to NEC 430-34. For a motor marked "thermally protected," overload protection is provided by the thermal protector [430-7(a)(12) and 430-32(a)(2)].

*Branch circuit short-circuit and ground-fault protection.* The branch circuit of the 25-hp motor shall have branch circuit short-circuit and ground-fault protection of not over 300 percent of a non-time-delay fuse [NEC Table 430-12] or $3.00 \times 34 = 102$ A. The next smaller standard size fuse is 100 A [NEC 240-6]. Since a 100-A fuse is adequate to carry the load, NEC 430-52(a), Exception 1 does not apply. If a time-delay fuse is to be used, see NEC 430-52(a), Exception 2(b). Where the 100-A fuse will not allow the motor to run, the value for a non-time-delay fuse shall be permitted to be increased to the next larger standard size, or 110 A. If these fuses are not sufficient to start the motor, the value for a non-time-delay fuse shall be permitted to be increased to 400 percent [NEC 430-52(a), Exception 2(a)].

*Feeder circuit.* The maximum rating of the feeder short-circuit and ground-fault protection is based upon the sum of the largest branch circuit protective devices (100-A fuse) plus the sum of the full-load currents of the other motors or $100 + 40 + 40 = 180$ A. The nearest standard fuse that does not exceed this value is 175 A (with time-current characteristic shown in Fig. 6.6 between the feeder damage curve and the 110 motor fuse). Both motor branch circuit and feeder time-current characteristic curves will asymptotically approach their nominal opening ratings.

*Remarks.* The foregoing example is adapted from National Electric Code—Chapter 9—Example 8: "Motors, Conductors, Overload, and Short-Circuit and Ground Fault Protection." The author wishes to acknowledge his gratitude to the National Fire Protection Agency (NFPA) for permission to use this example. The reader is encouraged to seek the original source (the *NEC Handbook,* 1993) where many other electrical design examples appear.

## Bibliography

Blackburn, J. L., *Protective Relaying: Principles and Applications,* Marcel Dekker, Inc., New York, 1987.

Lawrie, Robert J. (ed.), *Electric Motor Manual,* McGraw-Hill, New York, 1987. Articles originally published in *Electrical Construction and Maintenance* magazine.

Love, Daniel J., and Nasrollah Hashemi, "Failure Analysis of Components Due to 480 Volt Ground Faults," *IEEE IAS,* vol. 1A-22, July/Aug. 1986.

McPartland, J. F., *Practical Electrical Design,* McGraw-Hill, New York, 1986.

Paape, Kenneth L., "Tradeoffs in Motor Branch Circuit Protection," *IEEE IAS,* July/Aug. 1976.

Smeaton, Robert W. (ed.), *Switchgear and Control Handbook,* McGraw-Hill, New York, 1987.

## General references

"ABB Motor Protection Relays," *Application Guide 41-205M.*

Elmore, W. A., "Motor Protection," Chap. 7, *Applied Protective Relaying,* Westinghouse Electric Corp., 1982.

Fitzgerald, A. E., C. Kingsley, and S. D. Umans, *Electric Machinery,* McGraw-Hill, New York, 1983.

"Guide for AC Motor Protection," *ANSI C37.96-1976.*

Hughes, S. D., *Electrical Systems in Buildings,* PWS-Kent Publishers, 1988.

"IQ-1000 Motor Protection and Control Unit," *Technical Publication TD 17194,* Westinghouse Electric Corp.

"Motor and Generator Standards," NEMA.

## Further reading

Deutsch, A., "Relaying Overload Protection Through Proper Heater Selection," *Consulting/Specifying Engineer,* Sept. 1993.

IEC Standard 292.

Saporta, Vincent J., "Simplified Motor Control Conductor Protection Based Upon the 1984 National Electric Code," *IEEE IAS,* vol. 1A-22, May/June 1986.

Scheda, Francis A., "Transient Inrush Current in High-Efficiency and Standard Motors," *IEEE IAS,* vol. 1A-22, Jan./Feb. 1986.

Underwriter's Laboratories Standard 508.

# Protection and Coordination in Unit Substations

## 7.1 Foreword

Much of our work in overcurrent coordination at the electrical customer level will involve coordinating the devices in the articulated unit substations that operate as load centers in industrial, commercial, and institutional facilities. Our work will involve the following overcurrent devices:

- Incoming primary fuse or circuit breaker protecting a transformer
- Secondary main breaker(s) protecting a secondary bus
- Secondary feeder breakers protecting cables to distribution panels located within the substation room itself or located a considerable distance from the unit substation

The construction of a unit substation will have some bearing on our decisions, for example, whether the substation primary and secondary sections are interior or exterior. The distance between the primary and secondary sections will be important to us as we establish protective zones with our sensing devices. The notion of an articulated unit substation as an assembly of protective devices that comply with NEC requirements may be motivated by the existence (or desirability) of feeder taps on the substation secondary bus. In some circumstances, the notion of a unit substation as an element in a facility service entrance may suggest an interpretation of NEC Art. 230 that pertains to service entrances and the protection requirements therein.

## 7.2  Transformer Protection

The first overcurrent device we encounter is the transformer primary protective device. The NEC cites the requirements for unit substation transformer protection in Art. 450 (Fig. 7.1a to e). Related requirements appear in Arts. 240 and 310. The setting of the phase overcurrent protective device is limited by the same code restrictions on pickup and the same considerations of inrush and short-circuit withstand current discussed elsewhere in this text.

The NEC requires that any transformer over 600 V shall be protected on the primary side either by a fuse or by a circuit breaker. Where fuses are applied, their continuous-current rating shall not exceed 250 percent of the rated primary current of the transformer. Where circuit breakers are applied, they shall be set at not more than 300 percent of the rated primary current of the transformer. The 1993 NEC recognizes the prevalence of electronic fuses and establishes the maximum setting to be the same as the setting for circuit breakers: 300 percent.

There is nothing in this requirement that says that you may not select a fuse or circuit breaker to open at 100 percent of rated primary current or 200 percent or any value in between. It simply establishes the maximum settings. In most overcurrent coordination situations, you will need to select a device that opens somewhere between 100 percent primary current and the maximum.

Fuses provide short-circuit protection for the transformer and are frequently applied in combination with interrupter switches capable of interrupting full-load current. Fuses so selected can provide protection for secondary faults between the transformer and secondary side overcurrent protective devices, as well as backup protection for the latter. Transformer-overload protection can be provided by picking up a relay contact on the transformer temperature indicator to shed

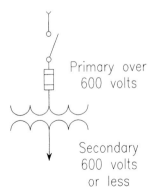

Primary over
600 volts

Secondary
600 volts
or less

**Figure 7.1a**  Rules for transformer overcurrent protection. Note that there is a fuse on the primary side of the transformer only. For transformers over 600 V, NEC 450 requires fuses rated at not more than 250 percent of rated primary current. Where 250 percent of primary current does not correspond to a standard fuse rating, the next higher size is permitted. As long as the primary fuse size does not exceed 250 percent of rated primary current, you do not need secondary protection.

Where circuit breakers are applied on the primary side, either at the transformer or at the supply end of the primary circuit, a circuit breaker may be rated at not more than 300 percent of rated primary current. Where 300 percent of primary current does not correspond to a standard circuit breaker trip setting, the next lower trip setting must be used.

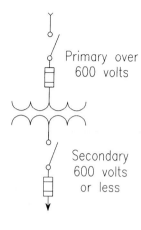

Primary over
600 volts

Secondary
600 volts
or less

**Figure 7.1b** Rules for transformer overcurrent protection. Note that there is a fuse on *both* the primary and secondary sides of the transformer. For primary circuits over 600 V, maximum fuse size may not exceed 300 percent of the transformer rated primary current. Maximum fuse size for a secondary less than 600 V may not exceed 250 percent of the transformer rated secondary current.

nonessential load or trip the transformer secondary side overcurrent protective devices.

It is usual practice that the fuse access door and the transformer main secondary overcurrent protective devices are interlocked to ensure that the fuse is deenergized before work on the substation interior is undertaken.

## 7.3 Medium-Voltage Power Fuses

We continue the discussion of medium-voltage power fuses begun in Chap. 3. The fuses with which we shall be concerned are fuses to be applied at voltages ranging from about 2400 to 34,500 V on transformers in the 225- to 5000-kVA range. Our selection will be determined from the constraints established by

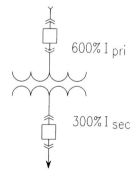

600% I pri

300% I sec

A transformer with a primary
rated over 600 volts
with a secondary
rated over 600 volts

**Figure 7.1c** Rules for transformer overcurrent protection. Note that there are circuit breakers on *both* the primary and secondary sides of the transformer. For a transformer primary over 600 V, the circuit breaker pickup may be no greater than 600 percent of primary current. On the same transformer for a secondary over 600 V the circuit breaker pickup may be set no greater than 300 percent rated secondary current.

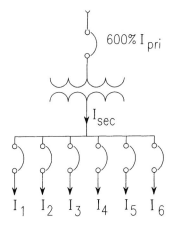

**Figure 7.1d** Rules for transformer overcurrent protection. Note that there are no more than (and only) circuit breakers on the secondary. The sum of the ratings of the circuit breakers is not permitted to exceed 300 percent of the rated secondary current.

$$I_1 + I_2 + I_3 + I_4 + I_5 + I_6 \leq 300\% \ I_{sec}$$

- Kind of installation (interior metal clad or exterior pad mount)
- Primary switch configuration
- Continuous current rating
- System grounding
- Time and current tripping characteristics required to coordinate with other overcurrent devices
- Protective practices of the system that currently prevail

Other factors such as safety, load growth, and changing duty requirements may have bearing on your decision.

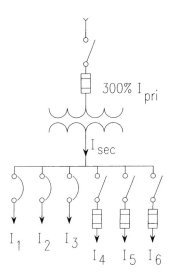

**Figure 7.1e** Rules for transformer overcurrent protection. Note the mixture of fuses and circuit breakers. The sum of the ratings of all the overcurrent devices protecting the secondary of the transformer is not permitted to exceed the rating permitted for fuses.

$$I_1 + I_2 + I_3 + I_4 + I_5 + I_6 \leq 250\% \ I_{sec}$$

The transformer primary is assumed to be over 600 V and the fuse protecting it may be sized no greater than 300 percent of rated primary current.

Whether you are starting a new system from scratch or whether you follow the practice that prevails, you are likely to face the decision about what type of fuse you should specify for a unit substation: current-limiting or expulsion fuse.

Current-limiting fuses with interrupting capacities on the order of 85,000 A are not easy to coordinate; expulsion fuses are easy to coordinate but lack high interrupting capacity at the point of application.

### 7.3.1 Expulsion fuse

The term *expulsion* in everyday discussion about primary fuses might be a cause for concern among electrical people who wonder if primary buswork of an indoor unit substation might be damaged by the operation of an expulsion fuse that is similar to the kind of distribution cutouts that are applied on utility poletop fuse installations. While it is true that gases are expelled from an expulsion fuse (there are "snufflers" that can be specified to keep these gases from contaminating nearby buswork), the arc is always contained within the expulsion fuse housing.

The range of voltages over which you may apply expulsion fuses is broader than with the current-limiting fuse. The ranges vary among manufacturers. For example, one manufacturer offers an expulsion fuse with a time-current characteristic that may be applied at voltages that range from 4.16 to 14.4 kV with continuous-current ratings ranging from 3E to 400E (S&C). You should compare this voltage range with the ranges for properly applied current-limiting fuses.

Some other things to keep in mind about expulsion fuses, particularly with respect to time-current characteristics and interrupting ratings follow.

The K (fast)- and T (slow)-rated links are designated universal links because of the complete mechanical and electrical interchangeability specified in the standards. K or T links of one manufacturer will be the same mechanically as corresponding K or T links of another manufacturer. The electrical characteristic of the K and T links have been standardized to meet the minimum and maximum current values required to melt the link at three time points on their characteristic curves. This ensures better coordination between links made by different manufacturers than is attainable with the N-rated link. The K and T links meet the single time-current requirement of the N links.

The three operating points that the K and T links are required to meet on their melting time-current characteristics are as follows:

- 300 s for fuse links rated 100 A and below; 600 s for fuse links rated 140 and 200 A
- 10 s

- 0.1 s as designated in Table 5 for type K fuse links and in Table 6 for type T fuse links (see tables in NEMA standards). These values provide essentially a band curve for each rating.

### 7.3.2  Current limiting

In the absence of specific instructions from a purchaser of metal-clad switchgear, current-limiting fuses have become the default device among manufacturers of unit substations. It happens this way because substation manufacturers assume that protection is preferred over coordination. The current-limiting fuse, by definition, cuts current off at one-fourth cycle. However, the current-limiting fuse may not clear transformer damage curves (as we see in Fig. 7.4). You may see that current-limiting fuses will give you the daylight you need to set short-time pickups higher than you can with a solid fuse, but it may cost you more than a solid fuse. It is worth the time to conduct your own research on cost comparisons between current-limiting and expulsion fuses. Make sure your comparisons are the same with respect to mounting styles, fittings and refills, and cost per phase or cost for all three phases. These are a sample of the choices you will face when deciding between a current-limiting and an expulsion fuse to protect the substation transformer primary.

Figure 7.2 is a screen display of the ANSI/IEEE transformer damage curves. One of the conveniences of overcurrent coordination software is that it plots the curves according to the standard that you apply.

In Figs. 7.3, 7.4, and 7.5, all time-current characteristic curves are plotted at 13.8 kV with a current scale × 10. The transformer is 2500 kVA, Δ-Y with 5.75 percent impedance.

In Fig. 7.3, you can see how the solid fuse has a nice bend in the middle that makes it easy to coordinate with the damage curve for frequent single-phase-to-ground faults. The diagram indicates the three-phase fault damage pickup at 420 A and the 57 percent displacement at 240 A, indicating that a single-line-to-ground will damage a transformer "sooner" than a bolted three-phase fault. This makes sense because fault current flowing through one transformer coil only creates unbalanced thermal and mechanical stresses.

Note the constant energy (linear) time-current characteristic of a current-limiting fuse shown in Fig. 7.4. This plot indicates limited protection for the transformer. If we could see where the fuse time-current characteristic intersected the one-fourth cycle (time) point we would see that the current-limiting fuse offers higher short-circuit protection than the solid fuse. But you may need to size a current-limiting fuse at a higher (or lower) multiple of primary current in order to get its time-current characteristic to clear a damage curve or a low-voltage main breaker curve.

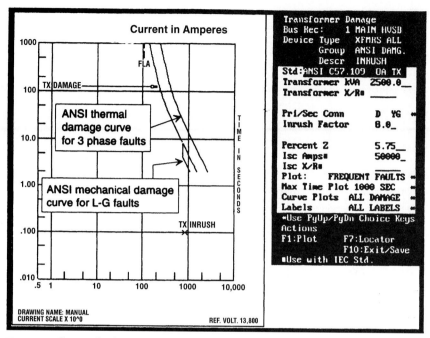

**Figure 7.2**   Screen display of coordination software transformer protection curves. Over-current coordination software allows you to quickly evaluate various protection strategies with respect to ANSI and NEC requirements. *(Actual screen output courtesy of SKM Analysis)*

You should also be mindful of the fact that when current-limiting fuses are applied in circuits protected by surge arrestors which have voltage ratings less than the voltage rating of the fuse, overvoltages may be great enough to exceed the safe volt-time characteristics of the arrestor.

Figure 7.5 demonstrates that for a current-limiting fuse that is applied to a Δ-transformer there will be an 87 percent displacement of the damage curves for line-to-line faults (420 A × 87% = 365 A). In general, the selection of a transformer primary fuse may be undertaken as a procedure that considers only the NEC requirements or may be cast as a challenging optimization problem that involves satisfying the competing requirements of short-circuit protection, transformer damage reduction, and the "reach" of the primary fuse into secondary ground faults (see Example 7.5).

### Example 7.1   Protecting a Category II Transformer

*Situation.*   An industrial plant or similar facility served by a 2500-kVA 12-kV:480-V transformer with 5.75 percent impedance. The protection consists of power fuses on the primary and low-voltage, direct-acting circuit breakers with series overcurrent trip units on the secondary side and associated feeders. Refer to Fig. 7.6.

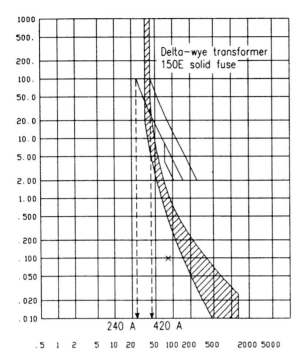

**Figure 7.3** Comparison of solid fuse TCC with transformer damage curve for frequent faults in a Δ-Y transformer.

*Requirements.*    Determine parameters for transformer protection.

**solution**  This is a Category II transformer, and, with metal-clad or metal-enclosed secondary switchgear, the fault frequency can be considered infrequent. The transformer damage curve that applies is reproduced in Fig. A.14.

$$I\ pu = I_{rated} = 2500/\,(\sqrt{3} \times 0.48) = 3007\ at\ 480\ V$$

and so, a tabulation of plot points can be applied

| Time | I pu | Equivalent I |
|------|------|--------------|
| 1000 | 2.3 | 6916 |
| 300 | 3.0 | 9021 |
| 100 | 4.0 | 12,028 |
| 50 | 5.0 | 15,035 |
| 7.0 | 10.0 | 30,070 |
| 8.0 | 17.39 | 52,296 |

For 50 s and less

$$t = 1250/I^2 \text{ such as } 1250/5^2 = 50\ s$$

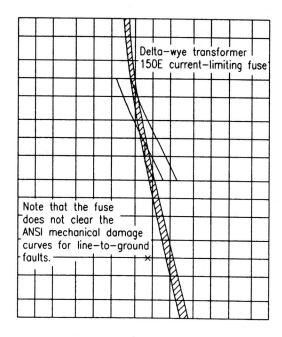

Delta–wye transformer
150E current–limiting fuse

Note that the fuse
does not clear the
ANSI mechanical damage
curves for line–to–ground
faults. ──────×

5  1  2  5  10  20  50  100 200  500  2000 5000

**Figure 7.4** Comparison of current-limiting fuse TCC with transformer damage curve for frequent faults in a Δ-Y transformer.

as shown. The maximum possible current with an infinite source is

$$I = 1/0.575 = 17.39 \text{ pu}$$

where $t = 1250/17.39^2 = 4.13$ s

This is the termination of the transformer through-fault protection curve.

On the primary side, rated current is

$$I \text{ pu} = I_{rated} = 2500/(\sqrt{3} \times 12) = 120.3 \text{ at } 12 \text{ kV}$$

To avoid fuse opening on magnetizing inrush, select fuse at about 150 percent of rated current. Thus $1.5 \times 120.3 = 180.4$, so 200-A fuses are selected and their time characteristics plotted. (See Fig. 7.6.)

The transformer secondary main and the feeders (not shown) have low-voltage circuit breakers with direct-acting overcurrent units. For this example, the transformer breaker long-time unit is set to pick up at 1.21 rated or $1.2 \times 3007 = 3608$ A at 480 V, where the time is 450 s. The short-time pickup is set at 2.5 $I_{rated}$ or $2.5 \times 3007 = 7518$ at 480 V. A time delay of 0.35 s is indicated to provide coordination with the feeders.

*Remarks.*   The protection plot of Fig. 7.6 shows good protection and coordination except for light secondary faults. The primary fuse curves cross the transformer

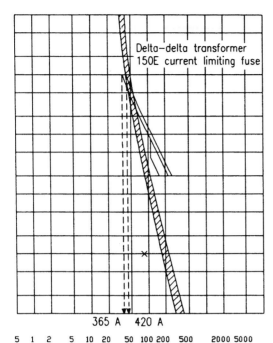

Delta–delta transformer
150E current limiting fuse

365 A     420 A

5   1   2    5   10  20   50  100 200  500    2000 5000

**Figure 7.5**  Comparison of current-limiting fuse TCC
with transformer damage curve for frequent faults in
a Δ-Δ transformer.

through the fault protection curve at about 13,000 A for three-phase faults and
at about 23,000 A for phase-to-ground faults. This means that the transformer is
not protected according to the standard for faults of this magnitudes or less by
the fuses. Such faults are possible. If they are in the transformer, damage has
already occurred and must become heavier before the source can be removed by
the fuses. If the fault is between the transformer and the secondary circuit
breaker, it must also develop to a heavier fault, which means more damage and
time; however, the probability of faults in this area will usually be small.

Typical industry data indicate that 480-V arcing phase-to-ground faults may be
as low as 19 to 38 percent of the rated fault value. Thus, for a secondary fault
maximum of 52,296 A, the primary current for the fuses would be $52,296 \times 0.19 \times 0.577 \times 0.48/12 = 220$ at 12 kV, just above the 200-A rating, and it is doubtful that
the fuses will give any protection until severe burning increases the fault current.

Secondary faults on the bus should be cleared by the secondary transformer circuit breaker, and the faults on the feeders by their circuit breaker backed up by
the transformer breaker. Thus, the primary fuses are backup for these faults if
they can see these secondary faults (ANSI, 1985; Blackburn, 1987).

## 7.4   Transformer Primary Circuit Breakers

Relay-protected systems can provide low-level overcurrent protection
for transformers, although in many cases the cost to do so is frequently

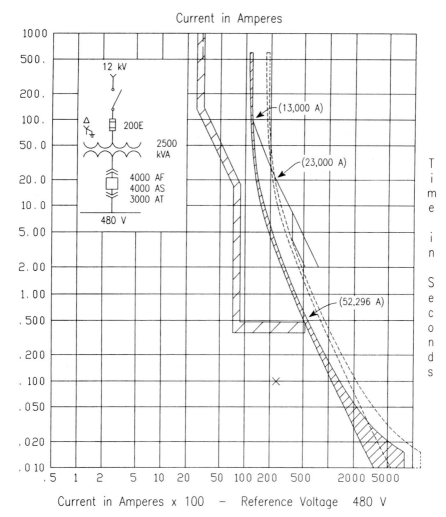

Current in Amperes x 100   –   Reference Voltage   480 V

**Figure 7.6**   Protecting a Category II transformer. Some protection specialists prefer to shift the transformer damage curves according to the line and winding currents for the various faults indicated in Fig. 3.3. The broken-line fuse curve indicates an implementation of an alternate method of tracing time-current characteristic curves for a single-line-to-ground fault by shifting the fuse curve instead. The three-phase fault time-current characteristic of the 12 kV fuse is shifted to the right 1.73 times (1/.577) the three-phase bolted fault value (and referred to 480 V). This shift is roughly indicated as 13,000 A and 23,000 A on the log-log plot.

determined to be unjustifiable in the case of smaller transformers. In medium primary to low-voltage secondary situations, the relevant NEC requirement for phase overcurrent protection appears in Art. 450 and is detailed in the material earlier in this chapter.

As discussed in Chap. 3, one of the relays on the primary side of a Δ-Y transformer will see 15.4 percent more current during line-to-line secondary fault than would be seen by the primary relays during a three-phase secondary fault of the same current magnitude and at the same location. To prevent miscoordination, the primary relay time-current characteristic must be raised (relay effectively slowed down). The time delay of the primary relay is selected to coordinate with the curve of the secondary main that has been shifted to the right by 15.4 percent of the actual time current for three-phase faults. A line-to-line fault will develop only about 87 percent as much current as a three-phase fault on the secondary side of the same transformer. Note that the difference between the line-to-line and three-phase fault current is the same as the 15.4 percent shift in current of the curve for the secondary relay.

### 7.4.1  Instantaneous relays

Short-circuit protection may be provided by instantaneous relays. As a general rule, the instantaneous trip of the primary relay protecting a transformer should be set slightly above the asymmetrical value of the three-phase bolted fault current on the secondary side of the transformer. This setting provides instantaneous clearing of primary faults and delayed tripping of secondary faults, allowing the faster secondary breakers to open first on faults close to the substation that are also seen by the primary relay.

**Example 7.2    Program Instantaneous Set Point on Relay-Protecting Transformer.**
See Fig. 7.7.

*Situation.*    The circuit shown in Fig. 7.7 requires short-circuit protection on the transformer.

*Requirements.*    Calculate instantaneous setpoint on inverse overcurrent relay.

**solution**    The general expression is

$$\text{Instantaneous Trip Setpoint} = \frac{(110\%)\,(I_F^{\max\,3\phi})(\text{Asymmetry Factor})}{(\text{Transformation Ratio})(\text{CT Ratio})}$$

Therefore

$$\text{Instantaneous Trip Setpoint} = \frac{(1.1)(18{,}460)(1.45)}{\left(\dfrac{4.16}{0.48}\right)\!\left(\dfrac{300}{5}\right)}$$

$$= 56.6$$

For an electromechanical relay you would set the magnetic element (Function 50) at 60. For a microprocessor relay you would program an equivalent pickup and remove the 110 percent tolerance factor in the preceding equation.

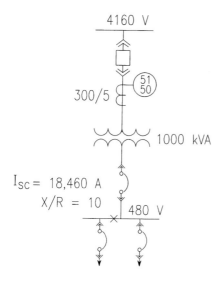

4160 V

300/5    51 50

1000 kVA

$I_{SC}$ = 18,460 A

X/R = 10    480 V

**Figure 7.7** Program instantaneous trip setpoint or relay protecting transformer. This instantaneous device cannot be coordinated with any other device that sees the same fault current unless there is sufficient impedance between the devices to discriminate fault current levels.

*Remarks.* This instantaneous element cannot be coordinated with any other relay with an instantaneous element in a series path with it unless there is sufficient impedance to reduce fault current between the two devices. You may opt to disable the instantaneous element of this relay or the relay in your own upstream primary unit substation.

### 7.4.2 Coordination of primary fuses with main breakers

You will find that a fuse current rating of approximately 200 percent of the transformer rated current will usually override the transformer magnetizing inrush current and still provide adequate fault protection. The transformer main secondary breaker should be equipped with tripping functions selected and set to meet the following requirements:

- Provide overload protection for the transformer (long-time pickup and long-time delay).

- Provide short-circuit and arcing fault protection for the bus and feeder breakers.

- Enable the transformer main secondary breaker to be selective with the feeder or group feeder breakers, that is, the time-current characteristics of their respective series overcurrent devices should not overlap.

To enable selective operation between the primary fuse and a main secondary breaker (that is, where the breaker is able to clear a secondary fault before there is any risk of damaging the fuse thermally), the total clearing time of the breaker should lie below the short-time curve of the fuse for all values of current equal to and less than the maximum value of symmetrical fault current that can flow through the transformer to a secondary fault. The short-time curve of the fuse lies below the minimum melting time curve. If some overlap of the breaker and fuse curves cannot be avoided, then it is desirable to set the breaker so that it will always trip even though the fuse may be damaged thermally. This can be accomplished by keeping the total clearing time of the breaker below the minimum melting time curve of the fuse.

Complete selectivity between the primary fuses and the secondary main breaker is desirable but is generally difficult to obtain. *The current rating of the fuse should not be arbitrarily increased to give complete selectivity at the expense of sacrificing adequate protection.* Partial overlapping of the primary fuse and secondary main breaker characteristic curves should not be objectionable when it is realized that the concurrent operation of the fuses and breaker is only for secondary faults, which are rare.

## 7.5   Secondary Main Breakers

First of all, there is nothing immediately wrong with the absence of a main breaker on a unit substation as long as the downstream circuit breakers are configured in a fashion that complies with the NEC. Article 230-71 indicates that no more than six switches (or breakers) be present at the moment that a firefighter needs to cut power to a building in trouble. When you can afford a secondary main breaker on a unit substation, however, you should specify it. The majority of unit substations are built with main breakers. Not only does it make it easy for the firefighter and the electricians, but it makes it easier for you to avoid cascading outages farther upstream from the unit substation.

The decision about whether or not to specify a secondary main breaker cannot be made without consideration of the NEC requirements for transformer protection. Article 450-3 specifies that maximum overcurrent level at which the transformer protection devices may be set. You may operate a substation with no secondary protection, but if you do, you must determine primary full-load current and size a circuit breaker to be set to trip at no more than 300 percent of full-load current, or you may use a fuse, in which case it can have a trip rating no greater than 250 percent of full-load current.

On the other hand, transformers with primaries rated 600 V or less require primary protection rated at 125 percent of full-load current when no secondary protection is present and 250 percent as the maximum rating of the primary feeder overcurrent device when secondary protection is set at no more than 125 percent of transformer rating. This is an important rule when we coordinate 480-V substation feeder breakers with downstream 208/120 transformers that provide power to single-phase receptacle and lighting circuits. (See discussion in Chap. 5.)

Certain exceptions to these requirements for smaller sized transformers, detailed in NEC Art. 450-3, are intended to permit the application of protective devices having standard ratings normally available. The permissible fuse rating is generally lower than circuit breaker setting because of the difference in the circuit opening characteristic in the overload region.

It is worthwhile recognizing how much an improvement in functionality microprocessor-based trip units have over solid-state trip units. The first mass-market solid-state trip units can be traced to the 1960s. They offered an order of magnitude more flexibility than the thermal-magnetic devices that preceded them. The first mass market microprocessor-based trip units offered another order of magnitude of flexibility over the solid-state trip units starting in the early 1980s. There is a great deal of literature available from electrical equipment manufacturers on the subject of microprocessor-based trip units and the circuit breakers to which they provide the driving intelligence. It is not fair to say "they are all the same" any more than it is fair to say they are all different. There are a few critical considerations that you should keep in mind when selecting a state-of-the-art circuit breaker, however. They are, in no particular order of importance.

- UL listing. (This may be required by local authority or your insurance company.)

- User friendly. (Always important, but it is a rather subjective quality.)

- Basic models, with subsequent models providing increased function levels with the flexibility to meet specific distribution system requirements.

- As many as five-phase and two ground time-current characteristic adjustments, providing increased levels of protection.

- Interchangeable rating plugs establish the circuit breaker's continuous ampere rating. The rating plugs are frequency sensitive, and specific types are available for 50- or 60-Hz system applications. Rating plugs may be applied as low as 50 percent of sensor rating.

*Rating plugs.*    All protection function settings on the face of the trip unit are expressed in per-unit multiples of the plug ampere rating. For example: 1000-A main breaker with a 1.2 multiplier with ground-fault protection.

*Auxiliary power module.* This module provides 32-V dc output and is applied for bench testing. It is equipped with a unique plug-in connection suitable only for plugging into the keyed receptacle for this manufacturer only.

*Power-relay module.* The module provides control power for operating the readout display, internally mounted signal relays, and light-emitting diodes. The internal relays provide for remote indicators wired in a conventional manner.

- The fourth auxiliary current transformer is supplied when the optional ground-fault protection function is selected in the trip unit. A side-mounted four-point terminal block is provided to prewire the mode of ground-fault sensing, residual, zero sequence.

- Zone selective interlocking (ZSI) for coordinating time delays with downstream devices so the circuit breaker closest to a fault trips instantly.

- *You must buy trip unit test sets and related hardware for each manufacturer. They are not interchangeable.*

Troubleshooting display information:

- Overload in progress, overload trip, short-delay trip, instantaneous trip, ground-fault trip, making current release trip, override trip, test in progress, rating plug problem, data memory problem, program memory problem.

- Are manufacturer's automatically building to NEC requirements such as the 480 Y 1000-A rule about ground protection?

- Are rating plug sensor ratings adjustable?

- Can you reprogram the trip unit without tripping the breaker?

- Can the breaker be tested in service?

- RMS sensing will permit discrimination between a lightning strike and a fault by computing the energy under the time-current characteristic.

**Example 7.3   Determine Interrupting Capacity of Secondary Main Breaker**

*Situation.* A unit substation as indicated in Fig. 7.8.

*Requirements.* Establish the basis for selecting a steel frame breaker with regard to its interrupting duty.

**solution** Maximum three-phase fault is 24,969 A. (Refer to Fig. 7.8.)

*Remarks.* Even though there are strategies available for opening devices "long" before withstand limits are reached, it is far better to have a device able

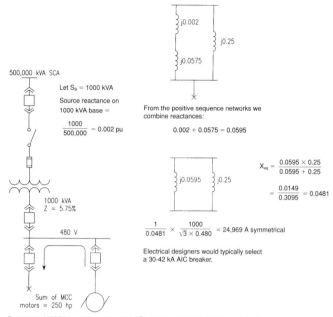

**Figure 7.8** Determine interrupting capacity of substation breakers.

to withstand the maximum available short circuit. The NEC requires it for customer-owned premises. The situation may be quite different in utility protection practices.

## 7.6 Secondary Feeder Breakers

Coordinating secondary feeder breakers with the next downstream overcurrent device is considerably more complex than coordinating the substation main breaker with the feeder breaker that is located within the same cladding. The likelihood of the feeder breaker seeing a fault is much greater than the main breaker seeing a fault within the substation cladding.

Feeder breaker trip functions may need to have an instantaneous function that the substation main breaker does not need. In the early years of a substation, the use of feeder breakers may be unknown and thus designated as a spare. You may want to purchase all trip functions for the electrical people who follow you. If you go this far, you may want to specify all the components for a complete ground-fault system (neutral sensors, zero sequence current transformers, and the like) so that the downtime needed for secondary cubicle preparation may be kept to a minimum.

Other hints:

- Connect neutral sensor so that polarity relationship toward source is identical for phase and neutral sensors. You may peruse UL standard 1503 that deals with wiring and functional details for neutral sensors.

- Some manufacturers will default to (virtual) instantaneous tripping regardless of time-band setting shown on trip unit unless special wiring is undertaken. Consult with the manufacturer. Ground-fault protection systems may be highly customized. Trip units and fittings are designed for maximum flexibility.

- In double-ended substations, some provisions are made for voltage surges on ground-fault currents with breakers in the withdrawn position.

### 7.6.1  Cable protection

The restraints imposed by the National Electric Code on pickup settings are considerably more restrictive for devices protecting cables and transformers (rated 600 V or less) than for the same apparatus rated over 600 V. For example, the circuit breaker setting for low-voltage services and feeders cannot exceed 100 percent of the cable ampacity in contrast to the 600 percent allowed for medium-voltage services and feeders. If the low-voltage protective device is nonadjustable, the National Electric Code will permit the next higher standard rating provided that the device rating does not exceed 800 A.

The feeder breakers are typically selected to match the cable connected to it. The rules for protecting these conductors rated 600 V or less is in accordance with their current-carrying capacity as given in NEC 230 and 240, unless motors are involved.

It is very important that you specify frame *and sensors* for feeders with some feeling for the future demands that will be placed upon the feeder. It does not make sense for you to specify 1600-A frame breakers when the feeder cable will only carry 800 A. Neither should you specify 400-A sensors or an 800-A frame breaker if you expect to fully load the feeder breaker. The industry notation that indicates AF (for amp frame) and AT (for amp trip) is only a partial feeder breaker specification.

In the case of microprocessor-based trip units, you must also indicate the *sensor* rating. You should specify sensor ratings *equal* to frame ratings unless you are working with severe financial constraints. Even then, subjecting an electrician to possible danger while changing sensors on feeder breakers, or shutting down the secondary section of a substation, is not worth the cost in the long run.

### 7.6.2  Small transformer protection

The zone is between a feeder breaker contained within a unit substation to a downstream transformer. Typically, these are "lighting or receptacle transformers" that step down 480-V feeders to 208 V, or 208-V feeders to 480 V (the 277-V line-to-neutral voltage applied for bulk lighting circuits).

You may think of the overcurrent protection requirements as identical to any transformer circuit we covered earlier in this chapter and in Chap. 5. You either do or do not have another downstream device to coordinate with. The rules of NEC 450 will apply, though you will always be dealing with transformers with both primary and secondary windings below 600 V. Most lighting and receptacle transformers are rated below 500 kVA. Where larger transformers are applied to supply single-phase loads, you will need to set the feeder breaker or select the fuse to clear the transformer inrush point. Remember, also, that line-to-neutral ground-fault current will exist between the grounded secondary of the 480/277 Δ-Y substation transformer and the primary delta winding of the 208/120 Δ-Y lighting or receptacle transformer. That is why ground-fault tripping is a desirable function on substation feeder breakers.

### 7.6.3  Motor feeder protection

Most of the rules for motor feeder protection were first discussed in Chap. 6. They are no different in the case in which the feeder is fed from a secondary breaker or fuse in a low-voltage unit substation except that there are some common situations worth noting as follows:

- Three-wire, 480-V distribution systems are sometimes built where motor circuits are the larger part, if not the only load on the substation. When this arrangement prevails, you need only concern yourself with phase coordination and annunciating a ground condition (in delta-connected systems).

- The difficulty in attaining ground-fault coordination between the substation feeder ground-fault relay and the instantaneous trip device is in the motor starter breaker. We alluded to this problem in Chap. 4.

- Motor starters supplied directly from the secondary bus of the unit substation. When microprocessor-based motor controllers are applied, your overcurrent coordination problems are reduced.

The rules for protection of a feeder to a motor control center are established in NEC 430-62. The pickup of this circuit breaker shall not exceed the setting of the highest branch circuit short-circuit protective device plus the sum of the full-load currents of the remaining motors. You should check that the circuit breaker curves will lie above a point defined by the acceleration time of the largest motor and the sum of the locked rotor current for this motor plus the sum of the full-load currents of the other motors. By largest motor, we mean the motor with the longest acceleration time and the highest starting inrush current.

---

### Transfer Considerations in Standby Generator Applications

When disconnected from the utility, large motors generate a residual internal voltage which is initially the same as the preinterruption value because the magnetic flux in the core as well as the rotor speed cannot change instantaneously. The residual voltage is reduced in magnitude and its frequency decays as the magnetic energy in the motor gradually dissipates due to losses. Reconnection of the motor to the power bus after a short delay can cause dangerously high transient torques and currents in the motor. The damage may not be apparent at first but it is cumulative over a number of out-of-phase reclosures and often results in collateral failures (such as single-line-to-ground insulation failure) which hide the original cause.

There are three methods to prevent problems associated with high-speed open-transition retransfers:

- Complete the retransfer before the internal motor residual voltage has time to fall less than 80 degrees behind the reconnected source voltage.
- Provide an OFF delay during the transfer to permit the residual voltages to decay to levels of 20 percent or normal, which will be safe regardless of closing angle and to allow time to trip off synchronous motors
- Delay closing into the alternate source until the first available in-phase condition detected by synchronizing relays.

(*Nochumson and Schwartzburg*)

---

In the case of motors, it is permissible for the protection device to be set higher than the continuous capability of the conductor (to permit coordination on faults or starting the largest connected motor while the other loads are operating at full capacity) since running overload protection is provided by the collective action of the overload devices in the individual load circuits. If you use protective devices rated 800 A or less that do not have adjustable settings that correspond to the allowable current-carrying capacity of the conductor, the next higher device rating may be indicated. There are other exceptions that are allowed in NEC Art. 240-3 such as capacitor and welder circuits and transformer secondary conductors.

You should confirm that the trip unit in the feeder breaker (or the dual-element fuse in the case of a fused unit substation) has the appropriate range of settings for a motor circuit protection situation, particularly, in switchgear arrangements where the motor starter is built onto the substation bus. The instantaneous settings of the devices that protect motor feeders must be high enough to ride through the starting inrush current and must not trip on the fault current contributed by the motor itself when a fault occurs on another feeder. It is possible for an induction motor, under certain conditions, to generate a fault current that exceeds its starting current. (Such may be the case with large, lightly loaded two-pole motors fed from a system with a low X/R ratio). The maximum setting of the instantaneous trip device permitted by the NEC is 700 percent of the full-load current, but this pickup value ignores the asymmetrical dc offset portion of the inrush current to which the instantaneous (magnetic) trip devices respond. The NEC recognizes this and, in an exception, permits a setting of 1300 percent of the motor full-load current. Confirm with the manufacturer that the trip unit associated with the motor feeder circuit breaker will have a range of settings up to 1300 percent. Typical settings will range from 8 to 11 times the full-load current depending on the dc offset, which is a function of the motor size and the number of poles.

## 7.7   Unit Substation Overcurrent Coordination

Let us put everything that we have discussed up to this point together. You will need to know something about overcurrent coordination when you have the responsibility of reviewing the manufacturer's customer-approval shop drawings; however, your concern may not be limited to the protection issues.

### Example 7.4   Typical Phase Overcurrent Coordination Study

*Situation.*   A customer-owned 2000-kVA secondary unit substation as shown in Fig. 7.9.

*Requirements.*   Coordinate all protective devices shown in Fig. 7.9.

**solution**   Refer to Fig. 7.10.

First, establish fixed constraints.

- Fault level:

$$\frac{2000}{\sqrt{3} \times 480} \times \frac{1}{0.0575} = 41,806 \text{ A Three-phase bolted fault}$$

   Devices are plotted beyond this point, but it is understood that no tripping current exists beyond 41,806 A.

- Transformer inrush and damage curves are plotted for an ANSI C57.12 dry-type transformer. Inrush factor = 8 times full-load amps.

- The extremely inverse relay with the 150/5 CT ratio picks up at 150 A. On the ABB CO-11 relay, for example, this would be Tap 5 with a time dial setpoint of 3.00. With an instantaneous tap set at 50, the short-circuit pickup will be

$$\frac{150}{5} \times 50 = 1500 \text{ A}$$

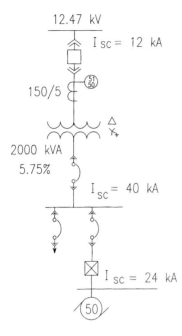

**Figure 7.9** Typical 2000-kVA substation.

Now the trip setpoints of devices associated with the substation are as follows:

- 2500-A main breaker with a fully rated 2500-A sensor will have

    LTPU = $2500 \times 1.10 = 2750$ A
    LTD = 2.50 s
    STPU = $2500 \times 1.5 = 3750$ A
    STD = 0.21 s
    Inst = $10 \times 2500 = 25{,}000$ A
    $I^2t$ = OUT

    Breaker AIC is confirmed to be 100 kA, which is more than sufficient for this application.
- The 50-hp motor startup curve is constructed from a nameplate full-load ampere rating of 65 A and an inrush factor of 6. The locked rotor transition point is estimated to be at 10 s.
- A motor circuit protector (MCP) with 430-A pickup within its range is applied in conjunction with a medium-speed overload device (OL) with a 125 percent heating factor.
- The thermal-magnetic feeder breaker can be fit nicely between the main and MCP + OL time-current characteristics. A 400-A unit is selected with an instantaneous pickup of $6 \times 400 = 2400$ A.

*Remarks.* There is a lot of "daylight" in this coordination study. Particularly in the case of protective device retrofit situations, you will discover considerably more difficulty in coordinating devices.

Note that under certain conditions, it is desirable that a trip unit remember that it has seen a fault condition for a short time after the

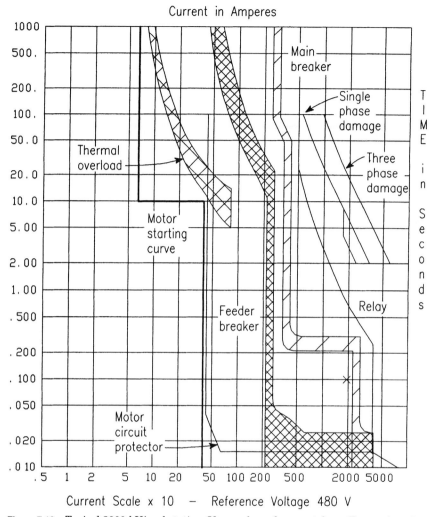

**Figure 7.10**  Typical 2000-kVA substation. If many branches are taken off one substation feeder and the branch loads are similar (all motors or all lights), the largest rated branch circuit should be checked for coordination with the upstream feeder. If the largest feeder will coordinate and the breaker devices have similar time-current characteristics, they generally will coordinate.

fault has cleared (to avoid a situation somewhat like short cycling of a heating, ventilating, and air conditioning (HVAC) system or the automatic reclosing of a utility circuit breaker). Some manufacturers build their trip units with logic so that repeated overloads will trip the breaker even though only one such overload would have been insufficient to case a trip. For at least one manufacturer, this logic is built into the long-time delay function. The ground-fault protection scheme is also provided with memory so that intermittent ground faults can still cause a trip.

### 7.7.1 Classical ground-fault coordination

As discussed in earlier chapters, there are three (classical) methods of ground-fault protection on low-voltage systems: source, zero sequence, and residual.

Figure 7.11 indicates the time-current coordination relationships among protective devices that are virtually independent of the fault-sensing method. The main breaker is set one step slower than the slowest feeder breaker ground-fault protection. Thus, for external faults, the main ground-fault relay waits for the feeder breaker to clear the fault before tripping its breaker and will provide backup protection if for any reason the feeder breaker fails to clear the circuit.

The ground-fault protection on subfeeder 3 could even be of the instantaneous type if selectivity with downstream protective devices on ground fault is not necessary. If the downstream circuit were a branch circuit, you may select an instantaneous type device with a sensitivity on the order of 15-A ground-fault current.

To protect against substation *internal* arcing faults to ground (or even inside a motor control center or switchboard—the principle still applies)—a main breaker and a time-delay ground-fault protective device in the *transformer neutral* connection are required. On internal faults to ground, all of the ground-fault current flows from the substation enclosure through the main breaker ground-fault protection to the transformer neutral. After timing out internal, the main breaker is tripped to extinguish the fault. In the absence of a secondary main

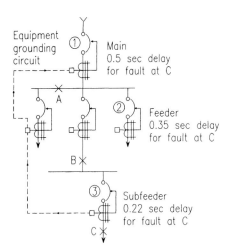

**Figure 7.11** Classical ground-fault coordination. The time delays between breakers correspond to about 12, 22, and 30 cycles. Where ground-fault protection is applied in unit substations in health care facilities, NEC 517-17(b) requires a six-cycle separation between tripping bands of the service and feeder ground-fault devices. Coordination shall include consideration of the trip setting, the time settings, and the total time required for opening each level of the ground-fault protection system.

breaker, the ground-fault protective device can transfer trip the primary metal-clad breaker or fuse (if so equipped).

### 7.7.2   ZSI of ground-fault coordination in a unit substation

The problem with the internal fault-clearing sequence in the foregoing section is that the main breaker still needs to "time out." That timing out period may be up to 30 cycles and it can be very destructive, especially if the main breaker does not have a 30-cycle withstand rating. One approach to coordinating phase and ground-fault protection that has been made possible by solid-state technology is ZSI. Do not let the name of the technology fool you into thinking it is very complicated.

Zone = the same zone we know from the zone around a bus or a transformer.

Selective = the same selective we use in the context of coordination.

Interlocking = the same way we interlock primary switches with main breakers.

Take three points in series, A-B-C, as shown in Fig. 7.12. Power flows from A to C as in a unit substation from the secondary main breaker to a feeder breaker to a downstream power panel.

In ZSI, breakers exchange signals and can disable each other's time delays.

If A, B, and C all see a fault, then the fault is somewhere downstream of the feeder breaker. The feeder breaker picks up and trips with normal time delay.

If only point A sees the fault and B does not, then the logical comparison results in the conclusion that the fault is on the bus. The main breaker will trip *with no time delay.*

Implementation of ZSI of ground-fault protection (Fig. 7.13) requires a pair of control wires between relays of each successive coordination step. The control leads add exposure to possible faults on these control leads. This should be considered when ZSI schemes are specified and applied.

## 7.8   Double-Ended Substation Coordination

Overcurrent coordination issues in double-ended substations require special attention because of the possibility that faults will be fed from two sources and because we sometimes need to squeeze in an intermediate level of overcurrent protection. We deal with double-ended substations with end-user secondary utilization voltages in this chapter

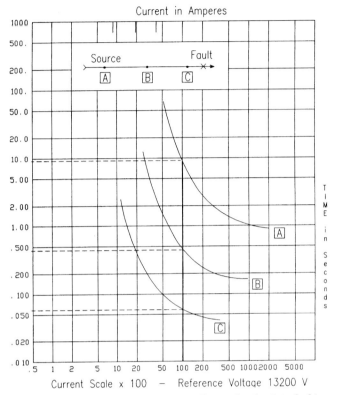

Current in Amperes

Current Scale x 100  —  Reference Voltaqe 13200 V

**Figure 7.12**  Zone interlocking concept. Zone selective interlocking effectively allows you to disable the ground-fault and short-time phase fault time delays programmed into series-applied overcurrent devices. The log-log plot shown in the figure uses some exaggerated inverse overcurrent time-current characteristics for illustrative purposes only.

If the fault is between points A and B (representing a bus fault, for example) you will want to trip "instantaneously" so that the time delay between A and B (9.0 − .4 = 8.6 s) is eliminated. You can save a lot of fault stress on the bus by overriding the time delay on device A with a command to trip "instantaneously." If the fault is between points B and C, however, or downstream from C (representing feeder or subfeeder faults) you may want to let upstream devices "wait" while the downstream devices clear the fault. Because of the half duplex communication among ZSI devices, there is a rudimentary form of breaker failure protection in some ZSI schemes.

and deal with medium-voltage, double-ended substations that typically comprise the consumer-utility interconnect in Chap. 9. The distinction is important because, among other things, the tie breaker in double-ended, *medium-voltage switchgear* does not always have overcurrent relays. The normally open tie breaker for medium-voltage

Source with grounded neutral
not shown for clarity

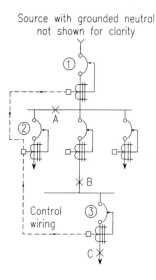

Control
wiring

**Figure 7.13** Zone interlocking method of ground-fault protection coordination. *Fault at A (bus fault)*: No restraint signal from downstream devices. Main breaker 1 is tripped instantaneously. *Fault at B (feeder fault)*: No restraint signal from downstream devices. Feeder breaker 2 is tripped instantaneously. Restraint signal sent to main breaker 1 to delay its tripping. *Fault at C (branch circuit fault)*: Subfeeder breaker is tripped instantaneously. Restraint signal is sent to upstream devices to delay their tripping.

switchgear is equipped with control devices that automatically open the main breaker and close the tie in the event of the loss of primary voltage or transformer fault (sometimes with manual bypass for closed transition switching), but there is no sensing of fault current at the halfway point of the lineup to section the switchgear.

By contrast, the normally open tie breaker for the typical low-voltage substation is usually equipped with overcurrent devices for reasons that have much to do with operating expediency and the desirability of breaker interchangeability. The tie breaker is a duplicate of the main breakers and *may* have the same continuous-current rating. Whether or not the tie breaker has the same continuous-current rating or a slightly lower rating (sometimes done for economy), the tie breaker is still another overcurrent device that has to be coordinated with respect to the two opposite mains.

### 7.8.1  Main-tie-main phase protection

When the tie breaker is closed, the procedure for coordinating phase devices is essentially the same as for a single-ended, three- or four-wire radially fed substation. All the usual considerations regarding transformer and motor inrush, transformer and cable protection still apply. Article 450-6 of the NEC brings particular issues to bear upon the matter of secondary ties between multiple source transformers.

Consider the situation in which the tie breaker is closed because of either a transformer failure or the loss of voltage on the other service conductor. There are three phase-fault situations indicated as F1, F2, and F3 in Fig. 7.17. Assume power flows from the left transformer. For a fault F2 occurring on a downstream feeder breaker on the opposite bus, we want selectivity with the tie and the main. For a fault F3 occurring between the feeder breaker and the tie, we will want the tie to open. For the fault at F1, we will want the main breaker to trip. If the primary fuse is not properly selected, the transformer fuses will open before the main. In a single-ended configuration, this lack of selectivity may be tolerable.

### 7.8.2 Coordinating ground-fault protection

For a single-line-to-ground, the system signals an open breaker to trip except when the tie breaker is closed (Figs. 7.14 to 7.16). Then if the fault is downstream from the tie breaker, the open main breaker is signaled to trip, and only the tie breaker trips. If the fault is upstream from the tie breaker, then the closed tie and main breakers are signaled to trip.

The systems shown in Figs. 7.15 and 7.16 operate on a summation principle where the transformer neutrals are grounded at the transformers. The service equipment connections to ground are made in the switchgear on the line or source side of the main protectors as required by the NEC for separately derived services. The phase-current sensors and electronic programmer are either integrally mounted or mounted externally. For a line-to-ground fault on the left bus or feeders fed from the left bus, a secondary current proportional to the fault current will flow in the trip unit associated with breaker 52-1/M1. Likewise, for a single-line-to-ground fault current will flow in the trip unit associated with breaker 52-1/M1. Likewise, for a line-to-ground fault on the right bus or associated feeders, a secondary current proportional to the fault current will flow in the trip unit. If these currents are above the electronic programmer's current settings and persist beyond the time-delay settings, the respective breakers will trip. The trip units may be selectively coordinated with the tie breaker 52-BT/T and feeder breakers by the selection of suitable current and time-delay settings. The neutral current sensor secondary windings, in addition to being connected to their associated trip unit, are interconnected with each other in a loop circuit. This ensures that the system remains nonresponsive to normal neutral loading, regardless of the possible diverse paths taken by the neutral return current, yet responsive to ground-fault current regardless of its return path to the source supplying fault current. Each breaker has an auxiliary "a" contact that controls when the neutral current sensor secondary winding and associated trip unit are interconnected. The contact mode open or close is similar to the breaker, that is, when the breaker is closed the associated contact is

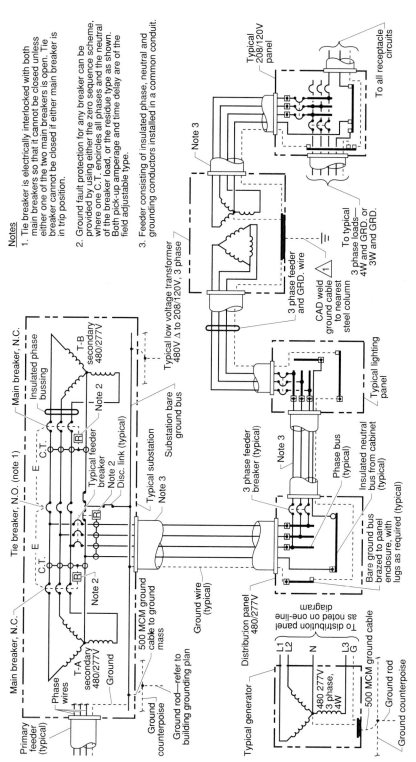

**Figure 7.14** Double-ended substation with ground-fault protection. Transformers have the same kVA rating, the same impedances, and the same voltage taps, and are supplied with power from a common source. (*Courtesy of EDSA Micro Corporation*)

**Notes**

1. Tie breaker is electrically interlocked with both main breakers so that it cannot be closed unless either one of the two main breakers is open. Tie breaker cannot be closed if either main breaker is in trip position.

2. Ground fault protection for any breaker can be provided by using either the zero sequence scheme, where one C.T. encircles all phases and the neutral of the breaker load, or the residue type as shown. Both pick-up amperage and time delay are of the field adjustable type.

3. Feeder consisting of insulated phase, neutral and grounding conductors installed in a common conduit.

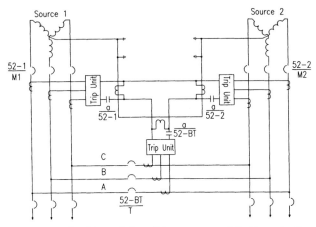

**Figure 7.15** Double-ended switchgear ground-fault protection scheme—modified differential. This scheme depends upon proper polarity markings of the sensing elements of the mains and the tie. Polarities are arranged so that there will be no current flow through the relay coils for three-phase, line-to-line, or single-line-to-ground currents. The single-line-to-ground fault current may return over with that of the ground paths and the neutral conductor, or it may be divided between the two in any proportion, without upsetting the proper flow of the current through the relay coils. The line-to-neutral load caused by unbalanced line-to-neutral current on a feeder circuit has two parallel paths by which it may return to its source at one or both of the transformers. One path is by means of the neutral conductor and the other is partially by the neutral conductor to the ground point near one transformer and then by ground to the neutral of the source transformer. With the current transformers and relays connected as shown, these extraneous currents flowing in the neutral conductors will cause no adverse action on either of the relays. It will not add to or subtract from the required ground-fault current flow in the relay coils, nor will it introduce any current flow in the relay coils for non-ground-fault conditions. These conditions will be true for any combination of breaker positions (open or closed) of M1, M2, or T.

closed and vice versa. As long as one breaker remains open (open transition), any neutral current returning to one of the sources via the main neutral bus of the other source and the neutral point ground interconnection is accounted for via the circulating currents circulating in the loop circuit. If ground-fault current total or partial for a given fault enters at the ground point of the source *not* supplying the fault, it can travel through the neutral conductor back to the neutral point of the source supplying the fault. As it passes through the neutral sensors, it induces secondary currents that result in a flow of current in the sensor loop circuit. By requiring one breaker to remain open, it ensures that at least one of the three neutral sensors will be disconnected by an open auxiliary contact from its associated breaker

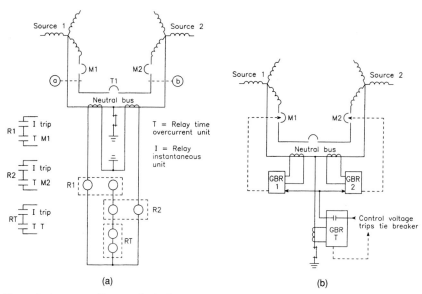

(a)                                                      (b)

**Figure 7.16a and b**  Two methods for double-ended switchgear ground-fault protection. Double-ended substations present special selectivity problems among feeders, ties, and mains under arcing-fault conditions. Selectivity may be obtained by grounding the neutral at only one point, at the center of the secondary section, and placing a sensor on the ground strap between this point and the secondary section ground bus. The relay associated with this sensor trips the tie device. Sensors for tripping each main device (shown as GBR in the figure) are located on the neutral, on each side of the point where the ground strap is connected. All feeder-neutral connections are made on the source side of these breakers.

The ground relays are interlocked to trip the tie device first, if it is closed. When the tie is open, ground-fault current returns to the transformer that is energizing the fault by flowing from the secondary section enclosure and ground bus through the single ground strap to the neutral bus, and through one neutral sensor back to the transformer neutral point. Since only the neutral sensor sees the fault current, only one main device trips and nuisance trips are prevented. The main breaker relays will not operate when load current flows in the neutral because their control voltage is obtained through a normally open contact of the tie breaker relay.

trip unit. This sensor then provides the driving force to ensure that the current flows around the sensor loop circuit instead of entering the breaker electronic circuitry. This prevents any mitigation of the ground-fault signal produced by ground-fault current flowing through the phase sensor of the circuit breaker. The secondary loop circuit helps provide accurate response to the flow of the ground-fault current. This summation scheme can be applied if one or both sources are emergency generation (Westinghouse, 1994; General Electric, 1991).

### 7.8.3  Tie circuit protection

According to NEC 450-6, both ends of each tie conductor shall be equipped with a protective device that will open at a predetermined temperature of the tie conductor under short-circuit conditions. This protection shall consist of one of the following:

A fusible link cable connector, terminal, or lug, commonly known as a limiter, each being of a size corresponding with that of the conductor and of construction and characteristics according to the operating voltage and the type of insulation on the tie conductors

Automatic circuit breakers, actuated by devices having comparable time-current time characteristics.

**Example 7.5   Double-Ended Substation Coordination Study.**   See Fig. 7.17.

*Situation.*   A double-ended unit substation as shown in Fig. 7.17.

*Requirements.*   Coordinate all phase and ground-fault protective devices.

**solution**   See Fig. 7.18. First establish fixed constraints.

$$\frac{200 \text{ kVA}}{3 \times .480} \times \frac{1}{0.0575} = 41,806 \text{ A } (3\phi \text{ symmetrical bolted fault short-circuit current})$$

This short-circuit value assumes that the double-ended substation is fully loaded on one end only and that the tie breaker cannot be closed such that both sources

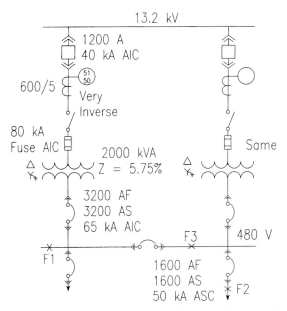

**Figure 7.17** Substation main-tie-main phase and ground-fault protection. This is the classic double-ended unit substation. This configuration offers another contingency in the case of a transformer failure. Backfeeding through a feeder breaker may even be possible with certain low-voltage circuit breaker trip units that have terminals and software for reverse connection.

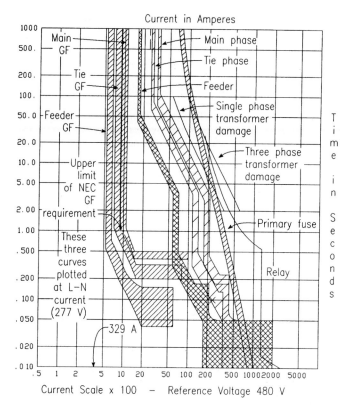

**Figure 7.18** Substation main-tie-main phase and ground-fault protection. Overcurrent coordination like this is only possible with carefully selected components. Such circumstances are usually only possible with new switchgear. Underlying the nicely coordinated curves, however, is the concern for coordinated fundamentals (withstand and interrupting duties, for example). Where steel-frame power breakers are applied, you should confirm 30-cycle withstand ratings. Sometimes the 30-cycle ratings hold even when the short time function is used with the instantaneous function disabled. (They can remain closed in order for zone selective or conventional timing to proceed.) Instantaneous trip characteristics may be achieved through instantaneous position on the short time switch.

will contribute to a fault at F1, F2, or F3. For operational reasons, however, you may want a "make before break" main-tie-main arrangement to switch between power sources without an interruption of service. Keep in mind that with both mains and the tie closed you increase the short-circuit availability by lowering the impedance (transformer reactances in parallel) and doubling the number of fault current sources. The additional fault current *may* by offset by the actual kVA load on either end of the substation. For instance, many electrical people prefer not to load either transformer more than 50 percent so that either end may hold the load of both secondary sections in the event of a transformer failure. Figure 7.18 shows time-current characteristic curves beyond the 41,806-A threshold. It should be understood that there would not be enough fault current to drive overcurrent devices beyond the 41,806-A threshold unless the main-tie-main arrangement, or transformer loading, motor backfeed results in greater fault current availability.

- Three-phase and single-phase transformer damage curves for Category II transformers are plotted as discussed earlier in this chapter. Note that these linear "curves" indicate infrequent faults only. Remember that the ANSI damage curves assume 10 or more *through-faults*. That is one major fault every five years, assuming a 50-year life for a transformer. In some facilities, this may be a realistic number of faults; in others not. The overuse of the frequent-fault impedance "leg" of the Category II transformer damage curve results in primary fuse sizing that errs on the side of protection. If you think that you are likely to see fewer than 10 faults in the lifetime of the transformer or have high-speed relaying upstream, then do not be afraid to apply the Category II infrequent fault curve.

- Transformer inrush is plotted at the 0.10-s, 10 times full-load current point ($2403.8 \times 10 = 24,038$ A).

- The very inverse 50/51 relay protects the cable. If the cable ampacity is given (by the manufacturer) as 480 A nominal for the type of service feeder construction to the substation, then with the 600/5 CTs, the overcurrent pickup will be $480/(600/5) = 4$. The instantaneous short-circuit pickup is set at 10 times the overcurrent pickup. This is a standard default in many overcurrent coordination software packages and has been shown in previous chapters to be a reasonable assumption. The 4800-A instantaneous pickup setpoint ought to clear a short circuit on the far end of the service feeder at the terminals of the transformer primary switch.

*The foregoing discussion completes the fixed constraints that normally prevail in coordinating the overcurrent devices in a double-ended secondary unit substation.*

Primary fuse is selected to be current-limiting 125 E. Since primary full-load current is 2000 kVA/($\sqrt{3} \times 13.2$ kV) = 87.7, the NEC will permit a fuse size up to 300% $\times$ 87.7 = 263 A. We begin by plotting ($150\% \times 87.7 = 131$ A) the 125-E fuse. It is worthwhile noting that the primary fuse may provide a certain degree of protection against faults on the secondary side of the transformer. As indicated earlier in this chapter, and elsewhere in this book, the minimum arcing fault current may range from 19 to 38 percent of the three-phase bolted fault value. Given that we have 41,806 for a three-phase bolted fault, then

$$41{,}806 \quad \times \quad \frac{480}{13{,}200} \quad \times \quad \frac{1}{\sqrt{3}} \quad \times 0.38 \quad = \quad 329 \text{ A}$$

| $3\phi$ bolted fault-infinite bus | transformation ratio | $\Delta$-Y reflection | arcing empirical factor | | |

Assuming an arcing empirical factor of 19 percent, the same formula yields 165 A. In each case, an arcing fault on the secondary is within "reach" of the 125-E primary fuse beyond. A fuse sized at the NEC maximum of 300 percent may *not* pick up secondary arcing faults. Of course, it takes the primary fuse a long time to see the arcing fault, which is why secondary main breakers are indicated.

*Phase protection:*  For both mains with fully sized 3200-A sensors and rating plugs set at 100 percent with effective pickup equal to 3200 A

Mains:  LTPU = $1 \times 3200 = 3200$ A
LTD  = 4.0 s
STPU = $6 \times 3200 = 19{,}200$ A
STD  = 0.20 s
Inst  = $12 \times 3200 = 38{,}400$ A
$I^2t$    = IN
AIC   = 65 kA

Tie:  LTPU = $0.8 \times 3200 = 2560$ A
LTD  = 2.0 s
STPU = $4.0 \times 3200 = 12{,}800$ A
STD  = 0.1 s
Inst  = $12 \times 3200 = 38{,}400$ A
$I^2t$    = IN
AIC   = 50 kA

Note that the instantaneous pickup is below the three-phase bolted fault value. You may opt to set this pickup lower to err on the side of protection; however, there is little advantage in this because there is virtually zero impedance between the tie and the main and (fortunately) very little chance of a bolted fault within the switchgear cladding.

*Feeder breaker:*  For a fully sized 1600-A sensor and rating plug set at 100 percent

LTPU = $1 \times 1600 = 1600$ A
LTD  = 2.0 s
STPU = $4 \times 1600 = 6400$ A
STD  = 0.1 s
Inst  = $12 \times 1600 = 19{,}200$
$I^2t$    = IN
AIC   = 50 kA

A hidden assumption in the selection of this breaker is that there is not sufficient fault current backfeed from motors to require a higher interrupting rating. Even if half of one end of the substation were motors, then 1000 kVA ($\sqrt{3} \times 480$) $\times 4 \cong 4800$ A would be a reasonable estimate of motor load fault current contribution. This amount of fault current is usually not enough to require the next larger feeder breaker interrupting rating. Large motor connected load may have broader implications for coordinating protective devices around magnetizing inrush constraints—especially if the substation is single-ended and all the motors are required to start simultaneously. Some protection engineers prefer to indicate maximum motor starting constraints on their finished log-log plots.

*Ground-fault protection:*  It is worth noting that the definite pickup current values in this and other ground-fault trip units come from line-to-neutral voltages, in this case, 277 V. Coordination of the main-tie feeder is straightforward stacking of pickup current and time delays.

Main GFPU = 1000 A    Time = 0.50 s
Tie GFPU = 800 A     Time = 0.30 s
Feeder GFPU = 600 A    Time = 0.10 s

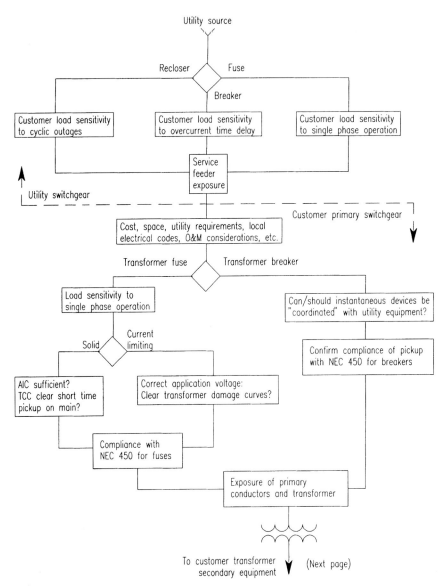

**Figure 7.19a and b**   The figure is a pseudo-flowchart to guide you through the some of the key decisions involved in selecting protective devices for low-voltage secondary unit substations. For clarity, some of the boxes that belong in more than one branch of the decision tree are not repeated. It is offered to the reader as a tool to rough out a structure for the complex considerations involved in overcurrent protection design.

*Remark.* Before issuing setting to a test technician, you should confirm that your settings match the range of possible settings on the trip unit nameplate. Manufacturers are continually improving their products; however, there may be considerable disparity in technical literature matching nameplates, published onion-skin TCCs, and setpoint options programmed into coordination software protective device libraries.

## 7.9 Flowchart for Selection of Substation Breaker Trip Functions

See Figs. 7.19*a* and *b*.

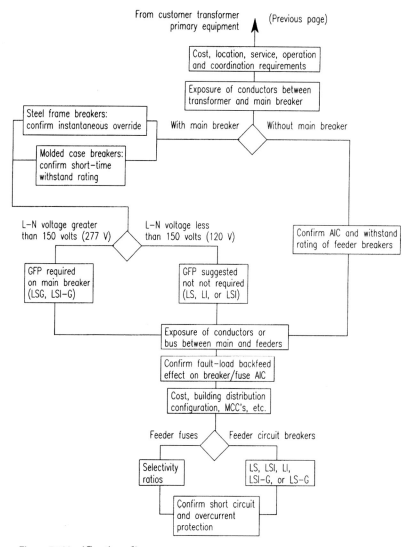

**Figure 7.19b**  (*Continued*)

## Bibliography

ANSI/NFPA 70-1993, *1993 National Electric Code.*

Blackburn, J. L., *Protective Relaying: Principles and Applications,* Marcel Dekker, Inc., New York, 1987.

*CAPTOR User Manual,* SKM Analysis, Manhattan Beach, Calif., 1994.

GE Electrical Distribution and Control, "Ground-Fault Protection for Solidly Grounded Low-Voltage Systems," Application Engineering Information, GET-6533A-0691BLE, 1.

*1993 NEC Handbook,* National Fire Protection Agency, Quincy, Mass., 1993.

Westinghouse Application Data 29-762, Westinghouse Electric Corporation, Pittsburgh, Pa., 1994.

### General references

"IEEE Guide for Protective Relay Applications to Power Transformers—Appendix A," *ANSI/IEEE Std. C37.91-1985.*

"IEEE Guide for Transformer Through-Fault Current Duration," *ANSI/IEEE Std. C57.109-1985.*

"IEEE Standard General Requirements for Liquid-Immersed Distribution, Power, and Regulating Transformers," *ANSI/IEEE Std. 57.12-1980.*

Smith, Robert L., *Electrical Wiring—Industrial,* Van Nostrand-Reinhold, 1982.

Westinghouse Communications Department, *Westinghouse Consulting Application Guide,* Westinghouse Electric Corporation, Pittsburgh, Pa., July 1991.

### Further reading

Johnson, Gorden S., "Overcurrent Protection for Emergency and Standby Generating Systems," *Electrical Construction & Maintenance,* April 1983.

Johnston, Frank C., "Specifying Fire Pump Circuit Protection," *Specifying Engineer,* Sept. 1984.

# Protection and Coordination for Bulk Distribution Switching Stations

## 8.1 Foreword

Plants that require bulk distribution are typically made up of many smaller buildings that are spread over large areas. This scattering of load over large areas is quite common for hospitals, shopping centers, chemical plants, colleges and universities, and water treatment plants. Loads in excess of about 10 MW now have switchgear operating at the medium voltage level for which the electrical consumer is responsible. Switchgear is the customer's own responsibility and is engineered, operated, and maintained by in-house or outside resources or a combination of each. Sometimes the electrical consumer supplements purchased power with its own generation.

Although our focus has been and shall continue to be upon overcurrent protection and coordination, medium-voltage switchgear is the limit for which overcurrent alone can be depended upon to provide sufficient protection. Directional overcurrent and differential protection must be applied to reach protection goals. As indicated in earlier chapters, differential protection is the fastest and most reliable protection strategy. It is complex in a way that is different than the way in which overcurrent protection is complicated (there is not the concern for coordination among series devices, for example) and it frankly deserves a dedicated textbook of its own.

The examples provided in this chapter will give you a sufficient sample of the issues involved in directional and differential protection. You should consult more authoritative sources especially if, for example, you are preparing bidding documents for a new lineup of switchgear. Again, the author knows of no protective device manufacturer who is not eager to help you specify your protective equipment correctly—even at the switchgear design stage. Most manufacturers have experts on staff who will flag a potentially erroneous specification. You should not be shy about consulting them.

## 8.2   Medium-Voltage Breakers

Our discussion of medium-voltage breaker application principles in Chap. 3 resulted in the following rule of thumb: If the available symmetrical short-circuit current at a time of interruption (or the higher first-cycle symmetrical short-circuit current) is not more than 80 percent of the circuit breaker symmetrical current-interrupting rating, any X/R ratio will be satisfactory and therefore need not be calculated. For example, if your breaker is rated to interrupt 61 kA and the available short-circuit current is 80 percent × 61,000 = 48.8 kA, then you need not analyze the circuit to determine X/R ratio.

This 80 percent condition is often sufficient to justify the circuit breaker interrupting rating. The available short-circuit current may be as great as 100 percent of the circuit breaker interrupting rating as long as the X/R ratio does not exceed X/R = 15 for five- and three-cycle circuit breakers and 10 for the eight-cycle circuit breakers. But if the X/R ratio is greater than these limits, multipliers from curves in ANSI/IEEE C37.010-1979 should be applied. These evaluations require calculating or conservatively estimating the system X/R ratio at point of fault.

A conservative X/R ratio can be obtained from vector analysis of the short-circuit current and X/R ratios of the various sources: utility, motors, and generators. One way is to factor the various source short-circuit currents into effective reactance and resistance components by considering that *reactance component = short-circuit current × sin (tan$^{-1}$ (X/R)); the resistance component = reactance component divided by X/R ratio.*

The arithmetic total of reactance components divided by the arithmetic total of resistance components will produce an acceptable X/R ratio for use with the total short-circuit current. Simplifying estimates tending toward a higher X/R ratio will be on the safe side in the medium-voltage circuit breaker applications.

In some cases, circuit breakers with adequate interrupting capacity may have inadequate close-and-latch ratings. This sometimes happens when motors make a significant fault-current contribution. ANSI/IEEE C37.010 deals with just this situation. In essence, the calculated first-cycle short-circuit symmetrical RMS current should be multiplied by a factor of 1.6 to obtain an asymmetrical RMS current value to be compared with the close-and-latch rating of the circuit breaker expressed in asymmetrical RMS amperes. If the circuit breaker close-and-latch rating is inadequate, then a second evaluation can be made by reducing the induction motor short-circuit contribution, from Table A.3, "Multipliers for Source Short-Circuit Current Contributions."

We provide a solved problem at the end of this chapter to review overcurrent protection fundamentals in medium-voltage switchgear.

## 8.3  Instrument Transformers

The quick and dirty rule of thumb regarding current transformer ratio selection is to specify current transformers at 100 to 150 percent of the circuit's full-load amperes. There are several examples in this book where we apply the 100 percent rule, and in others we apply the 150 percent rule. The rule has to be applied in the right circumstances, of course. You may need to know how load current will change (thus, multiratio current transformers). You may need to know whether the protection circuit will be shared with a metering circuit. You may find that the 150 percent rule is more appropriately applied to metering circuits.

Voltage or potential transformers are generally less difficult to specify. Scaling bus potential to the relay input terminals is fairly straightforward: line-to-neutral voltages, usually 120 VAC, are used to drive watt-hour and voltmeters and some (not all) switchgear control functions. In some arrangements, the potential transformers provide single-phase power to the dc battery charger which controls the tripping and closing circuits of the medium-voltage breakers. Some applications of voltage transformers require special attention to connection polarity.

Connection polarity is an especially important issue in current transformer circuits. Current transformers have one primary and one secondary terminal marked to indicate the relative instantaneous polarities of the primary and secondary. At any instant, when current is flowing in the marked secondary terminal, current is flowing in the marked primary terminal. In other words, if you consider the direction of current only, you can make current transformer connections by assuming the marked secondary is a continuation of the marked primary.

A current transformer rating of C50 refers to a calculated value. The 50 stands for 50 V. C100 refers to 100 V, C200 to 200 V, and so on up to C400. You may need to ask yourself whether 50 V is enough to operate the relays. If you think you need 100 V, then specify C100 and expect to pay extra for it.

Examples 8.1, 8.2, and 8.3 are provided to give you some confidence in dealing with instrument transformer application particulars.

**Example 8.1   Determine Current Transformer Ratio for Simple Radial Circuit with Instantaneous Protection**

*Situation.*   Two relays are in series with a transformer (an impedance element) in between. See Fig. 8.1.

*Requirements.*   Size current transformers on both sides of the transformer.

solution   The full-load amperes of the 3750-kVA transformer at 13.8 kV is 156.8 A.

$$150\% \times 156.8 = 235.2 \text{ A}$$

Select the 300/5 current transformer.

The full-load amperes of the 3750-kVA transformer at 2.4 kV is 903 A.

$$150\% \text{ of } 903 = 1354.5 \text{ A}$$

Select the 1200/5 current transformer.

*Remarks.*   The upstream instantaneous element is there for cable protection. We will return to this issue in Example 8.5 when we will need to determine the inverseness of the relays we wish to apply.

**Example 8.2   Determine Current Transformer Ratio for Looped Distribution Circuit**

*Situation.*   The circuit is shown in Fig. 8.2. The upstream tie breaker is normally open and the switches at each of the low-voltage secondary unit substations are normally open so that we are dealing with an overcurrent problem in which normal current flows in one direction only.

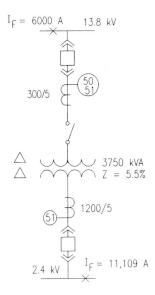

**Figure 8.1**   Determine CT ratio for simple radial circuit with instantaneous protection.

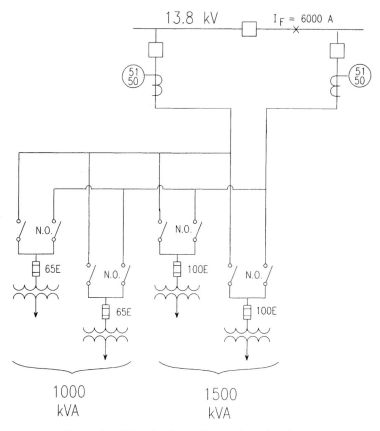

**Figure 8.2** Determine CT ratios for medium-voltage breakers protecting a looped distribution circuit. Note that one primary switch is open at each substation and that effectively this looped distribution network is operating radially. When the source tie breaker is normally open (as we assume here), the pickup point of overcurrent relays may be programmed with respect to the full-load amperes of the largest transformer on the loop.

*Requirements.*    Determine the current transformer ratios of the upstream breakers.

**solution**    We add up the total connected load

$$1.0 + 1.0 + 1.5 + 1.5 = 5.0 \text{ MVA} = 5000 \text{ kVA}$$

$$\text{at } 13.8 \text{ kV: } 5000/22.8 = 219 \text{ A}$$

$$150\% \text{ of } 219 \text{ A} = 329 \text{ A}$$

We could try a 300/5 CT or a 400/5 CT.

*Remarks.*    The selection of current transformers based solely on load and overload currents can result in inadequate relay protection for the application. You need to look at saturation at three-phase and single-line-to-ground fault current levels, especially in the case of low-ratio current transformers (*IEEE IAS,* July 1993).

In situations where coordination is close, the appropriate selection of current transformer can provide the daylight needed for reasonable compromises. Inverse curves shift left and right along the current scale as current transformer ratios are varied.

Appendix Figs. A.16 through A.18 are three key tools used by protection specialists involved in current transformer specification. It should be noted that burden ratings of current transformer were formerly expressed in terms of volt-amperes, but it is more accurate to express burden in terms of impedance of the load and its resistance and reactance component, which is now standard. It is usually enough to add series burden impedances arithmetically. Any inaccuracy will be on the safe side.

### Example 8.3   Select Current Transformers for Medium-Voltage Feeder Protection

*Situation.*   A typical medium-voltage distribution feeder as shown in several circuits in this book (Figs. 8.1, 8.2, 8.4, 8.5, 8.6, 8.9, 8.11, and 8.13 of this chapter, for example). Some basic information about the feeder has been determined to be the following: Full-load steady-state current is 90 A maximum. From a short-circuit study, maximum fault current has been determined to be 2500 A and minimum fault current is 350 A.

*Requirements.*   Select an appropriate current transformer + relay tap combination for phase protection. Assume that the CT will be driving an electromechanical relay.

**solution**   It is customary to select a CT on the basis of 150 percent of full-load current. Let us explore the selection process in a little more detail, taking exciting current and instrument transformer cable resistances into account. We will apply the current transformer excitation curves of Fig. A.16. We will also require relay manufacturer tap burden data, which is generally available in the technical literature that accompanies the relay. It is important to distinguish between the instrument transformer *winding tap* and the *relay tap* burden. In both phrases, the word "tap" appears, but the phrases refer to two different numbers.

*Full Load Current.*   Assume that we have a multiratio instrument transformer with winding taps, as shown in Fig. A.16. Our 150 percent rule would suggest that we first choose the 150/5 CT because $90 \times 150\% = 135$ A, and 150/5 would be the next CT winding tap higher. Instead, let us begin with the 100/5 winding tap to demonstrate the iterative, trial-and-error nature of the selection process and to demonstrate how an appropriate selection at full-load current may not be appropriate for other current levels.

With the 100/5 CT, the transformation ratio of 20:1 results in a $90/20 = 4.5$-A secondary CT current. By selecting tap 5 on the 100/5 CT, we avoid tripping the circuit upon maximum load since tap $5 \times 100/5 = 100$ A, which is just above the 90-A maximum.

*Minimum Fault Current.*   The foregoing conclusion assumes that exciting current is virtually zero. This is generally not the case in fault conditions and is the reason the 150 percent rule may fail us. To examine CT performance under fault conditions, we need two critical pieces of information: (1) the relay tap burden, and (2) the CT lead resistance. As previously indicated, relay tap burden is available from the manufacturer. If you were to consult the application literature, you would find (along with thermal capacities, contact options, and current element information) tables that indicated burden in volt-amperes according to the amp tap ranges and indicating accessories available with the relay. Burdens in terms of ohms generally decrease as relay taps (within a given element) increase. For example, the burden tabulation for one relay manufacturer indicates 9.5 ohms at the 0.5-A tap, 9.3 ohms at the 1.5-A tap, 5.3 ohms at the 5-A tap, and 3.5 ohms at 10 A (20 times tap). These will vary among electromechanical and microprocessor-based relays. Such reduced burdens improve CT performance in fault conditions, but the price we pay for this advantage is that at low taps there may not be enough voltage to drive the relay. From manufacturers, then, we obtain 2.64 VA as the burden on the 5-A relay tap, and from control cable manufacturers we obtain 0.4 ohms as the CT lead resistance. From Fig. A.16, the CT secondary resistance is 0.082 ohms. We convert VA data into ohmic data by the familiar formula $P = I^2R$, so that total resistance on the CT secondary circuit is

| Relay burden, $2.64/5^2$ | $0.106\ \Omega$ (ohms) |
|---|---|
| Lead resistance | $0.40\ \Omega$ |
| CT secondary resistance | $0.082\ \Omega$ |
| TOTAL on CT secondary | $0.588\ \Omega$ |

The voltage resulting from 5 A flowing through a secondary with 0.588 ohms resistance is $5 \times 0.588 = 2.94$ V. From the CT characteristic of Fig. A.16, exciting current $I_e$ for 2.94 V on the 100/5 curve is about 0.26 A.

Now the primary current just to initiate operation of the relay (with a given amp range element) is the sum of the secondary and exciting currents times the transformation ratio. In this situation that is $20 \times (5.0 + 0.26) = 105.2$ A. This is simple scalar addition, and in many situations it is appropriate. (See *Remarks* following.) The more orthodox approach, however, is to add secondary current to exciting current at 90 degrees. When we do, the total is $5^2 + 0.26^2 = 5.007$, giving a primary pickup of $20 \times 5.007 = 100.14$ A. With a minimum fault of 350 A, this is either (by scalar addition) $350/105.2 = 3.3$ or (by phasor addition) $350/100.14 = 3.5$ times the relay pickup. Either way, the 3.5-A tap will be a reasonable choice. You can see that scalar addition is a reasonable approximation. This CT ratio + relay tap combination would be generally regarded as acceptable since the tap falls in the middle range of taps available on typical electromechanical overcurrent relays. With a reduced relay tap burden on a microprocessor-based relay, the foregoing procedure situation may result in a different specification.

*Maximum Fault.*    For the maximum fault current of 2500 A, the secondary current (neglecting $I_e$) should be $2500/20 = 125$ A. From the manufacturer's literature, we read that at 20 times the relay tap, the burden is 580 VA. Tabulating all secondary burdens thus,

| Relay burden, $580/100^2$ | $0.058\ \Omega$ |
|---|---|
| Lead resistance | $0.40\ \Omega$ |
| CT secondary resistance | $0.082\ \Omega$ |
| TOTAL on CT secondary | $0.540\ \Omega$ |

The voltage required to pass 125 A through the relay would be $125 \times 0.540 = 68.13$ V. As can be seen from the excitation curve of Fig. A.16, this is not possible;

the CTs on the 100:5 tap can produce only 12 to 15 V before saturation, and from the curve a maximum of around 20 to 25 V. Thus the 100:5 ratio tap on the multiratio CT is not an optimal selection.

*New Iteration.* Consider another instrument transformer + relay combination. Fortunately we have a multiratio current transformer that will allow us to change the transformation ratio as required throughout the life of the feeder circuit. Let us try the 400/5 tap with the 80:1 transformation ratio. With this tap used, the load on the secondary of the current transformer is 90/80 = 1.13 A when the feeder is at full load. The next closest relay tap is 1.5, which may be sufficient for full load but not under the given fault conditions.

To confirm the suitability of the 1.5-A relay tap under fault conditions, we repeat the preceding methods. The manufacturer reports the CT burden to be 3.5 VA. For the moment, assuming no exciting current, the primary pickup would be 1.5 × 80 = 120 A. With 0.211 Ω, from Fig. A.16, the total burden is:

| | |
|---|---|
| Relay burden, $3.5/1.5^2$ | 1.56 Ω |
| Lead resistance | 0.40 Ω |
| CT secondary resistance | 0.211 Ω |
| TOTAL on CT secondary | 2.171 Ω |

The voltage required to develop 1.5 A in the relays is 1.5 × 2.171 = 3.26 V, and from Fig. A.16, exciting current $I_e$ = 0.026 A. Applying scalar addition for the worst case, the primary pickup would be 80 × (1.5 + 0.026) = 122.08 A. Thus, this relay tap + CT tap combination is sensitive to the 350-A minimum fault current. Minimum fault current would be 350/122.08 = 2.9 times the relay pickup current.

For the maximum fault, the secondary current neglecting exciting current $I_e$ would be 2500/80 = 31.25 A. The manufacturer data and scalar addition results in a relay burden that is not significantly different at this level than with the relay tap at 1.5 A. Using the total burden on the CT from the foregoing tabulation, the secondary voltage required to drive the relay is 31.25 × 2.171 = 67.84 V. This voltage appears in Fig. A.16 near the knee of the saturation curve. The exciting current $I_e$ that corresponds to 67.84 is about 0.21 A, which does not significantly decrease the fault current the relay sees. Maximum fault current would be about 2500/122.08 = 20 times the relay pickup.

Thus, application of the 150 percent rule, which suggested the CT ratio be sized at 150/5, has been superceded by the sensitivity required of the CT + relay combination. The optimal selection for CT ratio for the medium-voltage feeder is 400/5, available as one of many taps on a multiratio current transformer.

*Remarks.* In many cases, it is practical to add the burden impedances and the currents algebraically, though theoretically they should be combined according to the phasor addition laws. If any of the results demonstrated in the foregoing development leave you in the margins of performance limits for two different CT ratios, then you should apply phasor addition involving angles. Otherwise, scalar addition assuming a 90-degree angle will be adequate, since burdens are generally near unity power factor while exciting current lags 90 degrees (Blackburn, 1987).

Evaluation of Example 8.3 by the ANSI/IEEE standard provides equivalent results. With the 100:5 CT tap + relay tap 5 combination, the terminal voltage from the previous analysis would be 2500/2 × (0.106 + 0.4) = 63.25 V, which is the CT secondary current multiplied by the relay and the CT lead resistance. From Fig. A.16, we can determine that the C100 CT on the 100:5 tap can only supply 100(100/600) = 16.7 V, and since it should supply 63.25 V, the CT will be severely saturated. By using the 400:5 tap, the C100 CT can supply only 100(400/600) = 66.67 V. However, the voltage required is:

$$1.5 \text{ relay tap: } \frac{2500}{80(1.56 + 0.40)} = 61.25 \text{ V}$$

which is within the 66.67-V ANSI rating, so the error will be not more than 10 percent.

## 8.4 Generalized Overcurrent Relays

The classical 50/51/52 (instantaneous-overcurrent-breaker) circuit configuration sees a lot of general service. A few typical hookups serve a wide variety of needs. Figure 8.3 is a block diagram of a microprocessor-based relay. It contains both time and instantaneous functions but it can only be applied to one phase. (The manufacturer offers multiphase units as well.) Some protection designers prefer this arrangement because if one relay fails, only one phase need be taken out of service. Other designers prefer the multiphase + ground overcurrent relay.

By *generalized overcurrent relays,* we mean solid-state relays that may emulate induction disk time overcurrent relays, say, sweeping up samples from the current supplied by the instrument transformer. For

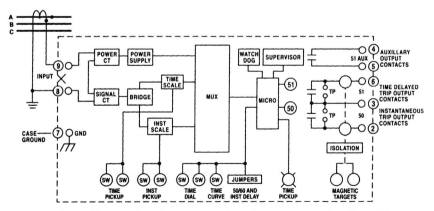

**Figure 8.3**  Block diagram for microprocessor-based overcurrent relay. One of the many advantages of microprocessor-based relays is that the influence of mixed-frequency harmonics is relatively minor. For faults containing a substantial dc component, however, the performance of such relays may vary considerably. *(Courtesy of Basler Electric Company, Inc.)*

example, a microprocessor can be programmed to integrate a function of current to provide a running sum incremented by each sample above the pickup point. When this running sum reaches a threshold, the relay trips.

Among the features of generalized overcurrent relays are the following:

- Time-current curves are obtained through the use of RC (resistor-capacitor) or digital timing circuits.

- Time-current characteristic curves and tap ranges are similar to those provided in induction relays. You should compare the two at, for example, 1.5-times pickup current.

- All of the time-current characteristics are included within the relay. A standard relay may be ordered before the coordination is completed, thereby allowing the physical construction to proceed. This is also an advantage as changes in the system configuration or coordination may be accomplished without a hardware change.

- Solid-state overcurrent relays have the same application as induction relays and are particularly useful where severe vibration specifications or seismic shock are imposed or where fast reset is required.

- Generalized overcurrent relays can provide faster reset times and have no significant overtravel. *Overtravel* is the term used in connection with the continuation of operation, due to the inertia of the mechanical disk, after the fault has been removed.

### 8.4.1   Overview of application principles

Before we discuss the coordination aspects of generalized overcurrent relays, let's have a look at tripping characteristics of these devices with respect to the requirements of bulk distribution circuits.

**Inverse.**   Long run, short rise. In other words, a relatively small change in time per unit of change in current. Provides phase or ground overcurrent protection on utility and industrial circuits. Especially applicable where the fault magnitude is mainly dependent on the system generating capacity at the time of the fault. Relay slope approaches a flat characteristic at high currents, giving a small change in operating time over a broad change in fault current magnitude.

**Very inverse.**   Provides phase or ground overcurrent protection on utility and industrial circuits. Especially applicable on subtransmission and distribution lines where the fault magnitude is mostly a function of the relative location of the fault to the relay. In addition, it provides better coordination with low-voltage breakers or a backup to other relays.

**Extremely inverse.**  Short run, long rise. In other words, a relatively great rate of change in time per unit of change in current. Applied on utility primary distribution feeders where sufficient time delay must be provided to allow a reenergized circuit to pick up without unnecessarily tripping during the inrush period, and at the same time to coordinate with main and branch cutouts and reclosers. Good for cold load pickup on distribution feeders.

**Short-time.**  Designed to provide overcurrent protection where fast operation is needed such as in residual ground relay in or where system stability is involved. Also applied in some bus or generator differential applications where restraint windings are not required.

**Long-time.**  Applied in motor circuit applications to override motor starting currents. Choose relay type based on starting time or motor.

**Definite-time.**  For use where fault current and generating capacity vary over a wide range. Relay has fixed operating time (per time dial setting) above approximately 10 times tap current, thus providing definite time-selective operation for coordination.

### 8.4.2  Coordinating inverseness

Figure 8.4 shows the family of time-current operating curves available with a solid-state inverse-time overcurrent relay applied to an industrial plant with four levels of overcurrent protection. The situation is somewhat rarefied, but it serves the purpose of illustrating once again the need to coordinate inversity itself, as well as pickup and time delays.

Similar curves are published for other overcurrent relays having different time delay characteristics. As is apparent, it is possible to adjust the operating time of relays. This is important since they are normally applied to selectively trip circuit breakers that operate in series on the same systems circuit. With increasing current values, the relay operating time will decrease in an inverse manner down to a certain minimum value.

### 8.4.3  Voltage drop considerations

Since a short circuit will collapse the voltage where an overload causes only a moderate drop, a voltage relay can be combined with an overcurrent relay. This setup means that the relay will operate at a higher

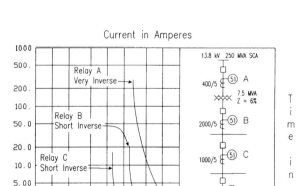

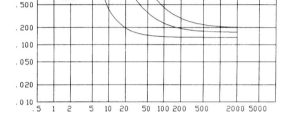

Current Scale x 100   —   Reference Voltage 2400 V

**Figure 8.4**   Selecting time-current curves and relay tap settings for an industrial plant distribution system. This schematic and coordination study shows various inverse relationships.

current value when voltage is nearly normal than when the voltage is very low. In this way, the relay distinguishes between a fault and an overload. The combination is fairly common because of the success of the application principle, and it is called an overcurrent relay with voltage restraint.

A short-circuit on an electric system is always accompanied by a corresponding—precipitous—voltage dip, whereas an overload will cause only a moderate voltage drop. Therefore a voltage-restrained or voltage-controlled overcurrent relay is able to distinguish between overload and fault conditions. Such relay characteristics are useful where it is necessary to set the relay close to or below load current, while retaining certainty that it will not operate improperly on normal load current.

### 8.4.4   Instantaneous elements

When an instantaneous element (50) is coupled with the time-delay element (51), its pickup current is set higher to override the delay element on large fault currents. But the instantaneous trip does not operate on moderate fault currents and system current transients, thus avoiding nuisance tripping. When two circuit breakers in series both have instantaneous overcurrent relays, their selectivity is dependent solely on their current settings. For example, when you have a 400/5 CT and observe that the instantaneous is set at 40, then $40 \times 80 = 3200$ A is what they both might see. Therefore, the relays must be set so that the breaker nearest the source will *not* trip when maximum asymmetrical fault current follows through the other circuit breaker. This requires sufficient impedance in the circuit between the two circuit breakers to cause faults beyond both circuit breakers to receive less current than faults near the source circuit breaker, so that the relays of the source circuit breaker can determine the fault location. If this differential is insufficient, selective operation is impossible with instantaneous overcurrent relays and the opening of the both circuit breakers on through-faults must be tolerated.

Usually, the impedance of a transformer is sufficient to achieve selectivity between an instantaneous relay on a primary feeder and the instantaneous trip coil of a low-voltage secondary circuit breaker. Also, the impedance of open distribution lines may be sufficient to provide the necessary differential in short-circuit magnitude to permit the use of instantaneous relays at both ends.

Generally, instantaneous relays at opposite ends of in-plant cable systems cannot be coordinated because the circuit impedance is too low to provide the necessary current differential.

Applications involving both phase overcurrent and residually connected ground relays should be reviewed carefully to determine if the steady-state and transient error currents are below the instantaneous pickup setting of the relay. The instantaneous element in a residually connected scheme may not be able to be set at all. Some solid-state instantaneous relays are designed to have inverse operating characteristics to allow a lower pickup setting without tripping during the transient portion of the error current.

Instantaneous attachments are generally furnished on all time-delay overcurrent relays on switchgear equipment so that they will be interchangeable, but they should be employed for tripping only when applicable. The fact that the relay setting study reveals that some of the instantaneous relays must be made inoperative should not be interpreted as a sign of a poorly designed protection system.

The instantaneous overcurrent element is designed to minimize transient overreach. The characteristic for phase faults is faster because the relay will be powered up. However, the tripping characteristic for ground applications is slightly longer to allow time to power up the relay. This longer trip time for ground applications is beneficial because it helps avoid nuisance trips.

### 8.4.5    Directional overcurrent relay—devices 67 and 87G

The basic overcurrent problem that we discussed in Chap. 3 was relatively simple and inexpensive to protect because it was a radial system. Consider the system in Fig. 8.5 which has multiple sources. The power systems of many large health care facilities are configured in this manner. In such systems, the fault current will flow from *both* ends of the distribution circuit. This makes coordination impossible.

If, however, every relay responds only to the flow of currents in the forward direction (toward its own zone of protection) as shown by the

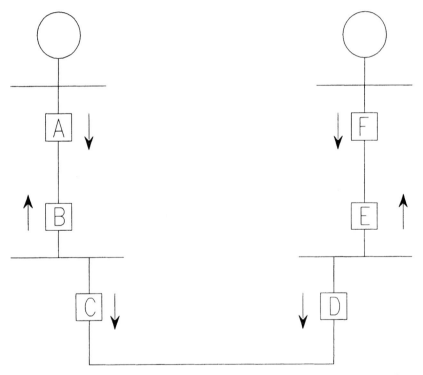

**Figure 8.5    Simplified loop circuit for directional overcurrent protection.** This simplified diagram indicates phase-current coordination among breakers A-C-E and breakers F-D-B with the application of overcurrent relays with standard elements. In many looped distribution systems, coordination of ground-fault protection using either definite time elements or inverse and instantaneous elements may be difficult. The choices for inverse elements may involve application of high time dial settings to allow sensitive pickup settings or higher pickup settings to allow lower time dial settings. With the first choice, less than optimum speed will result, especially at high currents, and with the second, less than optimum sensitivity. Microprocessor-based overcurrent relays can produce a hybrid tripping characteristic. (*Henville, 1993*)

arrows, and does nothing for currents in the reverse direction, then the loop system can be protected much like the radial system. Relays associated with circuit breakers A-C-E must be coordinated among themselves and relays F-D-B must be coordinated together. The overcurrent relays are made directional by using an additional directional relay at each location, and arranging the outputs of the directional and overcurrent units in such a manner that a logical AND operation between their outputs is performed. For example, if the contacts of the instantaneous elements are in series with the directional elements, then even though the instantaneous elements of nearby relays pick up, nothing will happen unless the contacts of the closest directional element are also closed.

Directional overcurrent relays consist of a typical overcurrent unit and a directional unit that are combined to operate jointly for predetermined phase angle and magnitude of current. In the directional unit, the current in one coil is compared in phase-angle position with a voltage or current in another coil of that unit. The reference current or voltage is called the polarization. The relay uses this (quadrature) voltage polarization to determine the direction of fault current. The overcurrent unit of the directional overcurrent relay is practically the same as for the usual overcurrent relay and has similar definite minimum-time, inverse, and very inverse time-current characteristics. The directional overcurrent relays can be supplied with voltage restraint on the overcurrent element.

The most commonly applied directionally controlled relay is the overcurrent unit that is effectively blind until the directional element detects the current in the tripping direction and releases or activates the overcurrent unit. Many directional relays are equipped with instantaneous elements, which in some cases operate nondirectionally, and unless it is possible to determine the direction of the fault by magnitude alone, the nondirectional instantaneous tripping feature should not be applied.

#### Example 8.4    Bus Tie Line Protected by Directional Overcurrent Relays

*Situation.*    The tie line between the buses shown in the circuit of Fig. 8.6. consists of a pair of 4/0 copper cables. The feeder relays have inverse characteristics similar to the moderately inverse ABB CO-8 with the following settings:

B1: Tap 5, Time Dial 4, Instantaneous 40

B6: Tap 5, Time Dial 6, Instantaneous 40

*Requirements.*    Select and set directional relays to protect the tie line within the limits of the cable ampacity and withstand capability.

**solution**    Three phase fault current levels (in amperes) have been determined to be:

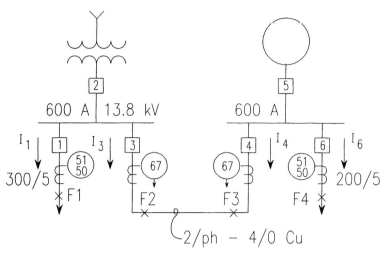

**Figure 8.6**   Bus tie line protected by directional overcurrent relays (schematic).

|          | $I_1$   | $I_3$ | $I_4$ | $I_6$ |
|----------|---------|-------|-------|-------|
| F1 Fault | 10,020  |       |       | 3900  |
| F2 Fault |         | 6120  | 3900  |       |
| F3 Fault |         | 5600  | 4184  |       |
| F4 Fault |         | 5600  |       | 9784  |

Refer to Fig. 8.7. From manufacturer ampacity tables for paralleled single-conductor 4/0 cable in nonmagnetic raceway at 75 percent load factor, the tie cable ampacity is $2 \times 295$ A = 590 A (Kerite 1990). This roughly matches the bus ampacity of 600 A. The selection of current transformer ratio for breakers 3 and 4 must take into consideration normal power flow between the buses when both sources are present and the power flow that would exist with only one source present. Selection may range from one to three times the normal load current with both sources present (sometimes called a CT ratio sizing "safety factor"). Let us leave the variable load and fault-current aspect to this problem aside for a moment so that we can study the settings of the directional relays. Let us work with a 600/5 CT ratio which assumes that each bus carries roughly half the load under normal operation.

The strategy for coordinating these relays has a symmetric aspect that is best illustrated by example:

- Coordinate B4 with B1 for a far-end fault at F1 (while ignoring fault-current contribution from the transformer).
- Coordinate B3 with B6 for a far-end fault at F4 (while ignoring fault-current contribution from the generator).
- Coordinate B2 with B3 and coordinate B5 with B4.

The directional equivalent of the ABB CO-8 is the ABB CR-8. By setting both taps on 5, we pick up at $600/5 \times 5 = 600$ A. We need only determine time dial settings that comply with the requirements of the foregoing coordination strategy. Figure 8.7 indicates:

Current in Amperes

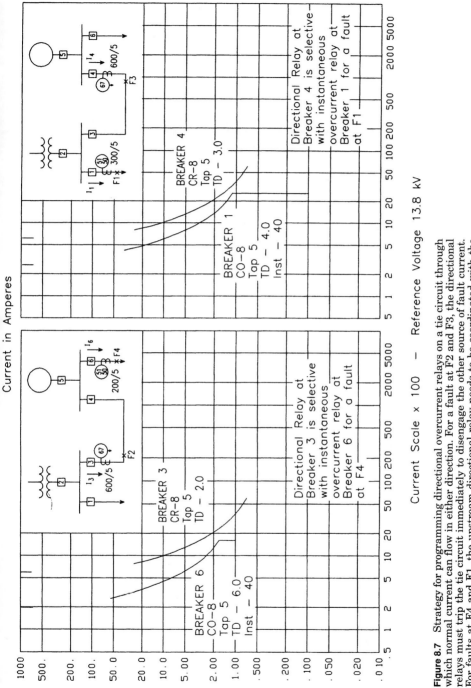

**Figure 8.7** Strategy for programming directional overcurrent relays on a tie circuit through which normal current can flow in either direction. For a fault at F2 and F3, the directional relays must trip the tie circuit immediately to disengage the other source of fault current. For faults at F4 and F1, the upstream directional relay needs to be coordinated with the feeder relay. The superposition of these two coordination studies is a complete strategy for directional overcurrent protection. A similar circuit appears in Fig. 8.12.

283

- Selective tripping of B3 and B6 for a fault at F4.
- Selective tripping of B1 and B4 for a fault at F1.
- For a fault at F2 and F3, the directional overcurrent relays must breaker the breaker immediately.

Remembering that B1 picks up at $300/5 \times 5 = 300$ A and that B6 picks up at $200/5 \times 5 = 200$ A, you can permute the other breaker tripping curves to confirm coordination at other fault locations. Since this tie line will act as a main to its respective opposite bus feeders, it should not have an instantaneous element.

*Remarks.* In cogeneration plants with two parallel sources, this relay may be applied in conjunction with another overcurrent relay driven by current transformers connected differentially to both lines. This directional configuration of overcurrent devices will provide time-current coordination with directional control to prevent false tripping on momentary reversal of power immediately following the clearing of a fault on one line. In the case of parallel lines, a "through" fault or overload that does not disturb the balance between the lines will not cause the relays to function. When a fault occurs that unbalances the current between the two lines, the differentially connected overcurrent relays receive the difference between the two currents and the breaker in the faulty line (Westinghouse, 1992).

### 8.4.6 Ground overcurrent relays

Where the system neutral is grounded and ground current can flow in the line conductors, the 51N relay connected to the common lead of the wye-connected secondary of three current transformers provides protection. This relay can be set to pick up at much lower current values than the phase relays because only unbalanced current flows in the current transformer neutral. That is how an arcing or high-resistance ground is detected and deenergized in time to prevent extensive damage.

Overcurrent relays for this form of ground protection are generally the same as those applied for phase protection, except that a more sensitive range of minimum operating current values is likely to be required.

Transformers and generators with grounded neutrals can be ground-protected by an overcurrent relay hooked up with a current transformer neutral-to-ground lead. These relays are set at low current values whether or not ground current is limited by neutral impedance or resistance.

### 8.4.7 Directional overcurrent ground relays

In Example 8.4, we discussed only directional phase-fault overcurrent protection. Where the ground-fault current in the relay is less than three times the load current, a dedicated single-phase ground relay is recommended to ensure adequate protection against ground faults.

Classical electromechanical directional ground overcurrent relays are built just like directional phase-fault protection devices. The operating coil of a directional-overcurrent relay connects in the neutral of the line current transformers as shown following. Neither normal load currents in the current transformer secondaries (even though unbalanced) nor phase-to-phase nor three-phase short-circuits will start current flowing in the neutral; only ground faults cause current flow through the sensing device.

A current polarizing coil is connected to a current transformer in the transformer neutral where current always flows in the same direction no matter where the fault occurs. Or, instead of a current-polarizing coil, a voltage polarizing coil may be connected across the open corner of a wye-delta connected potential transformer with a broken delta secondary. In normal operation the three voltages are equal and there is not potential across the relay coil. But a ground fault immediately senses a voltage across it, with a phase angle corresponding to the angle of the grounded primary phase.

Voltage coils of phase fault directional relays can be tied to the same potential transformers with a 60 degree connection (where current at 1.0 pf leads the voltage by 60 degrees). Alternate arrangements wye-wye potential transformers for phase fault relays; wye-broken delta auxiliary transformers for polarizing coil.

---

## Sensitivity of Ground-Fault Relays

A problem frequently encountered by relay engineers is obtaining sufficient residual time overcurrent relay sensitivity for the level of ground-fault current allowed to flow in the system. When system CT ratios are selected on the basis of main, tie, or feeder circuit capacity, the need for ratios of 2000/5 or even greater often arises. Application of electromechanical 0.5-A relays establishes the minimum apparent ground-fault sensitivity at

$$\frac{2000}{5} \times 0.5 = 200 \text{ A}$$

which, in the case of 400-A grounding, is generally not sufficient. One common solution is to use 0.1-A relays to achieve an apparent sensitivity of

$$\frac{2000}{5} \times 0.1 = 40 \text{ A}$$

However, the burden of a 0.1-A relay is *25 times as great* as that of a 0.5-A relay. With type IAC53 relays, the voltage at pickup across the 0.1-A coil is approximately five times the voltage at pickup across the coil of a 0.5-A relay. Thus, depending on the CT ratio and saturation characteristic, it may be that using a 0.1-A relay will not give greater sensitivity than using a 0.5-A relay. The best solution in this case is to use a 50/5 donut CT to measure ground-fault current directly; however, there are tradeoffs with the low-ratio CT because low-ratio CTs may not build up enough voltage across them to drive relays. Another solution to the problem of ground-fault current sensitivity is to use a solid-state relay with a higher-ratio CT. You should confirm that the time-current characteristic of the ground-fault protective function is appropriate for your application, however. In multiphase + neutral microprocessor-based relays, the phase and ground-fault time-current characteristics are not entirely identical (Powell, Elmore).

## 8.5    Special Application Considerations Regarding Microprocessor-Based Relays

In everyday language it is common to call microprocessor-based relays solid-state relays. While this is obviously true, it is not true that all solid-state relays are microprocessor-based. The chief difference has to do with the microprocessor's compact capability to store information. Solid-state relays (or static relays) that were the electronic equivalent of balance beams and polarized coils were rarely applied at the the electrical customer level. These early solid-state relays were constructed from transistors, resistors, capacitors, operational amplifiers, and, typically, protected utility transmission lines. It was a static backup relay, for instance, that was part of the protection circuit that caused the great Northeast power blackout during the middle 1960s.

Of course a microprocessor-based relay is composed of all of the components that make up a solid-state relay but with the additional feature (or requirement) that its intelligence (logic, memory) is managed by *software*. Although solid-state relays had a rudimentary form of software implicit in the switches, the dials, and the thumbwheels that were applied to manage the input-output characteristics of solid-state relays, the controls on a static relay are nothing like the software required to manage the input-output characteristics of a post-electromechanical, microprocessor-based relays that we see undergoing slow but steady implementation today. It is reasonable, given the enormous investment that manufacturers make in software development, that resident-in-memory software be considered proprietary. Some manufacturers reserve the right to request return of the memory components should the relay no longer be used as a protective device.

As you can see, we have a whole new set of issues to deal with when we apply microprocessor-based overcurrent relays. The software "problem" is one of them. The mixed blessing that password entry presents is another. The remainder of this section discusses a few others.

### 8.5.1    Power to the intelligence and output contacts

Generally speaking, the power that drives your circuit breakers will drive your solid-state relays. If you use a 125-V dc battery to drive your medium-voltage circuit breakers, you can tap the same battery to drive the solid-state relays. Since electromechanical relays have no "brains" to speak of (only coils, disks, balance beams, and so on), there is no need for a power supply to any internal circuitry. There are 125-V dc leads by which the relay contacts are wired up to the breaker. The 125-V dc source that trips and closes breakers never has any effect on the ability of an electromechanical relay to sense and act upon an abnormal condition.

The situation is different with microprocessor-based relays. Some units require a separate dc or ac source to sustain its intelligence; others use the power of the fault to drive the intelligence. Many engineers are concerned about the effect of an independent power supply. Their concern for sufficient energy in faults for a solid-state relay to remember its instructions may be reduced with the knowledge that the power requirement to send a trip signal to a breaker is on the order of milliwatts.

One manufacturer applies input current to provide both the power and the sensing quantity for the relay. Normal load current provides the energy for the internal power supply. A sensing input transformer provides the quantity to be scaled and measured by the *time* and *instantaneous* functions. Scaling of the input signal is accomplished by separate networks for time and instantaneous functions. The scale factors are established by the front panel pickup settings. "Null" pickup settings of 00 provide maximum sensitivity as a safety precaution for the installation process. Pickup occurs when the input current level is adequate to power the unit. Operating power from the power supply is applied to the microprocessor supervisor circuit. When the input current falls below an acceptable level, the supervisor circuit interrupts the microprocessor and halts further operation.

### 8.5.2   Reset, power down, and return to normal

Engineers have learned to deal with the problems inherent in electromechanical relay overtravel and short cycling of fault current. In microprocessor-based relays, reset occurs when the current level is less than the pickup. Some manufacturers provide an option with a circuit-board jumper which provides selection of either an instantaneous or a decaying reset characteristic. Instantaneous reset forces the timer to zero when the input current falls below 95 percent of setting. This fast reset characteristic prevents the ratcheting effect of electromechanical relay that may occur for repeated faults.

The fact that you may apply microprocessor-based overcurrent relays one-per-phase or one-for-three phases presents operational issues to be reckoned with. What do you do when one of the relays fails? (Most microprocessor-based relays have a watchdog circuit that will annunciate an unhealthy relay.) If it is a one-per-phase application, you may be comfortable with protection for two phases only for the few minutes it takes to swap one relay out for another. Your risks are considerably greater if you have one microprocessor-based relay protecting all three phases and a ground. One manufacturer reports 115 years as the mean time before failure for a utility-grade microprocessor-based relay, but this kind of data will be of no help to you if you are experiencing one relay failure a year. The best solution to state-of-the-art problems may well be the old-fashioned solution: have a spare ready. Have it programmed and tested in advance so that your exposure time is reduced. One of the advantages of a microprocessor-based relay is that it will tell you when it is not feeling well. Of course, digital antagonists will claim that an electromechanical relay will not be "ill" as often.

### 8.5.3   Equations for inverse curves

If you hold up to the light the 11 × 17 onionskin time-current characteristic curves of microprocessor-based and electromechanical relays with identical inversity, you will find that they do not exactly match. The mismatch is never enough to warrant the need for the selection of a more or less inverse curve (traditional inverse curve standards have been established by ANSI and IEC-International Electrotechnical Commission), but the mismatch is enough to cause some concern—particularly with regard to the time dial settings. Figure 8.8 is presented to give you an idea of how one manufacturer programs its inverse curves in resident memory.

The terms *time dial* or *lever* or *setpoint* still remain, however. In the application literature of the relay, each manufacturer will quantify how the microprocessor-based relay time dial differs from its electromechanical parent—usually on the order of fractions of a cycle. The time-current characteristic curves included in the Appendix should give you a feeling for the difference.

### 8.5.4   Effect of harmonics

Most waveform distortions are generated by nonlinear impedances, usually load impedances. Classical generators of harmonics are arc furnaces, saturated current transformers, arcing faults, transformer energization, capacitor switching, and thyristor-switching loads. Microprocessor-based relays will see all of these, and manufacturers work to measure and mitigate their effects. There is a wide variety of measurement principles indicated for such relays that produce different results among different manufacturers (Elmore, 1990).

Microprocessor-based overcurrent relays receive an analog input quantity—usually a 120-V ac, 0-5-A instrument transformer output—and convert it to a digital quantity with an A/D converter. The broader the breadth of the sample (8-, 16-, 32-, or 64-bit, for example) and the faster the sample rate (10-, 25-, or 64-MHz, for example), the more closely the converted digital quantity will resemble the actual analog output of the instrument transformer. Microprocessor-based relays use digital sampling, digital filtering, asynchronous sampling, and RMS measurement, among other conversion techniques.

**TIME ELEMENT
CHARACTERISTIC SHAPES**

All time characteristic curves follow the relation:

$$T = \frac{AD}{M^{N}-C} + BD + K$$

TABLE 3.

| Curve Type | Constants | | | | |
|---|---|---|---|---|---|
| | A | B | C | N | K |
| S | 0.2663 | 0.03393 | 1.000 | 1.2969 | 0.028 |
| L | 5.6143 | 2.18592 | 1.000 | 1.0000 | 0.028 |
| D | 0.4797 | 0.21359 | 1.000 | 1.5625 | 0.028 |
| M | 0.3022 | 0.12840 | 1.000 | 0.5000 | 0.028 |
| I | 8.9341 | 0.17966 | 1.000 | 2.0938 | 0.028 |
| V | 5.4678 | 0.10814 | 1.000 | 2.0469 | 0.028 |
| E | 7.7624 | 0.02758 | 1.000 | 2.0938 | 0.028 |
| B | 1.4636 | 0.0000 | 1.000 | 1.0469 | 0.028 |
| C | 8.2506 | 0.00000 | 1.000 | 2.0469 | 0.028 |
| F | 0.000 | 1.00000 | 0.000 | 0.0000 | 0.000 |

S= Short Inverse   M= Moderately Inverse   B= BS142 Very Inverse
L= Long Inverse    I = Inverse             C= BS142 Extremely Inverse
D= Definite Time   V= Very Inverse         F= Fixed Time
                   E= Extremely Inverse

Where **D** is the time dial setting (0.0 to 9.9) and **M** is the multiple of pickup. **A, B, C, N** and **K** are constants defining with the shape of the curve. The constants have been selected to provide a very close match to the characteristics of electromechanical relays. The constants are provided in Table 3 for each characteristic curve shape. Figure 2 illustrates the characteristic shapes.

**Figure 8.8**  Table of constants for inverse tripping characteristics of a solid state relay. (*Courtesy of Basler Electric Co., Inc.*)

Digital filtering and asynchronous sampling techniques will accommodate harmonic influences. A digital filter extracts the phasor components of the instrument transformer input. A low-pass filter ahead of the A/D converter is required to eliminate aliasing. Aliasing is a phenomenon that must be reckoned with whenever we pass from the analog into the digital world. Aliasing happens when samples are taken at a frequency that effectively masks the actual input frequency. A microprocessor-based relay that cleans parasitic frequencies from the current transformer secondary before the A/D converter sees it will be immune to the effect of harmonics in the sense that it extracts the fundamental waveform.

The synchronous sampling process has a high computational burden and the processing time between samples is limited by the number of samples required per cycle. Adequate sampling requires a sampling frequency at least twice that of the highest frequency to be measured. For example, sampling the 13th harmonic requires a 1560-Hz sampling frequency or 27 samples to execute the relay algorithm. However, the asynchronous sampling technique allows more efficient use of processing time by using fewer samples per cycle and accumulating the necessary number of samples over a number of cycles. Each sample is taken after a delay time of 2.0833 ms (8 samples per cycle), except that a millisecond is added to the seventh sample. This skew causes the RMS value calculated from the eight samples each cycle to undulate around the true RMS value. The average taken over time quickly approaches the true RMS value (Elmore, 1990).

We calculate faults as linear values and set relays on that basis. Fault currents have dc as well as harmonic components. Electromechanical relays do not respond to the dc component of fault current. Microprocessor-based relays will sense the component *and* the harmonic. In a large class of applications, dc effects die quickly. The number of cycles after the disturbance that saturation occurs varies with the offset, current transformer ratio, and primary and secondary X/R ratio. Harmonics should not be a problem unless the relay is set in the overload range and harmonic amplification occurs due to interaction with capacitors.

One other note of caution: All microprocessor-based equipment is susceptible to conducted and radiated electromagnetic noise. The internal electronics of a protection relay must be shielded from radiated interference. A common source of radiated interference is the hand-held walkie-talkie sometimes used in industrial plants and hospitals. Shielding techniques internal to µP-based relays can include metal shield plates and enclosures and metallic paints applied to plastic surfaces. Conducted electrical noise such as high-transient high-voltage spikes and electrostatic discharges must be effectively diminished before reaching sensitive electronic circuitry. ANSI/IEEE C37.90, the IEC series, and the IEC 801 series provide a number of standards for electrostatic discharge, application of transients, and high-frequency disturbances.

### 8.5.5  The human effect

It is fair to say that the electrical utility industry has been slow—at best, uneven—in its acceptance of solid-state protective devices. It is remarkable how the philosophies differ from utility to utility. J. L. Blackburn, to whose distinguished work this book constantly refers, discusses the element of "personality" in protection systems design. The personality factor in protection engineering is as real as symmetrical component sequence quantities.

In a decade, microprocessor-based protection has moved from laboratory experiments, through field trials, and into industrywide application. Our industry accepted digital relays much faster and more thoroughly than it did static analog relays for many reasons, including new and enhanced features, superior performance, higher reliability, and greater economy. We are moving away from electromechanical relays to avoid obsolescence, setting restrictions, and application limitations. Digital relays also reduce installation costs and labor-intensive maintenance.

Measurement and analysis improve any system and to this extent digital relay records provide systemwide information we need to make constant improvements in the design and efficient operation of electric power apparatus and systems. Fault location and routine event reporting are now part of every digital distance relay operation. Other breakthroughs are probably not far behind: improved high-resistance fault coverage, reduced load effects on relay characteristics, nonpilot schemes approaching the performance of pilot schemes, new protection schemes, faster industry response to new requirements, greater control of logic and relay characteristics by users, wider use of transient (traveling wave) relaying, and a continued trend in price/performance advancement (Phadke, 1988; Schweitzer, 1991).

## 8.6 Cable and Feeder Overcurrent Protection

### 8.6.1 Ampacities of medium-voltage cable

Since normal full-load current is the reference current level upon which all protection engineering begins, the ampacities of the cables that determine the upper limit of normal full-load current are important issues for protection specialists. The ampacities of cables operating at medium-voltage are indicated in NEC Tables 310-69 through 310-84.

Section 310-15(b) states that "under engineering supervision, conductor ampacities shall be permitted to be calculated by means of the formula:

$$I = \sqrt{\frac{TC - (TA + \Delta TD)}{RDC\,(1 + YC)\,RCA}}$$

where    $TC$ = conductor temperature in °C

$TA$ = ambient temperature in °C

$\Delta TD$ = dielectric loss temperature rise

$RDC$ = direct current resistance of conductor at temperature $TC$

$YC$ = component alternating current resistance resulting from skin effect and proximity affect

$RCA$ = effective thermal resistance between conductor and conduit systems

For example, the ampacity of an insulated, single conductor isolated in air, the ampacity, based upon a conductor temperature of 90°C and an ambient air temperature of 40°C at 15,001 to 35,000 V, would be 545 A. This ampacity would be the basis for setting the pickup on an overcurrent relay.

You should be aware that cable ampacities will differ considerably because of inductive and thermal effects. Three-phase ac cable systems are unique among circuit elements in the sense that their impedance is determined by the orientation among them. Underground cable systems, in particular, are subject to variations (usually reductions) in ampacity related to thermal bottlenecks. The Neher-McGrath study, which applied lumped parameter thermal "circuits" to electrical cable systems to determine cable ampacity is generally thought to be the outstanding study in this field. Cable ampacities are an important issue from an "installed cost of copper" standpoint. Perhaps it may become commonplace for adaptive overcurrent relaying to be applied to reduce the cost of overspecifying cable ampacities.

### 8.6.2   Medium-voltage cable shielding considerations

Many medium-voltage voltage distribution systems employ low-resistance grounding that allows 200 to 2000 A to flow during the solid single-line-to-ground fault. In most cases, the metallic shielding on those medium-voltage cables beyond the fault point carry part of the fault return current—just as the equipment grounding system of a low-voltage system carries ground-fault return current (Dedad, 1990).

This return current may then return along the shields of other conductors or other equipment grounding paths. The physics of inductance provides a path for ground-fault current that is physically close to the phase-current path—usually through the metallic raceway or through the ground wire since their conductance is much greater than the conductance of the shield. (For concentric copper tape shield cable construction, for example, a 12.5 percent overlap among successive turns is a common configuration.) Inadequate shield current-carrying capacity will cause shield overheating and cable damage; therefore, ground-fault protection coordination studies should address two specific shielding questions:

- What is the magnitude of the ground-fault current that will be carried by the metallic shield of the specific feeder with respect to its raceway/conduit/impedance configuration?

- Is the circular mil area of the metallic shields sufficient to carry the calculated ground-fault currents within the operational time frame of the specific ground-fault relay and overcurrent protection device?

As we indicated previously, the problem of an open-circuited, or high-resistance ground-fault path is generally avoided by pulling a dedicated ground conductor through the phase conductor raceway. Testing performed in 1986 by Paul S. Hamer and Barry M. Wood of Chevron Corporation resulted in provisional evidence suggesting that only 3 to 14 percent of available ground-fault current will flow through each cable metallic shield. Detailed information about the simulated ground-fault circuit and the various conduit, cable, and ground-wire configurations is available from the IEEE paper they published (cited at the end of this chapter), but the important result for us is that we use an empirical factor of 15 percent to estimate the quantity of current that will flow through a cable shield undergoing a ground fault.

Let us work with this number. We can illustrate its application with an example circuit, Fig. 8.9, very much like the radial distribution circuits we have discussed in Chaps. 4, 5, and 7. Assume that feeder No. 1 consists of three 4/0-AWG, 15-kV shielded conductors in a rigid steel conduit *without* a ground wire.

Should relay 50G for feeder no. 1 fail, the backup device (breaker 2) must clear the fault before the shield of his feeder is damaged. Assuming a 0.4-s offset from pickup for the ground overcurrent relay on the line side of breaker 2 and a circuit breaker operating time of 0.1 s, feeder no. 1 cable shield must be capable of withstanding its portion of

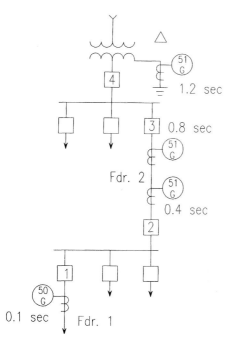

**Figure 8.9** Typical medium-voltage system with ground-fault relays. Times indicated are operating times of corresponding relay at a maximum fault of 1000 A at point F.

the 1000-A fault current for 0.5 s without sustaining damage. (Large medium-voltage motors connected to the other feeders would likely not contribute ground-fault current since motors are either connected in delta or have some kind of directional sequence overcurrent relays of their own.) The cable shield must be able to withstand 15 percent of 1000 A or 150 A for 0.5 s. Similiarly, feeder no. 2 shield must withstand 150 A for 1.3 s (0.5 s for feeder no. 1 plus 0.8 s for operation of the relay on the load side of breaker 3).

The cable industry has developed a performance equation (given in ICEA P45-482) that may be applied to determine the effective cross-sectional area of a shield required to withstand a given fault current for a given length of time.

$$\text{Area} = \frac{I_0 \sqrt{t}}{M}$$

where  $I_0$ = the ground-fault current in amperes
$t$ = time
$M$ = a factor dependent upon the construction characteristics
of the cable

$M = 0.63$ for cables rated 5 to 25 kV with a 90° rated cable with copper shielding and thermoplastic jacket such as PVC. This is not a complicated formula, but to avoid the calculations, you may obtain from the manufacturer a cable shield withstand curve such as the one that has been duplicated in Fig. 8.10. To apply this withstand curve, you need only confirm that the fault-current level and the time it persists fall below and to the left of the withstand limit line.

### 8.6.3  Medium-voltage distribution
### cable phase protection

When cable protection issues arise, we are almost always talking about a cable that will have power flowing from one direction or another. The protection problem must be recast in light of this as in the discussion on directional overcurrent protection earlier in this chapter. There is a working definition of a radial circuit that can help to classify our approach to feeder cable protection. A feeder is considered to be radial if, at any given relay application point, the maximum backfeed (fault current in the nontrip direction) is less than 25 percent of the minimum fault current for which the protective relay must operate. (Recall our discussion in Chap. 2 of the way in which the voltage collapse at the point of fault on a network will cause all power flow to reverse direction toward the point of zero voltage.) We use this definition to preface the following example of cable protec-

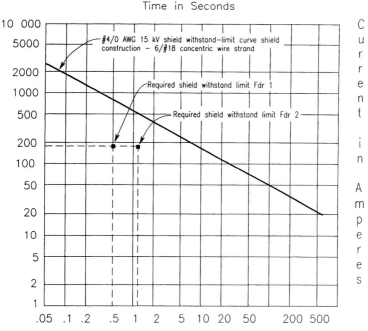

Figure 8.10   Medium-voltage cable shield withstand curve. Shield withstand limit curve of 4/0 AWG, 15 kV, 100 percent insulation, concentric wire strand shielded cable. Plotted points of required shield withstand limits of feeders 1 and 2 are shown relative to the withstand-limit curve. Required withstand limits fall within performance characteristics of shielding configuration used on cable in question.

tion in which it is assumed that there are no sources backfeeding into any fault on the system.

### Example 8.5   Simple Radial Bulk Distribution Circuit—Single Source

*Situation.*   Refer to the medium-voltage radial distribution subnetwork shown in Fig. 8.11. The impedances given are sequence impedances in actual ohms. Resistances are ignored and, in order to perform short-circuit calculations in longhand, positive-, negative-, and zero-sequence impedances are assumed to be equal. The transformer impedance is j5, referred to the 34.5-kV side. The breakers are controlled by electromechanical relays and are assumed to have adequate interrupting capacity.

*Requirements.*   Assuming that a coordinating time interval of 0.3 s accounts for all the real-time behaviors of protection circuit components discussed in Chap. 3, select current transformers and relay trip settings R1, R2, R3 for phase overcurrent protection on breakers B1, B2, and B3. Be mindful that each relay-breaker pair has an inherent time delay associated with it so that within some contexts it may be important to distinguish relay response and breaker operating times separately.

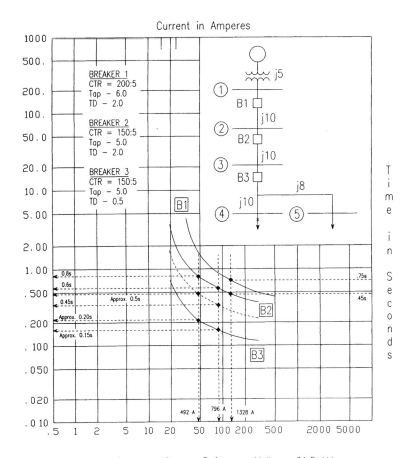

Current in Amperes

Current Scale x 10  —  Reference Voltage 34.5 kV

**Figure 8.11**  Simple radial circuit. In order to preserve an established coordination time interval throughout the range of available fault-current levels, you will need to carefully select time dial settings—usually by trial and error. Some overcurrent coordination software will execute an optimization algorithm based upon the constraints established by fault-current levels and a coordination time interval you select. In this study we see at 492 A that the coordination time interval between B3 and B2 may be almost $0.5 - 0.2 = 0.3$ s (broken line) or will be about $0.8 - 0.2 = 0.6$ s (solid line). There is nothing wrong with a 0.6-s coordination time interval unless it results in "squeezing" upstream devices or unless some component of the circuit cannot hold up to the fault current for an additional 0.3 s.

**solution**  We start at the far end of the circuit and work our way back to the source. As discussed earlier in this chapter, the choice of overcurrent relay will depend upon such issues as how fault magnitudes vary with respect to the relay application location and/or how small or large operating time needs to change over a broad range of fault-current magnitude. Let us work with a moderately inverse relay which provides a relatively moderate change in time per unit of change in current. Although all relay manufacturers have their own versions of a moderately inverse overcurrent relay, let us apply the ABB CO-7 relay reproduced in Fig. A.7.

*Breaker 3.* Suppose information in the schematic and information provided by a short-circuit study indicates that the minimum fault downstream from B3 will be a *line-to-line* fault. Such information would already be provided by the short-circuit study, but let us make an estimate of the fault current to generate some hard numbers to work with. Since our information is already given in ohms, we need only divide the line-to-neutral voltage by the series sum of the line impedances to calculate the three-phase bolted fault. The line-to-line fault is simply $\sqrt{3}/2$ times the three-phase bolted fault (since positive and negative sequences are assumed to be equal). Since $\sqrt{3}/2 = 0.866$

$$j0.866 \times \frac{(34{,}500/\sqrt{3})}{j35} = 492 \text{ A}$$

The point is to begin with the kind of fault that results in minimum fault current. We would like our relays to see this level of fault current as a minimum, but we do not want the settings so sensitive that we trip the breaker during normal load. As we have seen, arcing faults may hover just above full-load currents.

If we apply a CT selection safety factor of 3, which results in a prospective 492/3 = 164 A, we need to confirm that 164 A is above the normal load on that circuit. If not, then we would need to change the safety factor accordingly. If the maximum load on the feeder is confirmed to be, say, 100 A, we may proceed to the next step because the relay is programmed to allow normal load current to flow without tripping.

From the same short-circuit study, let us assume that all the design considerations discussed in Example 8.3 result in the identification of a 150/5 CT as the optimal selection for the high- and low-fault current levels. The 30:1 transformation ratio results in a 164/30 = 5.4 pickup setpoint on the relay. A half-tap setting is no problem for a microprocessor-based relay. In an electromechanical relay, however, we would have to opt for the integral tap setting of 5. (Recall from Example 8.3 that we like to keep our tap adjustments in the middle of the tap adjustment range where relay burden tends to be more linear.)

The relay is now set to pick up for any fault greater than 150 A. Since this subnetwork indicates that B3 has no other device to coordinate time with, we can simply set the time delay at its lowest time delay. On the CO-7 curve, the lowest setting is time dial (TD) 0.5. With this time dial setting, the time characteristic curve of the breaker 3 relay intercepts the time scale at approximately 0.2 s at the minimum fault-current level of 492 A. As we discussed earlier in this chapter, it is important that we distinguish between a relay's time dial setting and the absolute time its setting represents in a coordination study. We need to reckon with this distinction in the determination of the settings of R2.

*Breaker 2.* Since R2 must provide backup protection for R3, its current pickup level should be the same as the B3 current pickup level of 492 A but with an offset time delay. As we have discussed elsewhere in this text the vertical (time) displacement between the time-current characteristics of two series overcurrent devices can range from 0.2 to 0.4 s. For this situation let us try to maintain a 0.3-s interval between all three breakers for all levels of fault current. We cannot have too long a coordination time interval because circuit elements may be destroyed.

We cannot have too brief a coordination time interval because that may cause overtripping. With reference to the real-time behavior of the fault clearing period discussed in Chap. 1, we do not want the R2 contacts to close until B3 has had a chance to interrupt the fault current.

Since R3 picks up in 0.2 s at the 492-A level, we will want R2 to pick up in 0.2 + 0.3 = 0.5 s at the 492-A level. Which time dial setting will go through this point and yet maintain the 0.3-s minimum throughout the range of available fault currents? We usually have to guess. The broken line between B3 and B2 is a prospective time dial setting of 1.5 for B2 (*not* the same as 1.5 s). If you follow the time interval between B3 and the broken line at the 492 current level to higher current levels, you will see that the 0.3-s coordination time interval is *not* maintained. At 492 A, the time interval is just about 0.3 s, but as you follow current levels upward that interval gets shorter and shorter because of the logarithmic time scale. As indicated in Example 8.3, the actual inverse tripping characteristics may differ if the series-applied current transformers produce significantly different secondary current for the same fault current.

So it appears that we need either to pick another time dial setting or find out how far out we need to draw the R2 curve. To put the question another way: what is the *maximum* fault-current level that R2 is likely to see in backup mode? (R2 will need to look through another impedance to see a fault outside its primary zone of protection.) The maximum fault will be the three-phase fault on the load side of B3. Taking the line impedance between B2 and B3 into consideration:

$$\frac{34{,}500/\sqrt{3}}{j25} = -j796$$

This represents the maximum fault-current level. In the determination of which time dial setting to select, we need only consider fault currents between 492 and 796 A. Applying the CT 150:5 transformation ratio, the scaled-down current that the relay will see is $796/30 = 26.5$ A. Since we chose tap 5, this current is $26.5/5 = 5.3$ times the tap settings in both R3 and R2. Referring to the CO-7 time-current characteristic (and arbitrarily multiplying the current scale $\times$ 100), we can see that at the 796-A level, the CO-7 relay trips in about 0.15 s. Therefore, at 796 A, the R2 trip time should be $0.15 + 0.3 = 0.45$ s. We have two points now; we need only choose among the time dial settings the relay manufacturer makes available to us to choose which time delay preserves the 0.3-s coordinating time interval. In the matter of time delay adjustments, both electromechanical and microprocessor-based relays serve us well. Time delays are virtually continuously adjustable, not integral, as in the case of tap adjustments for electromechanical relays. A little manual trial-and-error curve fitting results in the selection of a time dial setting of approximately 1.5. With a little imagination you might be able to confirm that along the dashed line of Fig. 8.11 a $0.45 - 0.15 = 0.3$ s time interval exists between R2 and R3 at 796 A. Since this time dial setting has so little daylight timewise, we have plotted in a solid line the R2 trip curve with the time dial setting of 2. The $0.6 - 0.15 = 0.45$ s time interval at 796 A is equally as acceptable as long as downstream devices can withstand another $0.45 - 0.30 = 0.15$ s (or 9 cycles) of fault current.

Thus, R2 will not only provide backup protection should B3 fail, but it will initiate B2 tripping should a fault occur in its own primary zone of protection. Where the minimum fault on the load side of B3 was 492 A for a line-to-line fault, the minimum fault on the load side of B2 is $492 \times 35/25 = 688$. This is $688 \times 5/150 \times 1/5 = 4.6$ times the pickup value and R2 will trip in about 0.4 s.

*Breaker 1.*   We approach the selection of R1 settings the same way we selected settings for R2 as backup protection for R3, except for the fact that we shall have to deal with a normal maximum load current considerably larger than the 100-A load current we assumed farther downstream. Let us assume that 200 A is the normal load current. We can do this because we already know that the minimum fault current both R1 and R2 will see is 688 A. Applying the safety factor of 3 again, we get 688/3 = 229 A. We do not want B1 to trip at any current level lower than this. With this larger load current, we need another CT; try 200/5. This 40:1 transformation ratio results in a relay pickup value of 229/40 = 5.72 A. In order to coordinate with the R2 curve, the R1 curve will need to be shifted up and to the right. A shift to the right requires a larger pickup setting; try tap 6. This corresponds to a line current of 6 × 200/5 = 240, which is just above the 229-A normal maximum load-current level.

To determine the time dial setting, we must again determine the largest fault current seen on the load side of B2 and by the relay R1 backing up R2. The fault current on the load side of B2 is

$$\frac{34{,}500/\sqrt{3}}{j15} = -j1328$$

Thus, R1 and R2 will see 1328 × 5/200 = 33.2 A, which is 33.2/5 = 6.64 times the tap setting for R2 and is 33.2/6 = 5.53 times the tap setting for R1. Again, the current levels seen by the relays fall nicely in the middle of the relay tap adjustment range. By marking the 1328-A, 0.45-s point on the R2 curve, we can count up 0.3 s to the 1328-A, 0.75-s point. A manual trial-and-error process results in the selection of the 2.0 time dial setting. (You might want to nudge it a bit higher.) This time dial setting, at this pickup current level, preserves the 0.3-s coordination time interval throughout the range of fault currents available on the load side of B2.

### Summary of CT Ratios and Relay Settings

| Breaker | CT ratio | Pickup | Time dial |
|---------|----------|--------|-----------|
| B1 | 200/5 | Tap 6 | 2.2 |
| B2 | 100/5 | Tap 5 | 1.5 |
| B3 | 100/5 | Tap 5 | 0.2 |

*Remark:*   The advantage of the microprocessor-based relays, with their continuously adjustable pickups (or tap) adjustments, ought to be clear from this example. It is quite true that so-called half-taps on electromechanical relays virtually simulate microprocessor overcurrent relays in the matter of continuous pickup adjustments, but the in-service adjustment of an electromechanical relay requires careful attention to maintaining continuity of the breaker trip circuit. This concern is not present in microprocessor-based relays. In fact, many microprocessor-based relays may be programmed to adapt to a variety of load and fault conditions over the lifetime of a distribution feeder circuit. Distribution circuits that can only be operated in one configuration during certain times of the day because of fault duty limitations may be able to operated in more than one configuration if overcurrent relays can change their own settings automatically. Imagine how much faster we might have been able to trip any of the foregoing breakers had we not been constrained by the original "normal" maximum load current of 100 A. Microprocessor-based relays will allow you to program a variety of tripping setpoints based upon one or more independent variables. You may enjoy this flexibility or you may fear it (Bergen, 1986; Gross, 1979).

**Single source.** Directional overcurrent relays consist of a typical overcurrent unit and a directional unit that are combined to operate jointly for predetermined phase angle and magnitude of current. In the directional unit, the current in one coil is compared in phase-angle position with a voltage or current in another coil of that unit. The reference current or voltage is called the polarization. Such a relay operates only for current flow to a fault in one direction and will be insensitive to current flow in the opposite direction. The overcurrent unit of the directional overcurrent relay is practically the same as for the usual overcurrent relay and has similar definite minimum-time, inverse, and very inverse time-current characteristics. The directional overcurrent relays can be supplied with voltage-restraint on the overcurrent element.

The most commonly applied is directionally controlled, that is the overcurrent unit is inert until the directional detects the current in the tripping direction and releases or activates the overcurrent unit. Many directional relays are equipped with instantaneous elements, which in some cases operate nondirectionally. Unless it is possible to determine the direction of the fault by magnitude alone, the nondirectional instantaneous tripping feature should not be applied.

---

### Definition of Radial Circuit

A feeder is considered to be radial if, at any given relay application point, the maximum backfeed (fault current in the nontrip direction) is less than 25 percent of the minimum fault current for which the protective relay must operate.

---

Directional overcurrent relays are applied to provide sensitive tripping for fault currents in one direction and nontripping for load or fault currents in the other (normal) direction.

### 8.6.4  Multiple sources

We continue the discussion begun in the section on directional overcurrent relays to make a point about how directional relaying on tie lines can provide incidental bus protection as well. Let us consider the circuit of Fig. 8.12, which illustrates a power system with two sources. Practically all loads on utility power systems are fed from more than one source, so consider this situation as more the rule than the exception. Working with only two sources only will help illuminate some key ideas.

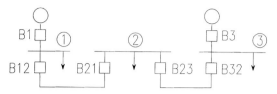

**Figure 8.12** Line protection for multiple sources. Schematic of a situation in which directional line protection provides incidental bus protection.

Note that a fault on bus 1, or the line between bus 1 and bus 2 need no longer interrupt service to buses 2 and 3. This, of course, presumes overcurrent coordination between the breakers. Suppose that there is a fault on the line between B23 and B32. As indicated in the directional overcurrent problem (Example 8.4), we want B23 and B32 to clear the fault. We do not want B12 and/or B21 to operate and interrupt service to bus 2. We would set B23 to trip faster than B21, and B21 to trip faster than B12. But suppose that the fault were on the line between B12 and B21 instead. With conventional overcurrent 50/51 relays, B23 would trip before B21, which would isolate bus 2 unnecessarily. When the fault may be fed from either left or right there is no way to coordinate the relay time delays for optimal selectivity.

To remove faulted lines correctly, we require relays to respond only to faults occurring on their forward or line sides—directional overcurrent device 67. In this case, B21 would operate first. On the other hand, with a fault on the line between B12 and B21, B23 would not operate and B21 and B32 could be coordinated so that B21 would operate first. These two breakers would not generally operate simultaneously since the short-circuit currents and coordination time delays would be different for the breakers to the left and the right of the fault point. Note, finally, that with directional relays the buses themselves are still protected (Bergen, 1986).

## 8.7 Bus Differential Protection

In buses, differential protection is provided to supplement overcurrent protection—particularly in main-tie-main switchgear configurations (see Fig. 8.13). The following factors determine whether this relaying should be provided:

- Degree of exposure to faults. In a majority of medium-voltage switchgear, the bus is metal-enclosed. In others, the bus is exterior and enclosed only by a fence.

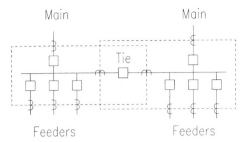

**Figure 8.13** Bus differential protection for main-tie-main switchgear. Note how current transformers determine the boundaries of the bus zones and how the protection zones overlap at the tie. This arrangement indicates current transformers applied on the load side of the feeders. Although the practice reduces the protected zone, there are situations in which the current transformers may be appropriately applied on the line side of the feeder breakers.

- Effects of bus failure on other parts of the system. The main-tie-main arrangement will allow servicing of each bus independently as long as you are careful about the internal construction details.

- If there are problems coordinating the system overcurrent relay settings. An example would be a system where several buses are required at the same voltage level, with one feeding another. This generally results in unacceptably high current ratings or overcurrent relay settings on the upstream fuses, switches, or circuit breakers.

- On buses fed by a local generator, bus differential relaying is recommended to clear the bus quickly and to hold the rest of the system together. The overcurrent relays used to protect a generator would take considerable time to operate.

It is possible to fashion differential relays from a judicious connection of overcurrent relays, but this kind of protective scheme is rare and not recommended. Manufacturers have easier and more economical ways to provide high-speed protection for buses.

## 8.8   Transformer Differential Protection

We broached the subject of differential relaying in Chap. 3 and we will work through some particulars here. As a general rule, transformers of 5 MVA and up should have differential protection. Some utilities do not require it in customer-owned transformers until the service transformer is at least 10 MVA. The reasons for this cutoff point may have more to do with economy than with any technical objections. Differential protection can be applied everywhere but, while relatively fast, it can be quite costly. Some utilities balance the cost of applying differential relaying, a high-speed grounding switch, or a very sensitive pressure sensor against the replacement cost of a 5- or 10-MVA transformer should a fault persist long enough to cause permanent damage. Much depends upon the grounding method of the subtransmission circuit feeding the transformer and the overall protection strategy applied by the utility.

In Chap. 3 we dwelled upon the input/output characteristics we require from transformer differential relays. One type of percentage differential relay that is applied for transformer protection has taps on the restraint windings that allow for different current transformer ratios to be applied in the power transformer primary and secondary circuits. Percentage relays indicated for bus protection applications typically do not have taps. Normally, all current transformers must have the same ratio and characteristics; however, solid-state relays are available for use with current transformers that have different ratios.

Differential relays with harmonic restraints have filters that block the fundamental frequency restraint unit while directing harmonic current to the restraint unit. The operating unit of this element receives only fundamental frequency current while harmonics are blocked. This causes the relay to be insensitive to the harmonic current that flows during transformer energization. An instantaneous trip unit is included in the operating circuit to provide fast operating times on very high internal faults.

These relays have current taps that are used to correct for mismatch between the currents from the current transformers in the primary and secondary circuits of the power transformer itself. Relay sensitivity can be adjusted by selecting an appropriate slope tap unless the relay has a variable percentage characteristic (Elmore, 1994).

### 8.8.1  Application principles

As with all applications of the differential principle in protection, instrument transformers need to be applied with considerable care. Wrong connections generally manifest themselves in a nuisance trip when the transformer begins to pick up load. One particular consideration involves the complications arising from variable transformer taps. Many transformers are equipped with variable tap settings which allow their secondary voltage to be adjusted as load changes. If automatic load tap changing results in an off-normal turns ratio, the relay will see a differential current during normal conditions and thus cause a nuisance trip. As you might imagine, the problem of undesirable error currents (see Fig. 3.6) is particularly onerous when primary and secondary currents have angular as well as magnitude differences (which is the case with all Y-Δ connections). Example 8.7 is adapted from from Stevenson (1982) to give you a sample of the nitty-gritty particulars involved in avoiding nuisance tripping in transformer differential protection schemes.

**Example 8.6   CT Connections for Transformer Differential Protection Using Auxiliary CTs**

*Situation.*   A three-phase customer-owned 345/34.5-kV transformer is rated at 50 MVA with an emergency rating of 60 MVA. The 345-kV side is Y-connected and the 34.5-kV is Δ-connected.

*Requirements.*   Using standard CT ratios available, determine the CT ratios, CT connections, and the currents in the power transformer and in the CTs such that secondary line currents as seen by the relay are in phase with the primary under normal load conditions. Refer to Fig. 8.14.

solution   The correct phase-angle relationship is obtained by connecting the current transformers on the Y side of the power transformer in Δ and those on the Δ side of the power transformer in Y. In this manner, the current transformer connections compensate for the phase shift created by the Y-Δ power transformer.

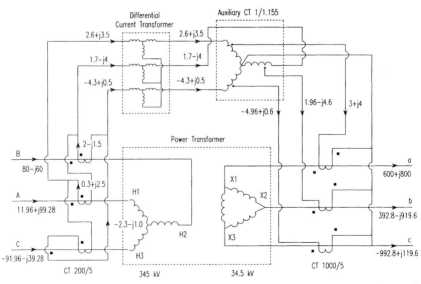

**Figure 8.14** Transformer differential protection. The strategy for balancing differential mismatch current that results from the angular difference between the primary and secondary winding of a Y-Δ power transformer is straightforward: simply connect the current transformers in Δ-Y to reverse the connection-induced phase shift. Much as an autotransformer is applied to make up small voltage differences, an auxiliary relay may be applied to a transformer differential protection circuit to reckon with the mismatch currents that result from load tap changing.

**solution**  In this situation, we use the emergency rating of the transformer so that the differential protective scheme does not trip the transformer when it is needed most. The full-load currents on each side of the transformer are:

$$\frac{60 \times 10^6}{\sqrt{3} \times 345 \times 10^3} = 100.4 \text{ A (primary)}$$

$$\frac{60 \times 10^6}{\sqrt{3} \times 34.5 \times 10^3} = 1004.1 \text{ A (secondary)}$$

Try the CT ratio of 1000/5 on the secondary side. Since the CTs on this side are connected in Y, the current flowing into the differential relay from this side will be

$$1004 \times \frac{5}{1000} \approx 5.0 \text{ A}$$

To balance this current, the line currents produced from the Δ-connected CTs on the 345-kV side must also be 5.0 A. This will require that each of the secondary windings of the Δ-connected CTs have a current of

$$\frac{5.0}{\sqrt{3}} \cong 2.9 \text{ A}$$

This current in the CT secondary winding requires CT ratios of 100.4/2.9 = 34.64 for the CTs on the 345-kV side. The nearest available standard CT ratio at this voltage is 200/5. If we can use this ratio, then 100.4 × 5/200 = 2.51 A and the line currents from the Δ-connected CTs to the differential relays would be

$$2.51 \times \sqrt{3} = 4.35 \text{ A}$$

This current cannot balance the 5.0 A produced by the 345-kV side. The remedy for this situation is to specify auxiliary current transformers which provide a wide range of turn ratios. Applying a set of three auxiliary relays, connected as shown in Fig. 8.14, with a turns ratio of

$$\frac{5.0}{4.35} = 1.155$$

will result in a balanced set of currents in the differential relay even when the transformer is operating at its short-time emergency rating. The foregoing procedure may be repeated using the 50-MVA rating to determine another auxiliary transformer ratio which might also be judiciously applied. The differential relay can be programmed to trip only upon a mismatch current that falls out of tolerance for normal load variations or may be programmed to trip only upon a preset *rate of change* of mismatch current.

For an assumed power factor of 0.8 lagging, the currents in the power transformer and the various CTs are shown in Fig. 8.14.

*Remarks.*  Notice that we have assumed that the magnetizing currents of the power transformers are negligible. This is a good approximation when the transformer is operating normally and the magnetizing current is very small. As we have discussed earlier in this text, transformer magnetizing current is rich in harmonics. The strategy to prevent tripping on transformer inrush is to supplement the differential relay with a harmonic restraint element to discriminate inrush current from fault current. "Normal" fault current tends to be a purer sinusoid of fundamental frequency (Stevenson, 1982).

Wherever possible, use standard relay schemes, applying relays specifically designed for your application. Instrument transformer and relay manufacturers will usually assist you in performing the (frequently messy) calculations you need to confirm acceptable performance of the scheme.

---

### Ways to Assure *Improper* Operation of Transformer Differential Relays

- Pay no attention to polarity marks.
- Consider the magnitude, but ignore the direction of the transformer phase shift.
- Pay no attention to system phase sequence.
- Fail to consider the no-load tap changer.
- Fail to consider the load-tap changer.
- Fail to consider the nature of the core of the transformer.
- Treat the third transformer winding improperly.
- Fail to examine current mismatch.
- Fail to set the relay to accommodate the mismatch.
- Use the right taps, but the wrong inputs to the taps.
- Fail to use proper inrush restraint.
- Ground the relay circuit improperly.
- Fail to include a proper neutral return circuit.
- For a wye-winding zero sequence differential using a product-type relay, match the current transformer currents exactly.
- Use a generator differential relay.
- Ignore a zigzag grounding bank inside the transformer differential zone.
- Parallel current transformers to avoid suing a multirestraint relay.
- Use a 20:1 auxiliary current transformer.
- Ignore current transformer relaying accuracy class.
- Use one set of differential relays for two transformers and switch them independently.

*(Walt Elmore, ABB. Used with permission.)*

---

## 8.9 Solved Problems

The medium-voltage main-tie-main switchgear arrangement comes up enough in practice that it is worth one last look at the coordination fundamentals. You need to be mindful of the operating configuration of your bulk distribution switchgear—particularly the consequences of operating two transformers in parallel.

**Example 8.7   MVA Class of Medium-Voltage Main-Tie-Main Switchgear**

*Situation.*   The 13.8-kV main-tie-main switchgear lineup in the schematic.

*Requirements.*   Determine the MVA class of the breakers. Let MVA = 100.

**solution**    See Fig. 8.15. We have three impedances in series

$$Z_{tot} = Z_{util} + Z_{line} + Z_{trans} = (1.5 + 5.0 + 0.0) + j(3.2 + 1.5 + 28.0) = 6.5 + j46.2\%$$

$$= \% |Z| = 46.6$$

Note that the transformer impedance had to be converted to the 100-MVA base; thus, $Z_{trans} = 100/25 \ (7\%) = j28\%$.

$I^F$ pu $= 100/46.6 = 2.14$. Therefore, the minimum interrupting rating of the breaker should be $100 \times 2.14 \rightarrow 214$ MVA.

By closing the tie breaker, the transformers operate in parallel, which *halves* the impedance, thereby allowing more fault current to flow into the switchgear.

$$Z_{tr}^{parallel} = j[(28 \times 28)/(28 + 28)] = j14\%$$

$$Z_{total}^{parallel} = (6.5 + 0.0) + j(18.2 + 14.0) = 6.5 + j32.2 = \% |Z| = 32.8$$

$I_{pu}^F = 100/32.8 = 3.05$. Therefore, the minimum interrupting rating of the breakers should be $100 \times 3.05 \rightarrow 305$ MVA.

*Remarks.*    This is a quick and dirty method in common use. The following example is a more rigorous treatment of the problem.

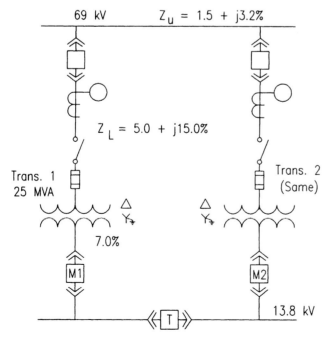

**Figure 8.15**

**Example 8.8 Determine MVA Class of Medium-Voltage Breaker**

*Situation.* The circuit of Fig. 3.2 (refer to Chap. 3).

*Requirements.* Determine short-circuit duty of breakers.

solution All calculations on per-unit basis. 7.5 MVA base.

$$\text{Base Current } I_b = \frac{7.5 \text{ MVA}}{\sqrt{3} \times 6.9 \text{ kV}} = .628 \text{ kA}$$

|  | $X$ | $R$ | $X/R$ |
|---|---|---|---|
| 13.8-kV System |  |  |  |
| $X = \dfrac{.628}{21} \dfrac{(6.9)}{(13.8)} = .015$ | .015 | .001 | 15 |
| *Transformer* | .055 | .0055 | 10 |
| *Total source transf.* | .070 pu | .0065 pu | 11 |

*3000 hp syn. motor*

$$X = .20 \frac{(.628)}{.197} = .638 \text{ pu at 7.5 MVA base}$$

*2500 hp ind. motor*

$$X = .25 \frac{(.628)}{(.173)} = .908 \text{ pu at 7.5 MVA base}$$

$$I_{3\phi} = \frac{E}{X} \text{ or } \frac{I}{X} \text{ where } X \text{ on per-unit base}$$

| Source of short-circuit current | Interrupting $E/X$ amperes | Momentary $E/X$ amperes | $\dfrac{X}{R}$ | $\dfrac{X(1)}{R(X)}$ | $\dfrac{1}{R}$ |
|---|---|---|---|---|---|
| Source transf. | $\dfrac{.628}{.070} = 8.971$ | $\dfrac{.628}{.070} = 8.971$ | 11 | $\dfrac{11}{.070}$ | $=157$ |
| 3000 hp syn. motor | $\dfrac{.628}{(1.5).638} = .656$ | $\dfrac{.628}{.638} = .984$ | 25 | $\dfrac{25}{.638}$ | $=39$ |
| 2500 hp ind. motor | $\dfrac{.628}{(1.5).908} = .461$ | $\dfrac{.628}{.908} = .691$ | 35 | $\dfrac{35}{.908}$ | $=39$ |
|  | $I_{3\phi} = \quad 10.088$ or 10.1 kA | 10.647 $\times 1.6$ 17.0 kA momentary duty | | Total 1/R | $=235$ |

$$\text{Total } X = \frac{I_b}{I_{3\phi}} = \frac{.628}{10.1} = .062$$

System $X/R = .062\,(235) = 14.5$ is mult. factor 1.0 from Table A.3.

Short-circuit duty $= 10.1$ kA

| Manufacturer's Type breaker | V max. | 3 sym. interrupting capability | | @6.9-kV oper. voltage | Close & latch or momentary |
|---|---|---|---|---|---|
| | | @V max. | Max. K1 | | |
| 75VCP-W500 | 8.25 kV | 33 kA | 41 kA | $\dfrac{8.25}{6.9}(33) = 39.5$ kA | 66 kA |
| 150VCP-W500 | 15 kV | 18 kA | 23 kA | $\dfrac{15(18)}{6.9}(39.1) = 23$ kA | 37 kA |
| | | | | (But not to exceed K1) | |

*Remarks.*   Either breaker could be properly applied, but price will make the type 150VCP-W500 the more economical selection. This example is adapted from "Vac Clad-W Medium Voltage Switchgear," Application Guide 32-265, and is used courtesy of Westinghouse-Cutler-Hammer.

It should be clear from the examples given in this chapter that solving the overcurrent protection problem is as rewarding as it is challenging. It is remarkable for its requirement for a combination of deconstructive, analytic thinking and reconstructive, synthetic thinking. In many ways, the overcurrent protection problem is more challenging than the the differential protection problem because of the aspect of the problem that demands that devices be coordinated (thus the title of this book).

As we have noted earlier, overcurrent protection is the backbone of any protection system no matter how high or low the voltage. It should also be clear, however, that unless you are doing overcurrent coordination on a regular basis, you risk making a mistake in (at least) optimization. In particular,

- Your technical library may not have information about CT and/or relay burdens. Example 8.3 was an example in which the rules of thumb for CT selection broke down.

- You may not have access to enough information to determine minimum and maximum fault-current levels.

- With regard to dc saturation of CTs, both the positive and zero-sequence networks will have unique X/R ratios at key points on the network where fault currents must calculated. As we discussed in Chap. 3, you risk blinding a relay with a high X/R ratio.

Here is where relay manufacturers can help you. The rule of the marketplace has resulted in positioning the most knowledgeable protection people on the staffs (or consultants to the staffs) of relay manufacturers. The author knows of no relay manufacturer who is not extremely eager to share application expertise with you, if not train you or completely analyze and engineer the entire protection system for you. It does not make good business sense to do otherwise. Another remarkable aspect of the electric circuit protection industry that the author has found to be generally true is that all the leaders in the protection art in North America and the world at large, most of whom have been cited in this book,* have good things to say about competitor products. Perhaps it is the sublime nature of the protection problem that unites its practitioners. At the very least, this textbook should help you become more sensitive to the fine points of the problem and to help you ask the right questions (and evaluate the work) of a regular practitioner.

Power system analysis and overcurrent coordination software manufacturers could also develop modules that reckon with the tradeoffs in selecting the appropriate CT + relay combination that we demonstrated in Example 8.3. Easy access to libraries of CT excitation curves, relay tap burdens, and control wire impedances would improve the chances for optimal selection if they could be cross-referenced. It would be extremely helpful to semiautomate the analysis of instrument transformer circuits, particularly how such circuits change impedance according to the configuration (single-line-to-ground, line-to-line, double-line-to-ground, etc.) of the fault. It would be extremely useful to apply software modules that guide the electrical designer through all the electric and economic considerations involved in engineering specialty protection circuits—beyond the overcurrent protection circuits discussed in this book. This is a new frontier in computerized protection engineering which would take nothing away from the art of it.

## Bibliography

Application literature for the BE1-50/51M overcurrent relay, Basler Electric, Highland, Ill.

Bergen, A., *Power Systems Analysis,* Prentice-Hall, New York, 1986.

Blackburn, J. L., *Protective Relaying: Principles and Applications,* Marcel Dekker, Inc., New York, 1987.

Dedad, John A., "MV Cable Shielding in Coordination Study, A Must!" *EC&M Magazine,* Jan. 1990.

Elmore, Walt, "Ways to Assure Improper Operation of Transformer Differential Relays," ABB internal memorandum.

Elmore, W. A., S. E. Zocholl, and C. A. Cramer, "Effect of Waveform Distortion on Protective Relays," *Asea-Brown-Boveri Presentation to the Western Protective Relay Conference,* Spokane, Wash., October 23–25, 1990.

Gross, Charles, *Power System Analysis,* John Wiley & Sons, New York, 1986.

Hamer, Paul, and Barry Wood, "Are Cable Shields Being Damaged During Ground Faults?" *IEEE IAS,* Nov./Dec. 1986.

---

* If the author has missed a few, this will be corrected in the next edition.

*Kerite Power Cable Data Catalog 1990,* Hubbel/Kerite Company, Seymour, Conn., 1990.

Linders, J. R., and W. A. Elmore, "Relay Performance Considerations with Low Ratio CT's and High Fault Currents," *IEEE PES Power System Relaying Committee Working Group Report,* 92 SM 382-2 PWRD T-PWRD, July 1993.

Phadke, Arun G., and James S. Thorp, *Computer Relaying for Power Systems,* Research Studies Press, Ltd., Taunton, Somerset, England; John Wiley & Sons, Inc., New York.

Potochney, and Powell, "Application of Protective Relays on a Large Industrial Utility Tie with Industrial Cogeneration," May/June 1983.

Schweitzer, Edmund O., "Where Is Microprocessor-Based Protection Heading?" *Technical paper presented before the 1991 Fall Meeting of the Pennsylvania Electric Association's Relay Committee,* Hershey, Pa., September 11–12, 1991.

Stevenson, W. D., Jr., *Elements of Power Systems Analysis,* 4th ed., McGraw-Hill, New York, 1982.

Westinghouse Engineering Services Division, *Power Systems Coordination, C/E-24,* Westinghouse Electric Corporation, Pittsburgh, Pa.

## General references

"Guide for Protective Relay Applications for Power System Buses," *ANSI C37.97-1979. IEEE Red Book.*

Kresser, J. V., and J. L. Blackburn, "Line Circuit Protection," Chap. 10, *Applied Protective Relaying,* Westinghouse Electric Corporation, 1982.

Li, H. J., "Transformer Protection," Chap. 8, *Applied Protective Relaying,* Westinghouse Electric Corporation, 1982.

Li, H. J., "Station Bus Protection," Chap. 9, *Applied Protective Relaying,* Westinghouse Electric Corporation, 1982.

*Short Circuit Performance of Metallic Shields and Sheaths of Insulated Cable,* 2d ed., ICEA Publication P45-482, South Yarmouth, Maine, August 1979.

## Further reading

Elmore, W. A., "Effect of Waveform Distortion on Protective Relays," *Technical paper presented before the Western Protective Relay Conference,* October 1990.

Enabnit, Jr., Elgin G., "15 Kv Is Still Preferred Distribution Voltage for Larger Utilities," *Transmission and Distribution,* January 1991.

Henville, C. F., "Combined Use of Definite and Inverse Time Overcurrent Elements Assists in Transmission Line Ground Relay Coordination," *IEEE,* July 1993.

Schweitzer, Edmund O., "Practical Benefits of Microprocessor-Based Relaying," *Technical paper presented before the Electric Council of New England, Protective Relaying Committee Meeting No. 55,* Stamford, Conn., May 5, 1989.

"Underground Feeders for Local High-Voltage Distribution," *Consulting/Specifying Engineer,* June 1993.

# Protection and Coordination at the Utility Interconnect

## 9.1 Foreword

Our treatment of the overcurrent coordination problem ends at the consumer-utility interconnect. The treatment we shall discuss is nearly identical to our treatment of overcurrent coordination in earlier chapters except for the fact that we must take into account the obligations utilities have to other customers on your circuit. Some of the complicating factors that you and your local utility have to reckon with as far as protecting your service entrance from the supply side is concerned are the following:

- The existence of circuit reclosers
- Overloading distribution transformers
- Allowing ground faults to remain on delta systems
- High-speed grounding switches
- Operating contingencies at a large scale

When power is purchased in bulk and at medium voltage, the rules are established by the local utility. The switchgear requirements for the consumer-utility interconnect are determined as a matter of policy based on certain types of consumer groups (nongenerators versus generators, for example). The services for the few large commercial or industrial consumers, however, are determined individually. Each group represents a certain range of consumer maximum kilovolt-ampere requirements. A certain conductor size and service entrance box current rating is established for each group, and they are applied to all consumers whose maximum load at the time of installation falls within the kilovolt-ampere range. The equipment sizes and ratings generally permit a certain amount of load growth before their capacity is exceeding or before permissible service voltage drop limitations are exceeded.

## 9.2 Generalized Consumer-Utility Interconnect Protection Scheme

A look at a typical utility subtransmission system (from about 2.4 to 120 kV) would reveal that overcurrent devices are applied in fairly predictable patterns:

- circuit breaker + fuse
- circuit breaker + circuit breaker + fuse
- circuit breaker + recloser + fuse
- circuit breaker + recloser + sectionalizer

The path from the utility substation to your utility interconnect may involve a series of overcurrent devices such as circuit breaker + sectionalizer + recloser + sectionalizer + fuse, etc., until it is terminated at your switchgear (which you may, or may not, own). In urban areas, where lines are relatively short and the possibilities of faults are rather small, subtransmission lines are divided into three or four sections and protected by single-pole fused cutouts. In suburban or rural areas, the subtransmission lines may be quite long and prone to frequent overhead disturbances. Reclosers and sectionalizers are applied in tandem to remedy coordination problems that result from the lack of sufficient coordination time between fuses or circuit breakers applied in series.

A large part of the following discussion has been adapted from the following ANSI/IEEE standards that deal with consumer-utility interconnection protection:

- ANSI/IEEE Standard C37.95-1973 *Guide for Protective Relaying of Utility-Consumer Interconnections*
- ANSI/IEEE Standard 242-1986, *IEEE Recommended Practice for Protection and Coordination of Industrial and Commercial Power Systems*

Most utilities have design guidelines for electrical designers that detail the requirements for electrical service connection to the utility system. The reader is encouraged to seek these references in their original form.

Figure 9.1 represents a grouping of protective schemes that appears in ANSI/IEEE Standard 242 to which we shall refer throughout our discussion. It features single-feed customer-owned main-tie-main switchgear with generation on one bus. The cluster of protective devices that protect the generator is indicated as Group F. We will not discuss this group in any depth in this text. The cluster of protective devices that protect the plant feeders is indicated as Group E. We have discussed the protection schemes in this group in earlier chapters. In this chapter we will dwell principally on the protective devices of Groups A through D.

### 9.2.1   Utility supply: Group A

You should have some idea of where your utility feeders are coming from geographically as well as electrically, especially if you are either a

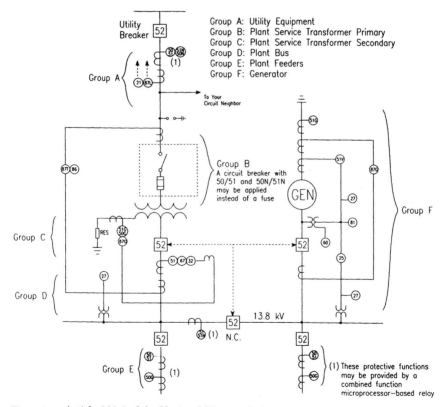

**Figure 9.1**   Article 230-2 of the National Electric Code indicates that a building shall be served by only one service and that the service overcurrent device be an integral part of the service disconnecting means. The exceptions to this rule recognize switchgear capacity limitations, redundancy in emergency circuits, buildings of large area or multiple-building facilities, and differences in voltage. (*Adapted from IEEE Std. 242. Used with permission.*)

large customer, a cogenerator, or both. Knowledge of who your utility circuit partners are may help you explain outages even though you may have little control over them.

The protective equipment is usually on utility premises at a bulk distribution switching station. At the very least, you will have utility phase and ground overcurrent devices protecting the feeder to your plant. As indicated in earlier chapters, the more inverse relays may be used when coordination with fuses is needed or when it is required to ride over high inrush currents upon restoration of power after a service outage. (See Fig. 1.3.) Instantaneous elements may be applied when there is a chance that they will coordinate with your own instantaneous relay elements. When instantaneous elements are applied, they are set high enough so that they do not detect faults beyond about 80 percent of the distance to the next load-side overcurrent device.

Other devices that may exist at the utility switching station feeding your plant may include distance relays (Device 21) and line-pilot relays (Device 87L). Line-pilot relays are based on the differential principle and apply telemetry to communicate with both ends of the subtransmission or distribution line to your plant. If you are a cogenerator, it is more likely that you actually own (or at least have purchased) the line-pilot telemetry equipment that is installed at the upstream utility distribution switching station.

### 9.2.2   Service entrance: Group B

Where service entrance relaying is applied, it normally operates the main interrupting device. There are several schemes that can be applied to open the utility supply circuit breaker with Group A when there is no transformer protection circuit breaker and the fault currents are not sufficient to operate the relays of Group A. This is accomplished by employing transferred tripping schemes through the use of pilot wire, grounding switches, or power-line carrier audio tone or microwave signals.

Typical protective devices are as follows:

- *Overcurrent phase and ground-fault relays (Devices 50/51 and 50N/51N).*   Instantaneous phase-overcurrent relay settings for utility distribution feeders are usually set as low as possible considering, among other things, cold load pickup as discussed in Chap. 1. The instantaneous function (50) is frequently omitted to be selective with customer feeder relays having the instantaneous function.

- *Directional phase-overcurrent relay (Device 67).*   When applied for tie line protection, they look into the utility systems and detect faults on incoming lines, thus preventing overloading of in-plant generators and parallel lines. Also, their directional selectivity allows for sensitive settings that would not be possible with overcurrent relays.

- *Directional overcurrent ground-fault relays (Device 67N).*  These are applied in addition to directional phase-overcurrent relays (Device 67) for the complete protection of incoming lines in grounded systems. However, when supply transformers are involved, these relays (Device 67N) are considered optional in view of the reduced ground-fault possibility and possible use of ground relays (nondirectional) (Device 51N or 51G), which will operate to clear the ground fault. Also Device 67N requires polarization, and added cost of polarization is not justified.

- *Ground-fault detector relay (Device 64).*  This may be needed to clear a supply line ground-fault by disconnecting the supply line at the consumer end. This situation can occur when there are parallel supply lines or in-plant generator, and the utility end is opened by overcurrent relays. The system ground is thus removed and the supply line is then operating as a normally ungrounded system. An over- and undervoltage relay connected to the line-to-ground voltage transformer or an overvoltage relay connected to the broken delta secondary of three line-to-ground voltage transformers can be applied. Alternately, a sensitive power directional relay (Device 32) may accomplish the same purpose.

- *Consumer terminal of pilot relay systems (Device 87L).*  This can be applied to trip the service entrance circuit breakers as well as the utility supply circuit breakers.

### 9.2.3  Supply transformer primary protection: Group C

- *Overcurrent phase and ground-fault relays (Device 50/51 and 50N/51N).*  Instantaneous ground-fault relays (Device 50G) should be connected to core-balanced (ground-sensor) type current transformers for best results, although they can be applied with conventional current transformers in a residual connection with Relay 50N with good results on solidly grounded systems.

- *Transformer differential relays (Device 87T).*  These differential relays are arranged to cause both the primary and secondary circuit switching devices to trip and lock out through a lockout relay (Device 86). Differential protection is almost universally applied to large (above 5000 kVA) or important transformers when a primary circuit breaker or circuit switcher is applied. Harmonic restraint relays are applied to allow greater sensitivity and yet not operate on magnetizing inrush currents.

- *Pressure relays (Device 63).*    These are applicable to all transformers that have a sealed gas chamber above the oil level. They are more sensitive than differential relays for internal faults and are particularly useful for faults in tap-changing equipment. They can be applied in place of or in conjunction with transformer differential relays.

- *Transformer temperature protective devices (49).*    These are usually provided with all large oil-filled and dry-type power transformers. These devices are indicated for overload protection and in many applications merely annunciate the condition and/or activate cooling apparatus.

### 9.2.4  Supply transformer secondary protection: Group D

Basic protection here includes the following:

- *Overcurrent relays (51).*    These are required to protect against bus faults and to back up the in-plant feeder overcurrent relays. Where there is a primary circuit breaker with associated overcurrent relays, it is possible to eliminate these relays at the secondary circuit breaker without a great sacrifice in protection. Instantaneous attachments (50) cannot be applied here successfully without loss of selectivity between main and feeder relaying. Therefore, if high-speed protection against bus faults is desired, bus differential relays (87B) should be applied. Residually connected overcurrent ground relays (51N) are not needed because the transformer neutral ground relay 51G, described in the following paragraph, is more effective.

- *Transformer neutral ground relay 51G.*    This is connected in the grounded neutral lead of the transformer secondary. This relay is very sensitive and will back up feeder ground-fault relays. This relay usually trips the secondary breaker. A time-delay relay may be connected in series that will be activated at the same time to trip the primary breaker 62P if the fault continues after set time delay (1 to 2.5 s). This additional time-delay relay will protect the windings and terminals from ground faults. It is the only protection against bus ground faults when bus differential relays are not specified. A high-set 50G can provide additional protection for turn to ground faults in the transformer secondary winding. In a resistance-grounded system, the transformer differential relay sensitivity may be such as to be unable to recognize the low side-line-to-ground fault. In such cases, differential ground relay scheme 87G should be applied.

- *Directional overcurrent phase and ground relays 67/67N.*    These can be useful in those dual-service arrangements where the dual services are exclusively connected to a single consumer. Installation with in-plant generator utilizes directional relaying at this location to clear fault in the supply transformer from in-plant generator and bus sources.

■ *Directional power relay 32.*    These can be applied to disconnect the incoming line and the supply transformer upon utility tie loss in case of parallel operation or when there is an in-plant generator. For example, a sensitive relay can detect core power loss when the transformer is reverse magnetized from the secondary side.

The probability of an internal fault in a substation transformer is so small that many utility companies can justify deenergizing an entire subtransmission circuit should such a fault occur. In these cases, no protective device is installed at the distribution substation. There are several methods that are indicated to trip the circuit breaker at the subtransmission substation. In a few cases, the relays controlling this breaker can be set to recognize the minimum fault current for internal faults in distribution substations that are relatively close to the sub-transmission substation.

If the minimum fault current for such a fault is below the pickup setting of the relay, some other method must be applied to trip the circuit breaker on the subtransmission circuit. One method is the use of a grounding switch at the distribution substation. Upon operation of the transformer differential relays or sudden pressure relays, the grounding switch is closed to place a line-to-ground fault on the subtransmission circuit that will be recognized by the relays at the subtransmission substation.

Generically, these schemes are referred to as transfer trip schemes. You may recognize them by their use of pilot-wire relaying, audio tone, or microwave equipment.

## 9.3    Single-Feed Service

### 9.3.1    Single Service With Primary Fuse

The general aspect of reliability in the North American electrical power grid and the availability of high-quality switchgear makes single-feed service a perfectly reasonable and economical choice for a large class of bulk electric power consumers. Protection engineering has advanced to a state in which it need not be the principal determinant in the selection of service configuration or even the principal determinant in overall switchgear operating economics. In other words, do not let a protection wizard convince you that protection problems at your utility interconnect are so severe that you need to build more electric switchgear than you actually need. Services should be designed on the basis of initial and long-term economic aspects with protection engineering coming afterward—not the other way around. The electric power circuit protection art, while certainly not shy of personalities and individualized approaches, has evolved to such a state that any switchgear can be economically protected within the limits of what an electrical consumer can afford.

Let us begin our discussion of overcurrent coordination with a look at one of the simplest nonresidential consumer-utility interconnects. Refer to Fig. 9.2. The power fuse applied on the primary side of the transformer in a distribution substation must have time-current characteristics such that it will coordinate with both the circuit breaker on the secondary side of the transformer and the subtransmission circuit breaker, and protect the transformer in the case of an internal fault. Proper coordination with these devices usually will preclude the recognition of an overload condition by the primary fuse. If the circuit is to be opened on overload, it is the function of the device on the secondary side of the transformer to recognize the overload and open the circuit.

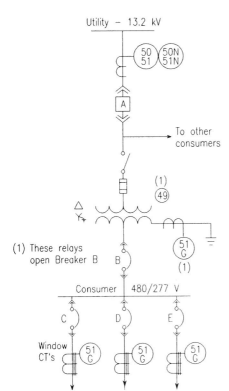

**Figure 9.2** This is the basic consumer-utility interconnect for a single service. It complies with the overcurrent protection requirements of Article 230—Part G (which actually refers you back further to Article 240 for fuse size and circuit-breaker setting). If you are buying power at 600 V or less and your load requirement exceeds 2000 A, the National Electric Code permits you to add a second service.

**Example 9.1  Protection for Customer-Owned Category III Transformer**  The schematic of Fig. 9.3 indicates that the customer owns a 12/16/20 MVA transformer with 10 percent impedance. This is a Category III transformer according to ANSI/IEEE C37.91. Transformers of this size typically have three ratings. We shall use the rating at maximum load. On the primary, and ambient rating on the secondary. Primary current is:

$$\frac{20,000}{\sqrt{3} \times 115} = 100.4 \text{ at } 115 \text{ kV}$$

On the secondary, the full-load current will be

$$\frac{12,000}{\sqrt{3} \times 12.5} = 554.26 \text{ at } 12.5 \text{ kV}$$

With the 10 percent impedance, the maximum three-phase bolted fault current on the secondary will be

$$\frac{1.0}{0.1} \times 554.26 = 5542.6 \text{ A}$$

To protect this transformer, the following devices have been selected:

- 100:5 current transformers applied at the primary
- Very inverse overcurrent relays set on tap 8 and thereby pickup at $8 \times 100/5 = 160$ primary A (or 1472 secondary A)
- The pickup of these relays for secondary phase-to-ground faults would be $1472/0.577 = 2551$ A
- The 12.5-kV feeders and transformer neutral have 300:5 current transformers with phase- and ground-fault pickups shown in Fig. 9.3.

This transformer bank is protected for through three-phase faults but not for secondary phase-to-ground faults. Differential and thermal protection is recommended for primary protection with overcurrent relays considered as the backup protection.

This example is adapted from the application examples indicated in the Appendix of ANSI/IEEE C37.91-1985. This standard and ANSI/IEEE C57.109 contain the bulk of the rules for transformer overcurrent protection. These rules have undergone considerable refinement in the past ten years as protection specialists engaged in dialog with transformer designers. While it is possible to apply the transformer damage curves by simply tracing the appropriate curves provided in the Appendix (overcurrent coordination software makes it even easier), it is instructive to refer to the ANSI application guidelines for further discussion of infrequent-frequent fault incidence zones and Category IV transformers. A student of the subject of transformer overcurrent protection will find in these standards a full complement of $I^2t$ curves, K factors, and assorted application caveats.

### 9.3.2  Single service with relayed secondary breaker

There is nothing in the rules that says you cannot apply a standard induction disk or microprocessor-based time-overcurrent relay on a

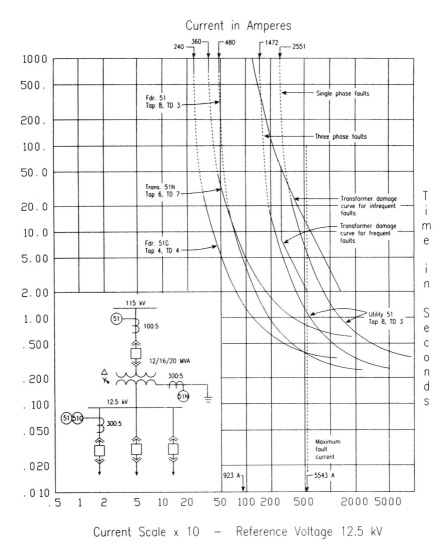

**Figure 9.3** The 115-kV primary-side overcurrent device, assumed to be near the transformer, will see only 58 percent of any single-line-to-ground fault current that flows into a fault on the secondary side. Thus, if we want to reflect the time-current tripping characteristic of the transformer primary breaker through the transformer, we need to multiply the primary pickup current times the transformer turns ratio times 1/0.58. This results in the primary breaker tripping characteristic shifting to the *right* by 1.732 × 160 × (115/12.5) = 2551 A for single-line-to-ground faults. This adjustment results in the observation that the transformer primary breaker does not protect the transformer for all frequent single-line-to-ground faults (possibly up to the maximum three-phase fault-current level) or even for all levels of infrequent fault-current levels. The unprotected condition might be improved somewhat with the selection of a transformer with a lower impedance, but this may compromise other aspects of the protection strategy. Sensitive settings with fast operation are usually not possible with overcurrent relays—particularly for internal faults—and differential protection is usually indicated.

low-voltage circuit as long as you follow the NEC low-voltage overcurrent protection rules covered in previous chapters. Where budgets allow, the combined application of a primary fuse and a secondary main breaker results in reasonably fast protection for both minimum and maximum fault currents as the following example indicates.

**Example 9.2    Single Service with Relayed Secondary Breaker**    See Figs. 9.4 and 9.5.

The primary fuse must carry at least transformer full-load current and must withstand the magnetizing inrush current of 10 to 12 times full load for 0.1 s.

The 125E primary fuse ought to be able to open for both the three-phase and the reflected phase-to-ground faults on the secondary side of the transformer. One way of reckoning with this requirement is the following:

Given that the transformer and secondary cable impedance result in a fault current of 29,000 A at the service bus, we can estimate that a single-line-to-ground arcing fault will be (at its minimum) 38 percent of the three-phase bolted fault

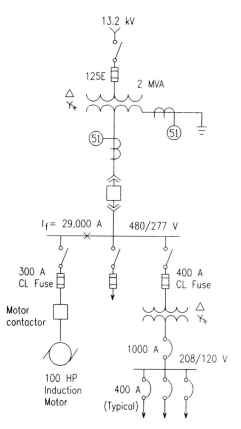

**Figure 9.4**  Article 230-208 contains the rules for overcurrent protection for services exceeding 600 V. Item 230-208(d) deals with the particulars when the service protection involves a medium-voltage circuit breaker. In general, circuit breakers shall not trip at current levels any greater than six times the ampacity of the service conductors. In this example, the full-load ampere rating of the service transformer is 2404 A, so, assuming that the service conductors are sized correctly, the secondary relay pickup of 6000 A is within the limit established by the NEC. Where fuses are applied, they shall not open at current levels any greater than three times the ampacity of the service conductor.

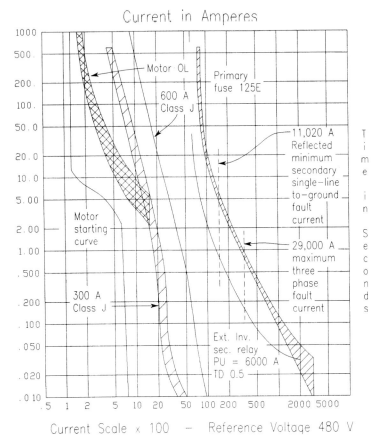

**Figure 9.5** Coordination study for Example 9.2. The current transformer + relay combination on the transformer neutral provides ground-fault protection required by the NEC. Coordinated instantaneous (short-circuit) protection may be possible if there is sufficient impedance between the consumer and the utility overcurrent devices. Much depends upon the actual construction particulars of the interconnect.

value (refer to discussion on arcing faults in Chap. 4), then the current at the fault would be

$$.38 \times 29,000 = 11,020 \text{ A at } 480 \text{ V}$$

Of course this is not the current the primary fuse will see. Through a Δ-Y transformer, this secondary current will be reflected into the primary as

$$\frac{11,020 \times .57 \times (480)}{(13200)} = 228 \text{ A}$$

Although it appears by the E-rating of the primary fuse that a secondary arcing fault will open the primary fuse "eventually," in about 5 s, the primary fuse may not open soon enough to avoid permanent transformer damage, hence, the secondary relayed breaker that will clear the fault in less than 1 s.

The motor is protected by the thermal overcurrent devices in the motor controller. The Class J current-limiting fuse provides short-circuit protection for the contactor and motor insulation.

The lighting transformer is protected by a fuse sized to carry the full load of the transformer. The secondary and breaker circuits are protected with magnetic circuit breakers (Smeaton, 1987).

## 9.4    Dual-Feed Service

The trend has been toward more dual-feed services because of so many mission-critical loads. Sometimes the duality refers to two independent utility circuits with one customer transformer. One circuit may be more reliable than another, such as one overhead and another underground. In a few cases, the duality refers to a single utility interconnect with two customer transformers.

The issue of dual service is frequently complicated by the cost of the second service. In many local jurisdictions, there are additional charges levied upon a second service.

### 9.4.1    Dual-feed service with single transformer

In Fig. 9.6, two independent transmission lines serve the single transformer substation. When economics permit, a second transformer should be provided. This kind of service is common in government facilities that are owned by the federal government (such as Veteran's Administration Hospitals) and, unlike the regulations that apply to private hospitals, is considered to be redundant service even though there is only one transformer.

The load bus will be subjected to a voltage dip during a fault. Bus voltage returns to normal as soon as a fault located on the utility side of circuit breakers A and B is cleared. However, service will be interrupted when clearing faults that occur between circuit breakers A and B or in the transformer.

High-speed relaying has been installed on the transmission lines to detect faults and isolate the faulted line.

Relays that control feeder circuit breakers D, E, and F must be coordinated with those on the main circuit breaker C, and relays that control the main circuit breaker C must be coordinated with the overcurrent relays on the high side of the transformer bank and with the overcurrent relay in the grounded neutral.

The reliability of power at the load may be increased by adding a second transformer and a second low-side bus tied to the first bus as suggested above.

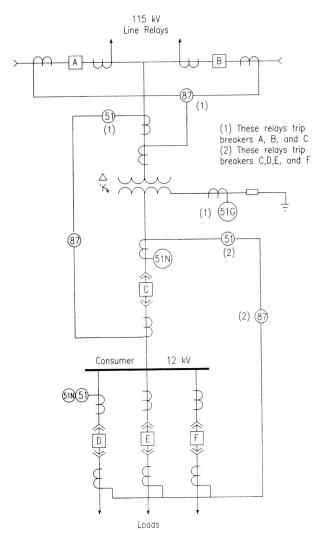

**Figure 9.6** Facilities that require more than one service are generally a mixture of continuous, batch process, and a few mission-critical loads that require backfeeding to permit riding through a major system disturbance. A few seconds of outage for many loads may not produce a critical situation; therefore, the choice of a service design and the related protection systems may emphasize rapid restoration of service rather than providing (frequently costly) uninterruptible service.

### 9.4.2  Dual service *without* transformation

In the service configuration of Fig. 9.7 one service circuit breaker or interrupter switch (sometimes called a circuit switcher) may be normally open and the other service circuit breaker or interrupter switch normally closed. The reasons for not operating in parallel in this instance are to minimize the short-circuit duty on the plant bus and to eliminate the need for directional relays (Device 67). Automatic transfer (Device 27) should be delayed to coordinate for faults on other portions of the system. The voltage will be depressed when a fault occurs until a circuit breaker or fuse opens to clear it.

Because of the setting requirement placed by the utility on the overcurrent, relays for circuit breakers may be difficult to obtain. Overcurrent blocking is applied to lock out both source lines in the event of a bus fault or a lack of coordination with fuses protecting the feeder circuit. Selectivity would depend on the instantaneous overcurrent relay (Device 50), tripping only the feeder circuit breaker for feeder faults.

### 9.4.3  Dual service *with* transformation

We shall discuss two schemes involving two customer-owned transformers fed by two independent utility lines.

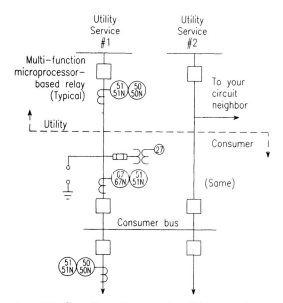

**Figure 9.7**  Sometimes the cost of a reliable second service requires that the protection strategies differ for each service interconnect. For example, some dual services have one overhead line and one underground service feeder.

- Without primary bus tie (Fig. 9.8)
- With primary bus tie (Fig. 9.11)

We need to pay particular attention to how far upstream from the customer switchgear the services are operated in parallel.

**Dual service *without* primary bus tie.**   Relaying shown in Fig. 9.8 is described for only one half of the system. Identical relaying (not shown) exists on the second half of this system.

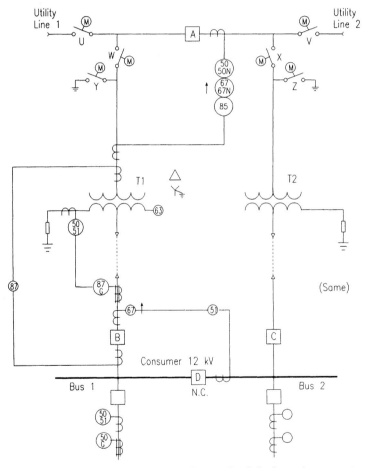

**Figure 9.8**  Consumers that require that each of dual services operate "independently" may encounter situations in which the protection strategies will differ enough to require significantly different trip settings on the service entrance switchgear to compensate for the different transient behaviors of overhead and underground subtransmission circuits.

Phase and ground faults on Line 1 will cause circuit breakers A and B to trip. Line 2 and the secondary transformer continue to supply uninterrupted power. Reclosing relays at circuit breaker A and the remote line terminal will automatically reenergize the line. If the fault is clear, it remains energized. Closing circuit breaker B, which may be done manually or automatically, will restore the power system to its normal condition. If the fault is permanent, as evidenced by an unsuccessful recloser, the motorized disconnect switch U will open automatically and isolate the faulted line section before circuit breaker A can reclose a second time.

Faults in the transformer or in the low-voltage cable may be detected by one or more of the following: Device (63), Device (87), Devices (50/51), or Devices (51G, 87G). They initiate opening circuit breakers A and B directly. They also initiate the opening of the remote circuit breakers on Line 1 by closing grounding switch Y. The faulted equipment can be isolated by opening disconnect W and circuit breaker B. Transmission Line 1 may then be reclosed to provide dual feed to the remaining transformer. Device (67) provides backup protection by detecting current flowing into transformers through circuit breaker B. Partial differential relay (51) will clear faults on bus 1 by opening circuit breakers B and D. Also, it serves as a feeder overcurrent backup device.

Each feeder is protected with Devices (50/51) and Device (50G). The feeder breakers are coordinated with circuit breakers B and D. The presence of grounding resistors in the transformer neutrals requires special attention to the differential relays that may not be sensitive enough to detect ground faults in the transformer cables. A "window" current transformer that encircles the incoming cables has been installed and connected to a sensitive ground differential relay (87G). The location of this current transformer leaves a blind spot in the ground differential relay zone between the cable termination and the circuit breaker. Therefore, an additional ground time-overcurrent backup relay (51G) is required to cover this area. The ground differential relays trip the same circuit breakers as their associated transformer of cable differential relays. The backup ground relay (51G) is connected to trip the bus-tie breaker D with sufficient delay to coordinate with feeder ground relays (50G), and then additional fixed times are added to trip the incoming circuit breaker and, finally, to trip the transformer differential relay. This three-step tripping sequence provides backup protection, respectively, for feeder faults, bus faults, the blind spot, and the transformer ground-differential relay. Feeder ground protection is provided by window current transformers that energize instantaneous overcurrent relays (50G).

**Example 9.3   Dual Service with Consumer-Owned Transformers and Emergency Generation**   Refer to Fig. 9.9 and 9.10. This example will show how load current can limit the effectiveness of the protection system.

*Situation.*   In the system of Fig. 9.9, we have two consumer-owned transformers with secondary automatic transfer and a limited amount of on-site emergency generation. The transformer secondary, the tie breaker, and the emergency-generator breaker are all electrically interlocked to "break before make." The feeder breakers have direct-acting trip devices and are manually operated. All critical loads are served from one bus that has an emergency generator that will start if both incoming lines are open. If voltage at one of the incoming lines returns (confirmed by a voltage-sensing relay), the generator is shut down, and the load is automatically returned to normal utility source.

*Requirements.*   Specify and coordinate all overcurrent devices given primary SCA = 1300 A.

*Solution.*   Given that the utility has 1300 A available at the 13.2-kV primary service drop, and your own transformers have 5.75 percent impedance, then total impedance to the secondary bus is (on 10,000-kVA base):

$$\frac{10,000 \text{ kVA}}{13.2 \text{ kV} \times 1300 \times 1.732} = 0.337 = z_1^{\text{utl}} \text{ pu}$$

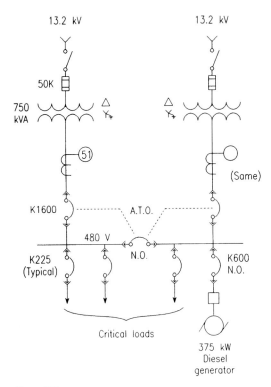

**Figure 9.9**

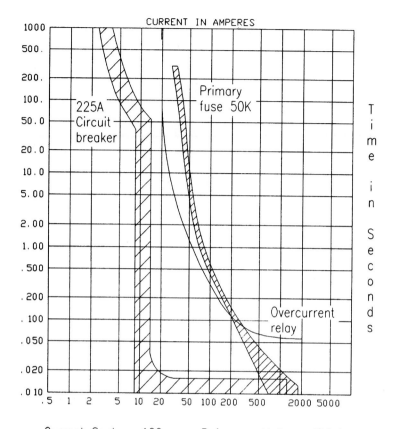

Current Scale x 100 — Reference Voltage 480 V

**Figure 9.10**

$$0.0575 \times \frac{10,000}{750} = 0.766 = z_1^{\text{tr}} \text{ pu}$$

$$z_1^{\text{total}} = 0.337 + 0.765 = 1.102 \text{ pu}$$

Letting $z_1 = z_2$, then

$$z_1 + z_2 + z_0 = 1.102 + 1.102 + 0.765 = 2.969 \text{ pu}$$

$$I_B = \frac{10,000}{\sqrt{3} \times 13.2} = 437.5 \text{ A}$$

$$437.4 \times \frac{13,200}{480} \cong 12,000 \text{ at } 480 \text{ V}$$

$$\text{Secondary } I_{3\phi} = \frac{1.0}{1.102} \times 12{,}000$$

$$\text{Then secondary } 3I_0 = \frac{3\,(12{,}000)}{2.969} = 12{,}100 \text{ A}$$

$$\text{Reflected secondary } 3I_0 = \frac{(\sqrt{3})(437.5)}{2.969} = 255 \text{ A}$$

The 750-kVA transformers are fed from 50K universal fuse links mounted on the cable poles. These fuses provide adequate protection for phase and phase-to-ground faults on the secondary of the transformers. The fuse size (50K) was chosen to be able to sense the reflected secondary phase-to-ground fault, but the 50K restricts the permissible loading to less than twice transformer nameplate. The fuse curve also restricts the secondary overcurrent relay setting. Another fuse with a slower time-current characteristic could have been used to provide more coordination clearance between the fuse and the secondary overcurrent relay but at a much greater expense. If a larger-ampacity universal fuse link is used, some form of a transfer trip is required.

Since there are not large synchronous motors connected to this service, the low-voltage or single-phase sensing device for the automatic transfer scheme can be a three-phase undervoltage relay. A negative sequence voltage relay with sufficient time delay could be used to initiate the automatic transfer if motor back-feed presents any problems.

The total clearing time curve of a 50K fuse at 100 s = 120 A with 255 A available for a bolted fault. The fuse will protect for secondary phase-to-ground faults. There must be at least 200 A of available fault current for adequate protection. The maximum loading is limited by the overcurrent relay pickup setting adjusted by a suitable safety factor to ensure that load current will not cause any unwanted tripping. One such factor of safety is 80 percent, but it could be any depending on the sensibility of the engineer. The loadability will be 80 percent of the relay pickup current. This factor limits the load to 1280 A ($0.8 \times 1600$) or 1065.

The setting cannot be made larger because the primary fuse size is limited to 50K to ensure clearing for secondary phase-to-ground faults. If the available primary short-circuit current were higher, larger primary fuses and, hence, higher overcurrent relay settings would allow higher total loads to be carried on one incoming line under emergency conditions (Smeaton, 1987).

**Dual service *with* primary bus tie.**    We assume that both tie breakers are closed. With this arrangement, the plant is protected not only from the loss of supply line but also against the failure of a primary bus or one transformer. The secondary sides of both transformers are tied together through a normally closed tie breaker or switch. This scheme could also be provided with an automatic transfer on the primary side of the transformer by closing the tie breaker or switch after the fault is cleared when one of the lines is faulted. A fault in the transformer and on the secondary side of the transformer is seen by one or more of the following protective devices:

---

## Transfer Considerations in Standby Generator Applications

When disconnected from the utility, large motors generate a residual internal voltage which is initially the same as the preinterruption value because the magnetic flux in the core as well as the rotor speed cannot change instantaneously. The residual voltage is reduced in magnitude and its frequency decays as the magnetic energy in the motor gradually dissipates due to losses. Reconnection of the motor to the power bus after a short delay can cause dangerously high transient torques and currents in the motor. The damage may not be apparent at first but it is cumulative over a number of out-of-phase reclosures and often results in collateral failures (such as single-line-to-ground insulation failure) which hide the original cause.

There are three methods to prevent problems associated with high-speed open-transition retransfers:

- Complete the retransfer before the internal motor residual voltage has time to fall less than 80 degrees behind the reconnected source voltage.
- Provide an OFF delay during the transfer to permit the residual voltages to decay to levels of 20 percent of normal, which will be safe regardless of closing angle and to allow time to trip off synchronous motors
- Delay closing into the alternate source until the first available in-phase condition detected by synchronizing relays.

*(Ref. Nochumson and Schwartzburg.)*

---

- Sudden pressure relay (Device 63)
- Transformer differential relay (Device 87T)
- Overcurrent relays (Device 51)
- Ground relays (Devices 51G and 87G)

Directional overcurrent relay (Device 67) provides backup protection by looking at current flowing to the transformer from the low-voltage side. Partial differential relaying is provided for only the source buses, using an overcurrent relay with time delay (Device 51). The relays protecting the feeders or circuits are not in the differential scheme. This scheme provides protection against bus faults and isolates the faulted section by opening secondary breakers or switches. Transformer differential relay should be considered for transformers of 5000 kVA or more.

When a tie circuit breaker or switch is normally closed, special relaying may be necessary to allow for the possibility of circulating current between bus sections.

If the system of Fig. 9.11 is operated with either primary or secondary bus tie device normally closed, faults on the utility system are normally cleared by the customer's protective devices. In order to secure continuity of service to your circuit partners, the setting and calibration of your protective equipment will probably need to be done with close cooperation with your local utility.

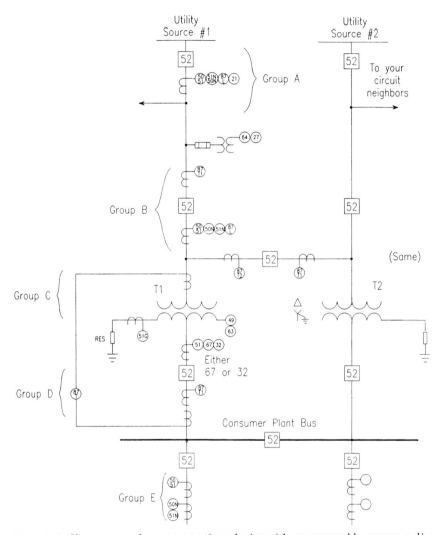

**Figure 9.11**  You may complement protective relaying with programmable process and/or circuit controllers so that when faults occur you may initiate an orderly shutdown of systems or opening circuits capable of adding fault current into the distribution system. Your supervisory system should be superimposed upon a conventional protective scheme (without replacing existing fuses or circuit breakers) unless you can start from scratch with one of the distribution control systems now on the market.

**Example 9.4   Dual Service Operated in Parallel**   Since the tie breaker shown in Fig. 9.12 is closed, the two 120/13.2-kV service transformers are operated in parallel. This requires careful consideration by the protection specialist.

The 120-kV lines are protected by pilot-wire differential relaying using metallic wires between the various terminals. There is also a transfer trip scheme on this pilot wire for use with the transformer protection.

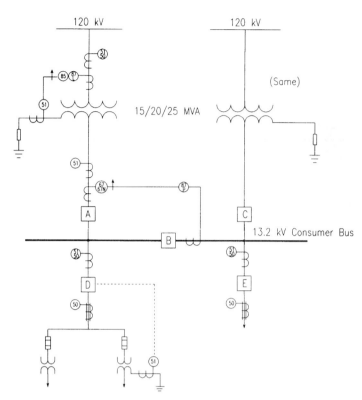

**Figure 9.12** Bus tie circuits within the same lineup of switchgear, including two incoming lines, are frequently specified without overcurrent protection relays. When overcurrent protection is provided for this type of circuit, relays are connected in a summation overcurrent connection. The application of this scheme provides the opportunity for selectivity between main or tie breakers and feeder breakers minimizing relay operating time delay.

The main power transformers, which are resistance-grounded, are protected with primary phase and neutral overcurrent relays, a fault pressure device, and an overcurrent relay in the transformer neutral-to-ground connection. All these devices initiate a transfer tripping function to the remote line terminal. The transformer neutral-overcurrent relay also trips the transformer secondary breaker.

The phase relays (67) are backup for the 120-kV line relaying, and the neutral relay is necessary for relay-relay coordination with the neutral overcurrent relay (51) on the other transformer for ground faults between the transformer and its secondary breaker.

The phase (51) overcurrent relays on the transformer secondary are somewhat redundant but do provide backup protection should the bus partial differential (87P) relays fail to function.

The 13.2-kV buses are protected by a partial bus-differential or bus-overcurrent scheme that acts as the feeder breaker backup as well as the bus protection. These relays operate to open the transformer secondary breaker involved and the normally closed tie breaker. If the tie breaker is open, the partial differential relays act as transformer overcurrent relays.

The feeder breakers D and E serve several fused transformers that are connected Δ-Y grounded. The reflected secondary phase-to-ground fault does not produce sufficient current for phase fuses to operate reliably. A neutral overcurrent relay is sufficient current for the phase fuses to operate reliably. A neutral overcurrent relay is indicated to sense the secondary phase-to-ground fault, and the tripping function is transferred to the feeder breaker.

The zero-sequence device and the instantaneous relay operate to provide very sensitive ground-fault protection on the feeder.

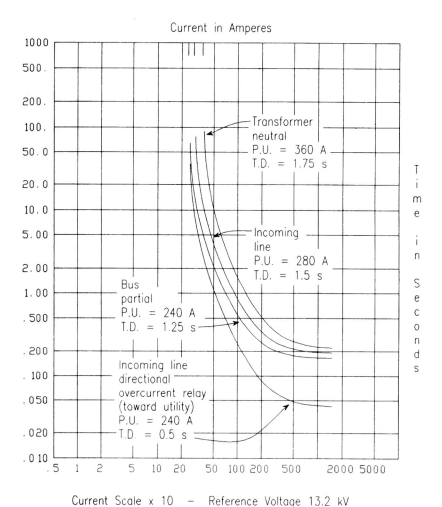

**Figure 9.13** Plots of ground or neutral protective devices *only* for utility interconnect of Fig. 9.12.

*Phase protection coordination.* The primary overcurrent relay must be selective in terms of pickup and time with the transformer secondary overcurrent relay. Under normal operating situations, since the two transformers are operated in parallel, the primary relay must coordinate with the partial differential relays with an ample coordination time interval.

For the situation in which one main transformer unit is out of service and a fault occurs on the bus normally served by the missing transformer, the load is carried through the tie switch. The partial differential on this bus now acts as an *overcurrent relay.* To save the load on both buses, the partial differential relays must be coordinated *below* the incoming line relays at the magnitude of current available from one transformer.

For faults on a feeder just off the bus, adequate selectivity must be maintained. Feeder breaker relay curves must operate first before the partial differential relay. The instantaneous element helps to achieve the necessary coordination by cutting short the feeder inverse time curve.

Appropriate coordination time intervals among instantaneous devices (discussed in Chap. 3) should be observed.

The directional overcurrent relay should coordinate with the incoming line relay of the *opposite* transformer (discussed in Chap. 8). The short time dial setting should be set to get as fast a trip as possible for faults in the transformer or the secondary cable so that the system's disturbance is kept to a minimum.

*Neutral protection coordination.* Similar arguments may be applied to coordinating the neutral and ground relays shown in Fig. 9.13.

## 9.5  Typical Service Configurations with Local Generation

The subject of cogeneration protection systems has been very well covered by engineers working on behalf of utilities and electrical customers. It is fair to say that we are likely to see more independent power generators rather than less—at least for a while. The reader is encouraged to seek the references and/or attend a technical seminar for more depth on the subject of local generation. For now, the following examples should provide you enough information to at least be able to ask a few helpful questions from the experts.

There are at least two types of service contracts that could be indicated when on-site generation is involved. The on-site generation is normally running and operating in parallel, backfeeding into the grid.

The other method would not allow any backfeed into the utility systems except for momentary swings for disturbances on the utility systems.

The 1978 public utility regulatory policies act required electric utilities to interconnect with independently owned generating plants. This act has brought about widespread interest in the unlimited backfeed service contract.

**Example 9.6    Single Service with Consumer Generation**    The local generation is connected to the same bus as the interconnection transformer. The transformer in Fig. 9.14 has a low-side circuit breaker and a motor-operated disconnect switch on the high side. In the device option box, the transformer has circuit breakers on both sides. In both systems, assume the local generator is insufficient to carry total load. Therefore, noncritical loads may be shed whenever the interconnection is opened. This can be done either manually or automatically. Much will depend on the generator control system and the governor.

The distance relays are set to reach through the transformer into the utilities' 115-kV transmission line and trip circuit breakers A and B. Ground faults on the utility system will be detected by zero-sequence ground voltage relay 59 connected to the transformer bushing-type potential devices. These devices are backed up with undervoltage 27 and underfrequency relays.

The overcurrent relays in the differential current transformer circuit encompassing the power transformer and circuit breaker A must be coordinated with the overcurrent relays connected to circuit breaker A bussing current transformers.

Relays on feeder breakers B and D must coordinate with the relays on the main circuit breaker A and the local generator breaker C for all possible operating conditions that include

- Generator only connected to the 12-kV bus
- Transformer bank only connected to the 12-kV bus
- Generator and transformer connected to the 12-kV bus

**Example 9.7    Dual Service with Two Feeds Operating in Parallel with On-Site Generation and Backfeed Allowed**    The system in Fig. 9.15 has a two-line service from the utility with the lines operated in parallel and a generator located on one of the two plant buses and with backfeed allowed. The 4800-V lines are fairly short cable lines that use a line-differential relaying scheme with an instantaneous overcurrent relay at each terminal to trip its respective breaker. The A51 and B51 overcurrent relays at breakers E and F are backup for line-differential relays. The plots for the coordination are shown in Fig. 9.16.

The A51 relays have contacts of the relays on position E in series with the contacts of the relays on position F. The A51 relays are functional at all times but especially when one line is out of service. The B51 relays, in effect, sum the current toward the plant bus to sense fault downstream when the system is normal.

The B67 directional overcurrent relays are set to coordinate with the opposite line A51 on the protected line. The A51 and B67 relays have compatible time-current characteristics to allow coordination.

The A67 directional overcurrent relays were chosen so that the characteristic more or less follows the generator decrement curve. The relays were calibrated to protect against faults at the utility substation. These relays must function whether both lines are in service or not.

The 87P-1 and 87P-2 relays are partial differential or bus overcurrent relays that are set to provide clearance under the A51 and B51 relays at the utility as well

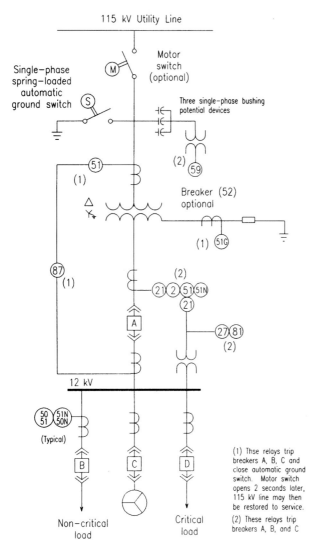

115 kV Utility Line

Single–phase
spring–loaded
automatic
ground switch

Motor
switch
(optional)

Three single–phase bushing
potential devices

Breaker (52)
optional

12 kV

(Typical)

B

C

D

Non–critical
load

Critical
load

(1) Thse relays trip
breakers A, B, C and
close automatic ground
switch. Motor switch
opens 2 seconds later,
115 kV line may then
be restored to service.

(2) These relays trip
breakers A, B, and C

**Figure 9.14**  Where consumers generate in parallel with the utility, protection strategies must include faults that occur on the utility subtransmission system as well. The magnitude of the fault current is determined by the impedance of the circuit elements involved—including the speed and fault support capability of the generator excitation system. When faults occur, bus voltages depress, generators unload, and (because of the relatively slow responses of the turbine governor) speed up. If synchronous motors are involved, they will slow down because of the reduction in voltage, thus pulling out of step with the generator and the governing source frequency.

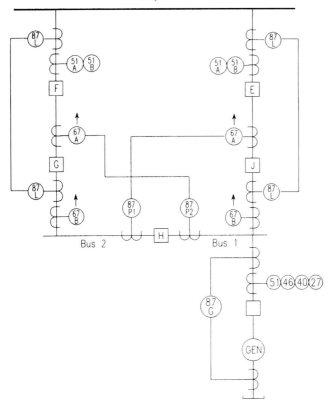

**Figure 9.15**

as provide time clearance over plant feeder breakers. The use of the partial differential scheme provides backup protection for the feeder breakers and also prevents a total shutdown of the facility in the event of a bus fault.

The generator has the usual complement of relays that include generator differential 87G voltage-controlled overcurrent relays 51/27, negative-sequence protection 46, and loss of excitation protection 40. This protection will allow power flow either into the plant load or out to the utility systems, provided that the load is balanced. Any uncontrolled fault on the incoming lines or on the utility system operates the voltage-controlled overcurrent relays 51/27 to trip the generator to isolate the fault. This arrangement provides a backup function because some other protective devices should have removed the fault from the system long before the generator relays are required to function.

### 9.5.1  Synchronizing relays

One of the most dramatic aspects of generating in parallel with a utility is the need to synchronize your machine with the utility's machine,

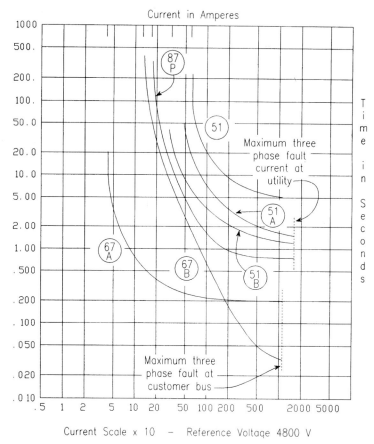

**Figure 9.16** Coordination study for circuit of Fig. 9.5 showing breaker coordination relationships only.

which in turn, is synchronized with the continental electrical grid. It is worth dwelling on the devices that allow us to do this.

Synchronizing relays may be applied for synchronizing and incoming generators to a power system in two ways: relay supervision of manual synchronization or automatic synchronization. The selection of either scheme should be based on the advantages and disadvantages of each for the system under consideration. Manual synchronization requires training, use of good judgment, experience, and the careful attention of the operator. Switchgear and generating equipment have been damaged as a result of misjudgment by an operator. Bent shafts of industrial-size turbine generators occur all too often when operators close circuit breakers when the systems are too far out of phase. Therefore, manual synchronizing is not recommended unless it is supervised with a relay that performs a synchronous verification.

It is recommended practice to include, as a minimum, a normally open contact of a synchronization relay that performs synchronizing verification in series with the closing circuit of a generator breaker, so the relay acts as a permissive device.

In this scheme, the operator performs all the normal manual synchronizing functions but cannot hold the breaker control switch closed until the relay senses that the systems are in synchronism; the generator must be in synchronism with the systems before the breaker control switch is closed. The relay monitors the voltages on each side of the breaker, and the relay's normally open contact closes; hence, the breaker is closed after a preset time delay period when

- The phase angle difference between the two systems remains less than a preset value.

- The voltage difference between the two systems remains within preset values.

The time delay is adjustable by using a time dial; the higher the time dial, the longer the delay. Normally, a low time dial is applied, so the slip frequency between the two systems must be small in order for the contacts to close within delay period. Synchronism check relays are available with fixed and adjustable closing angles. Typically, the closing angle is $20°$. The relay may not permit closure because the magnitude and phase angle of the voltages on each side of the open breaker are different due to load flow in the systems; however, the relay can be present to permit closure under these conditions.

## 9.6   Coordinating Consumer Switchgear with Utility Circuit Reclosers

For the purpose of sustaining continuity of power flow through overhead service conductors in adverse weather conditions, some facilities have automatic circuit reclosers installed upstream from the service entrance. The automatic circuit recloser is an intelligent overcurrent device that can not only be programmed to trip in a quasi-adaptive fashion, but it also has the capability of reclosing a preset number of times to clear temporary faults (such as galloping conductors) or isolate permanent faults on overhead lines (such as insulator failure). Reclosers are classified according to

- Application voltage, continuous current, and interrupting ratings
- The number of phases interrupted (one or three phases)
- The type of control (hydraulic, static electronic, or microprocessor)

- The kind of interrupting media (oil or vacuum)
- Operating states (automatic and/or manual) and speed of response

The mother standard for the application operation and maintenance of automatic circuit reclosers is ANSI/IEEE C37.61-1973. This publication contains details about standard ratings, operating characteristics, and some sample problems demonstrating application methodologies. As with any protective device, knowledge of present and future maximum and minimum fault-current levels at the point of application is assumed.

The virtual instant reset made possible by microprocessor technology has made the contemporary recloser superior to the electromechanical recloser. You can imagine what it must have been like having to figure induction disk overtravel into your strategy for establishing optimal settings, especially when fault current might change after fault inception. On the 10 time-dial setting for example, the approximate reset time is 6 s on the inverse time relay and 60 s on the very inverse and extremely inverse relays. With respect to the needs of contemporary electricity end users, this is practically forever.

Some appreciation for the action of circuit reclosers may be derived from reference to the schematic representation of a typical recloser operating sequence in Fig. 9.17. This is an oscillographic plot of current versus time. On the far left is normal load current; on the far right is recloser lockout. The four recloser actions between the initiation of the fault are ours to determine. It is common practice to allow 60 Hz between each recloser action. This provides time for utility sectionalizers to operate while no current is flowing.

Notice that the first two openings of the recloser are faster than the last two. The first two openings are called the instantaneous recloser response and the action may involve two cycles. This strategy will allow the recloser to remove the fault before a downstream overcurrent device (typically a fuse) has time to melt open. The last two openings are the time-delay operations and the action may involve 5 to 20 cycles. This strategy will allow the fuse to open on the longer 5-Hz openings and thereby lock out the faulted section of the line until electrical service specialists can intervene. During lockout, the contacts are held open until the recloser is reset manually. If a temporary fault clears before the recloser locks out, all mechanical operations cease and the recloser becomes ready to cycle over again when the next fault occurs.

Just knowing this much about reclosers allows us to visualize what a time-current characteristic of a recloser might look like. Unlike the time-current characteristic of a fuse or a relay that has only one response curve (or response band), the recloser has *two* time-current characteristics. The fast time-current characteristic should lie well

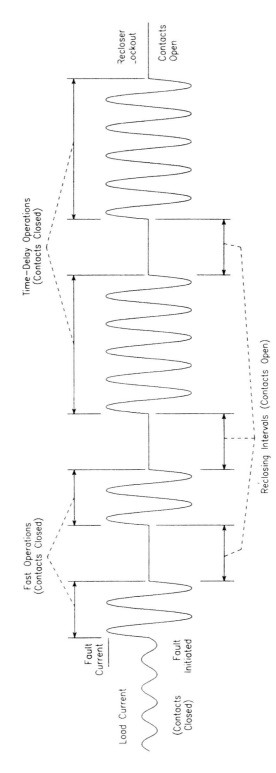

**Figure 9.17**

below the slow time-current characteristic (in terms of time, or hertz). Most recloser manufacturers offer several different tripping characteristics for each of the fast and slow response functions. Figure 9.18 indicates how a consumer-owned transformer primary fuse might coordinate with the fast and slow time-current characteristics of the upstream utility recloser. A consumer-owned transformer primary circuit-breaker time-current characteristic would fit between the two recloser responses in a similar fashion.

Coordinating our service fuses and/or circuit breakers with reclosers might be as easy as coordinating low-voltage fuses were it not for the fact that we must take heating and cooling into account when we coordinate reclosers with fuses. These fuses have to be coordinated with

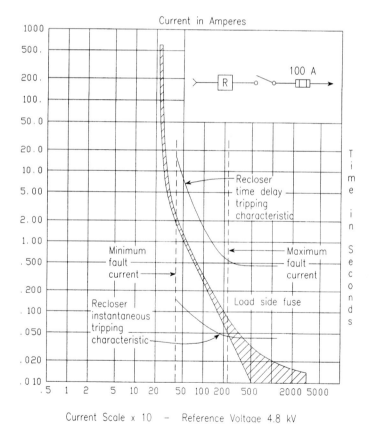

Current Scale x 10  –  Reference Voltage 4.8 kV

**Figure 9.18**  Note how the fuse time-current characteristic is effectively "boxed in" by the minimum and maximum fault-current levels and the slow and fast time responses of the recloser. Preloading (preheating) a primary fuse can sometimes reduce the fuse melting times between 30 and 50 percent. This should be considered when considering coordination with secondary devices, at time longer than about 0.5 s.

the reclosers or reclosing circuit breakers located on the secondary side of the transformer to prevent the fuse from any damage during the sequential tripping operations. The effects of the accumulated heating and cooling of the fuse element can be taken into account by adjusting the delayed tripping time of the recloser.

Proper coordination of trip operations of the recloser and the total clearing time of the fuse prevents the fuse link from being damaged during instantaneous trip operations of the recloser. The required coordination between the recloser and the fuse can be achieved by comparing the respective time-current characteristics and taking into account other factors, e.g., preloading, ambient temperature, curve tolerances, and accumulated heating and cooling of the fuse link during the fast-trip operations of the recloser.

If reclosing is done a few seconds after the initial fault, the overcurrent relay may not have completely reset, and if the fault is permanent rather than transient, the overcurrent relay may be "inched" out and the contacts closed to trip a device upstream of the device nearest the fault. This same type of operation may occur to fuses and other thermal devices. The heat buildup within the fuse must be dissipated before the fault current is reapplied to prevent false operation of an upstream device.

While reclosers benefit electricity end users, they present a challenge to protection specialists who must coordinate facility service protective devices around their action. For example, in a situation in which customer generation is present and adverse weather lies ahead, the service conductor may need to be disconnected from the utility via pilot wire or tone telemetry from an upstream recloser. Assuming that plant generators can supply the full plant load and your turbogenerator control system can respond quickly, it may well be that your generators may remain on-line upon loss of the utility supply. The feasibility of this "independent" condition or the feasibility of programming your system to "ride out" momentary disturbances should be examined with knowledge of and feeling for system behavior and system history.

## Bibliography

"Guide for Protective Relaying of Utility-Consumer Interconnections," *ANSI/IEEE Standard C37.95-1973.*

"IEEE Guide for Protective Relay Applications to Power Transformers—Appendix A," *ANSI/IEEE Standard C37.91-1985.*

"IEEE Guide for Transformer Through-Fault Current Duration," *ANSI/IEEE Standard C57.109-1985.*

"IEEE Standard Guide for the Application, Operation, and Maintenance of Automatic Circuit Reclosers," *ANSI/IEEE Standard C37.61-1973.*

Nochumson, Charles J., and William E. Schwartzburg, "Transfer Considerations in Standby Generator Application," *IEEE IAS,* Sept./Oct. 1979.

Power System Relaying Committee of the IEEE Power Engineering Society, "Computer Aided Coordination of Line Protection Schemes," *IEEE Report,* 90 TH 0285-7, 1989.

Stouppe, Jr., Robert L., and Richard M. Sientar, "System Protection and Coordination," Chap. 10 in Robert W. Smeaton (ed.), *Switchgear and Control Handbook,* McGraw-Hill, 1987.

Witte, J. F., et al., "Computer Aided Recloser Applications for Distribution Systems," *IEEE Computer Applications in Power,* July 1992.


## General references

Blackburn, J. L., *Protective Relaying: Principles and Applications,* Marcel Dekker, Inc., New York, 1987.

Gonen, T., *Electric Power Distribution System Engineering,* McGraw-Hill, New York, 1986.

IEEE Relaying the Consumer-Utility Intertie Working Group, "Considerations in Protecting the Consumer-Utility Interconnection," *IEEE I&CPS Technical Conference Rec.,* May 1983.

"IEEE Standard General Requirements for Liquid-Immersed Distribution, Power, and Regulating Transformers," *ANSI/IEEE Standard 57.12-1980.*

"Intertie Protection of Consumer-Owned Sources of Generation—3 MVA or Less," *IEEE Special Report 88TH0224-6-PWR,* 1988.

Powell, L. J., "An Industrial View of Utility Cogeneration Protection Requirements," *IEEE IAS,* Jan./Feb. 1988.

Rook, M. J., et al., "Application of Protective Relays on a Large Industrial-Utility Tie with Industrial Cogeneration," *IEEE Transactions PAS,* June 1981.

St. Pierre, Conrad, "Microprocessor-Based Load Shedding Keeps Industry Systems in Balance," *IEEE Computer Applications in Power,* Jan. 1992.

Westinghouse Protective Relay Systems Committee, *Plant-Utility Tie Circuit Protection Guide,* Westinghouse Industrial and Commercial Power Systems Applications.


## Further reading

Clark, H. K., "Microprocessor-Based Load Shedding for the Paper and Pulp Industry," *TAPPI Journal,* Dec. 1987.

Durkin, C., and E. Eberle, "Development of a Rate of Change Frequency Relay," *Transmission & Distribution,* Dec. 1969.

"Feasibility of Adaptive Protection and Control," Report by the IEEE Power System Relaying Committee, J. S. Thorp (chairman), *IEEE Transactions on Delivery,* July 1993.

Koval, Don O., "Power Systems Disturbance Patterns," *IEEE Transactions on Industry Applications,* May/June 1990.

McEachern, Alexander, *Handbook of Power Signatures,* 1989 Basic Measuring Instruments, Foster City, Calif.

"Optimum Load-Shedding Policy for Power Systems," *IEEE Transactions on Power Apparatus and Systems,* March 1968.

Slade, P. G., et al., "The Utility Requirements for a Distribution Fault Current Limiter," *IEEE Transactions on Power Delivery,* July 1993.

Vey, Larry, and Jim Iverson, *Grounding of AC Generators and Switching the Neutral in Emergency and Standby Power Systems, Part Two,* Publication No. 900-0262, Onan Corporation, Minneapolis, Minn., May 1991.

# Appendix

This appendix is provided to the reader as the starting point for the beginning of the development of a professional library. There is no substitute for reading the original sources from which most of the material in this book has been taken. This book is possible because of the assistance of many individuals in the industry. The choice of material is, of course, the responsibility of the author.

Just as this text is no substitute for the original sources, it is no substitute for hands-on technical training. The selection of material in this text is based upon the author's own experience, and you need to be exposed to other points of view. Protection engineering is an aspect of electrical circuit design where good people will disagree. A partial listing of technical seminars offered on the subject appears as follows:

IEEE Technical Training, Piscataway, New Jersey

NFPA Technical Training, Quincy, Massachusetts

Westinghouse Technical Training Center, Pittsburgh, Pennsylvania

ABB Technical Training, Coral Springs, Florida

University of Toledo, Toledo, Ohio

Georgia Technical Institute, Atlanta, Georgia

University of Wisconsin, Madison, Wisconsin

SKM Analysis, Manhattan Beach, California

EDSA Microcorporation, Bloomfield Hills, California

Much of the information in this book has been previously published by authors and editors in various trade magazines, manufacturer internal memoranda, engineering society journals, and the like. The author wishes to express appreciation to Paul Beck from *Consulting/ Specifying Engineer;* John Dedad and Richard Hathaway from *EC&M* Magazine; James A. Bright from Basler Electric; Mike Stump and Jim Lagroe from Westinghouse; Lon Lindell from SKM Analysis; Ali Nasli from EDSA Micro Corporation; George Powers from General Electric; Steve Shaeffer at Cooper-Bussman; Cary Cook from S&C Electric; Walt Elmore, John LaDronka, and Jim Santilli from Asea-Brown-Boveri; Mr. Dennis Berry from the National Fire Protection Association;

Michelle Phillips and Bill Hagen from the IEEE; Diane Devine- Mount from Marcel Dekker; and Bonnie Beacher from McGraw-Hill Book Company.

- ANSI publications are available from the American National Standards Institute, Sales Department, 11 West 42nd Street, 13th Floor, New York, NY, 10036, (212)642-4900

- IEEE publications are available from the Institute of Electrical and Electronics Engineers, Inc., Service Center, 445 Hoes Lane, P.O. Box 1331, Piscataway, NJ 08855-1331, (800)678-4333. The IEEE reprint department is available at (800)ASK-IEEE (FAX: 415-259-5045) and over the Internet at askieee@ieee.org

## A.1   Checklist for Coordinating Overcurrent Devices

The following is a summary of the principles you will need to apply in order to coordinate overcurrent devices.

- Budget 1 hour of engineering time for each protective device you need to coordinate. (See Chap. 1.)

- Determine *maximum* short-circuit levels at critical locations on the electrical network to be protected. In many cases—but not all—this will be the three-phase bolted fault. Adjust these figures as required for the manner in which fault currents are reflected between transformer primaries and/or secondaries. (See Chap. 2.)

- Determine *minimum* short-circuit levels at critical locations on the electrical network to be protected. In many cases—but not all—this will be the arcing or topological (zero sequence) minimum. Arcing faults may be estimated to be 38 percent of the bolted ground-fault current level. This will be your time-current reference point from which you will coordinate ground-fault protective devices. (See Chap. 2.)

- Plot the critical system short-circuit levels described above on horizontal axes. (See Chaps. 1 and 2.)

- Withstand and interrupting ratings of protective devices must match the level of fault current at the half-cycle point and at the device's interrupting point. Confirm that protective devices applied in series all have the withstand capability, while downstream devices "time-out." (See Chap. 3.)

- Fault-sensing devices must be specified so that minimum and maximum fault levels can be detected. Learn the nature of the phase- and ground-sensing elements to confirm that the sensing scheme will "reach" toward low fault current levels and/or will not saturate during maximum fault current levels. (See Chaps. 3, 4, and 8.)

- Manufacturer time-current characteristic curves must be obtained that match the protective device applied. These time-current characteristic curve plots must be normalized on a single voltage. (See Chaps. 1 and 3.)

- Transformer inrush: Inrush is 6 to 12 times full secondary load current and lasts for about 1 s. (See Chaps. 4 and 7.)

- Transformer protection curves must be shifted to the left by $1/\sqrt{3}$ or $2/\sqrt{3}$ according to transformer connection and grounding configuration. (See Chaps. 4 and 7.)

- Allow 16 percent margin for line-to-line faults on $\Delta$-Y transform. (See Chaps. 3, 4, and 7.)

- The requirements for setting transformer protective devices are indicated in National Electric Code Table 450-3(a) and (b). (All chapters.)

- Plot motor characteristic curve. It typically consists of inrush current, locked rotor current, and full load current. (See Chaps. 1 and 6.)

- Plot cable short-circuit withstand curves. This step is optional if you are familiar with the cable thermal characteristics. (See Chaps. 3 and 5.)

- Confirm that the clearing times of dissimilar devices are sufficient for fault sensing and opening. (See Chap. 3.)

- Confirm that current level multiples and trip times within the device tripping regions you have drawn conform to the requirements of the National Electric Code. (All chapters.)

- Do not overcrowd the study.

- Find a colleague to check your work.

## A.2  Some Handy Numbers

0.0—The time coordinate of all time-current characteristic plots for overcurrent devices begin at t = 0.0 when the fault first occurs.

0.004—Nominal opening time of a current-limiting fuse.

0.016—Number of seconds in one 60-Hz cycle.

0.048—Opening time of the fastest medium-voltage circuit breaker.

0.36—.208 kV $\times \sqrt{3}$ (see 2.77).

0.38—A single-line-to-ground arcing fault may be this percentage of a three-phase fault in some common application situations.

0.4—Number of seconds of time between electromechanical-based overcurrent relay time-current characteristic curves.

0.4343—Multiplying factor for conversion between log10 and natural log (see 2.3026).

0.57—The amount by which voltage is displaced during ground fault on a delta system.

$0.707 - 1/\sqrt{2}$ where $\sqrt{2} = V_{max}$ for sine wave only.

0.8—Number of hp per kVA at 1.0 pf at 480 V.

$0.832$—$.480 \times \sqrt{3}$.

$0.866$—$\sqrt{3}/2$.

1.0—Asymmetry factor of X/R = 0. (See also 1.732.)

1.0—Number of hp per kVA at 0.8 pf at 480 V.

1.17—Asymmetry factor for typical low voltage (below 600 V) industrial distribution system. (See 6.6.)

1.2—Reciprocal of 1/.36. In a 480-V system you may multiply transformer kVA by 1.2 to estimate full-load amperes. (See .832.) For example: 1000 kVA transformer × 1.2 = 1201 amps is the full-load current on the secondary.

1.6—Asymmetry factor that corresponds to a short-circuit power factor of 15 percent and X/R ratio of 25 in UL test circuits for circuit breaker interrupting ratings.

$1.732$—$\sqrt{3}$ shows up in the arithmetic of all three-phase circuits. The largest asymmetry factor. It corresponds to an X/R ratio of infinity. (See also 1.0.)

2.3026—Multiplying factor for conversion between log10 and natural log. (See .4343.)

2.777—The reciprocal of .36. On a 208-V system you can multiply transformer kVA by 2.7 in order to estimate full-load amperes. 1000 kVA at 208 V = 2.7 × 1000 kVA → 2777 V.

16%—The current margin between a primary and secondary device on either side of a Δ-Y transformer. The per-unit primary current in one phase for this type of fault is 16 percent greater than the per-unit secondary current which flows for a secondary three-phase fault.

6.6—X/R ratio for typical low-voltage distribution system. (See 1.17.) This is the X/R ratio at which manufacturer's test breakers 600 V and below.

12—Twelve times full-load amps. Commonly the limit of molded-case circuit breaker short-circuit interrupting capacity.

15—The X/R ratio at which manufacturer's test breakers greater than 600 V.

16—The percentage additional time and current margin between protective devices that are applied on either side of a Δ-Y distribution transformer.

25—X/R ratio for medium voltage (600–27,000 V) industrial distribution system. (See 1.6.)

37—As in ANSI/IEEE C37, one of the most commonly applied industry standards.

38—Most probable percentage of bolted single-line-to-ground fault current that an arcing fault causes. (See Chap. 3.)

44.4—Magic number for motors.

57—As in ANSI/IEEE C57 one of the most commonly applied industry standards.

110—Article 110 of the National Electric Code that indicates requirements for interruption capacity.

141—ANSI/IEEE Red Book, *Recommended Practice for Electric Power Distribution for Industrial Plants.*

230—Article 230 of National Electric Code pertaining to electrical services.

240—Article 240 of National Electric Code pertaining to overcurrent protection.

242—ANSI/IEEE Buff Book, *Recommended Practice for Protection and Coordination of Industrial and Commercial Power Systems.*

310—Article 310 of the National Electric Code pertaining to conductor ampacity.

377—$2\pi f$ with $f = 60$ Hz. Also the characteristic impedance of free space. A pure number.

430—Article 430 of the National Electric Code pertains to motor protection.

710—Article 710 of National Electric Code that pertains to circuits over 600 V.

746—Watts per horsepower.

1000—Average finger-to-finger impedance (in ohms) of a human being with normal electrolytic composition.

1201—Full-load amps of a 1000-kVA transformer at 480 V. You can round this off to 1200 A to *estimate* full-load current of, say, 250-500-1500 kVA transformers.

2777—Full-load amps of a 1000-kVA transformer at 208 V. You can round this off to 2800 amps to *estimate* the full-load amps of, say, 250-500-1500 kVA transformers.

## A.3   Estimated Clearing Times
## of Protective Devices

**TABLE A.1   Estimated Clearing Times of Protective Devices**

*Relayed Circuit Breakers, 2.4–13.8 kV*

|  | Type of relay | | |
| --- | --- | --- | --- |
|  | Plunger, instantaneous | Induction, instantaneous | Induction, inverse-time |
| Relay times, cycles | 0.25–1 | 0.5–2 | 6–6000 |
| Circuit-breaker | | | |
| interrupting time, cycles | 3–8 | 3–8 | 3–8 |
| Total time, cycles | 3.25–9 | 3.5–10 | 9–6000 |

*Large Air Power Circuit Breakers, Below 600 V*

|  | Frame Size | |
| --- | --- | --- |
|  | 225–600 A | 1600–4000 A |
| Instantaneous, cycles | 2–3 | 3 |
| Short time, cycles | 10–30 | 10–30 |
| Long time, seconds | over 100 s | |
| Ground fault, cycles | 10–30 | 10–30 |

*Molded-Case Circuit Breakers, Below 600 V*

|  | Frame Size | |
| --- | --- | --- |
|  | 100 A | 225–1200 A |
| Instantaneous, cycles | 1.1 | 1.5 |
| Long time, seconds | over 100 s | |

*Medium- and High-Voltage Fuses*

| High current | 0.25 cycles (for current-limiting fuses operating in their current-limiting range) |
| --- | --- |
|  | 1.0 cycle (for power fuses at maximum current) |
| Low current | 600 s (for E-rated fuses operating at 2× nominal rating: other ratings are available with different times at 2× nominal rating) |

*Low-Voltage Fuses*

| High current | 0.25 cycles (in current-limiting range) |
| --- | --- |
| Low current | 1000 s (at 1.35 to 1.5 times nominal rating) |

Adapted from ANSI/IEEE.

## A.4   Selected Time-Current Characteristic Curves

These curves are used at several locations in the book. The use of these time-current characteristic curves are for instructional purposes only. The next edition of this book is likely to use a different set of sample time-current characteristic curves in order to represent all manufacturers.

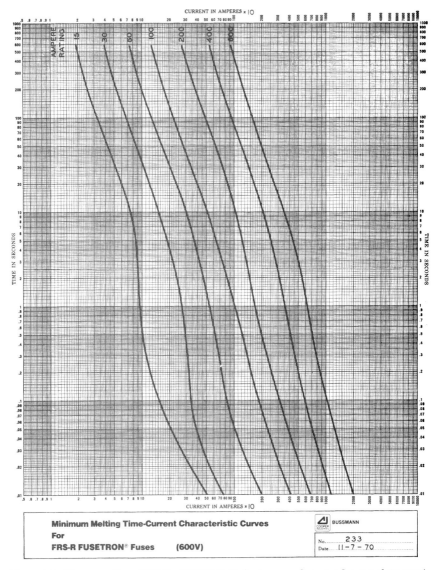

**Figure A.1**   Bussman Fuse FRS-R—TCC 233. Refer to manufacturer for complete specifications.

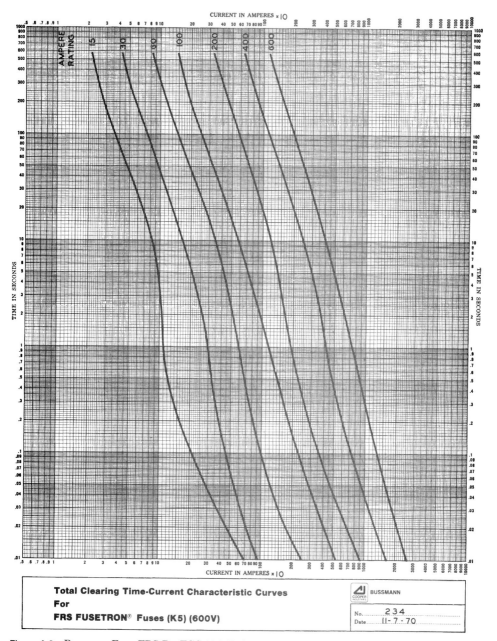

Total Clearing Time-Current Characteristic Curves
For
FRS FUSETRON® Fuses (K5) (600V)

BUSSMANN
COOPER

No. ....234....
Date .....11-7-70....

**Figure A.2**   Bussman Fuse FRS-R—TCC 234. Refer to manufacturer for complete specifications.

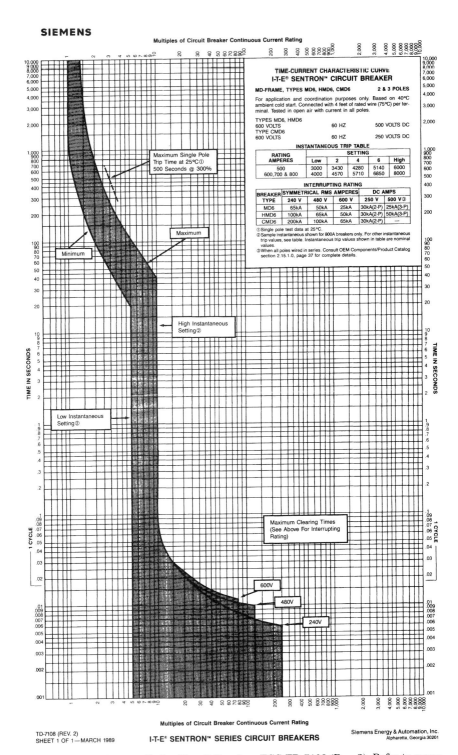

**SIEMENS**

Multiples of Circuit Breaker Continuous Current Rating

### TIME-CURRENT CHARACTERISTIC CURVE
### I-T-E® SENTRON™ CIRCUIT BREAKER

MD-FRAME, TYPES MD6, HMD6, CMD6    2 & 3 POLES

For application and coordination purposes only. Based on 40°C ambient cold start. Connected with 4 feet of rated wire (75°C) per terminal. Tested in open air with current in all poles.

| TYPES MD6, HMD6 | | |
|---|---|---|
| 600 VOLTS | 60 HZ | 500 VOLTS DC |
| TYPE CMD6 | | |
| 600 VOLTS | 60 HZ | 250 VOLTS DC |

**INSTANTANEOUS TRIP TABLE**

| RATING AMPERES | SETTING | | | | |
|---|---|---|---|---|---|
| | Low | 2 | 4 | 6 | High |
| 500 | 3000 | 3430 | 4280 | 5140 | 6000 |
| 600,700 & 800 | 4000 | 4570 | 5710 | 6850 | 8000 |

**INTERRUPTING RATING**

| BREAKER TYPE | SYMMETRICAL RMS AMPERES | | | DC AMPS | |
|---|---|---|---|---|---|
| | 240 V | 480 V | 600 V | 250 V | 500 V③ |
| MD6 | 65kA | 50kA | 25kA | 30kA(2-P) | 25kA(3-P) |
| HMD6 | 100kA | 65kA | 50kA | 30kA(2-P) | 50kA(3-P) |
| CMD6 | 200kA | 100kA | 65kA | 30kA(2-P) | — |

①Single pole test data at 25°C.
②Sample instantaneous shown for 800A breakers only. For other instantaneous trip values, see table. Instantaneous trip values shown in table are nominal values.
③When all poles wired in series. Consult OEM Components/Product Catalog section 2.15.1.0, page 37 for complete details.

Maximum Single Pole Trip Time at 25°C① 500 Seconds @ 300%

Maximum

Minimum

High Instantaneous Setting②

Low Instantaneous Setting②

Maximum Clearing Times (See Above For Interrupting Rating)

600V

480V

240V

TIME IN SECONDS

1 CYCLE

Multiples of Circuit Breaker Continuous Current Rating

TD-7108 (REV. 2)
SHEET 1 OF 1—MARCH 1989

**I-T-E® SENTRON™ SERIES CIRCUIT BREAKERS**

Siemens Energy & Automation, Inc.
Alpharetta, Georgia 30201

**Figure A.3** ITE Sentron Series Circuit Breaker. TCC TD-7108 (Rev. 2). Refer to manufacturer for complete specifications.

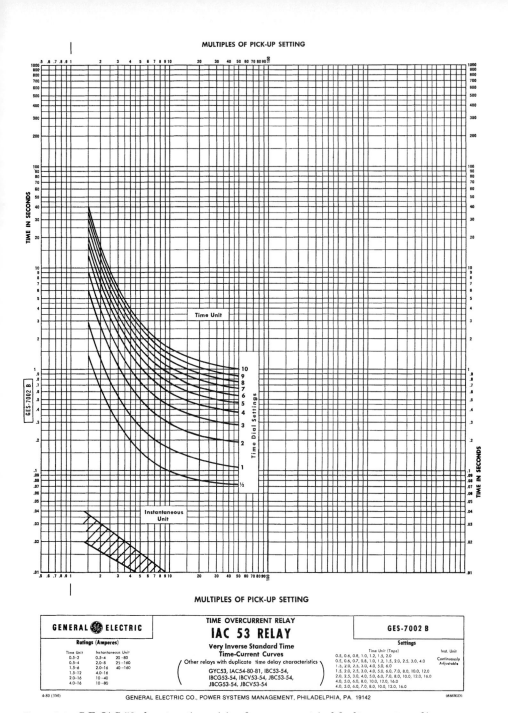

**MULTIPLES OF PICK-UP SETTING**

TIME IN SECONDS

GES-7002 B

Time Unit

Time Dial Settings

10
9
8
7
6
5
4
3
2
1
½

Instantaneous Unit

**MULTIPLES OF PICK-UP SETTING**

| GENERAL ⊕ ELECTRIC | | TIME OVERCURRENT RELAY<br>**IAC 53 RELAY**<br>Very Inverse Standard Time | GES-7002 B |
|---|---|---|---|

| **Ratings (Amperes)** | | **Time-Current Curves** | **Settings** | |
|---|---|---|---|---|
| Time Unit | Instantaneous Unit | ( Other relays with duplicate time delay characteristics ) | Time Unit (Taps) | Inst. Unit |
| 0.5–2 | 0.5–4 | 20–80 | 0.5, 0.6, 0.8, 1.0, 1.2, 1.5, 2.0 | |
| 0.5–4 | 2.0–8 | 20–160 | 0.5, 0.6, 0.7, 0.8, 1.0, 1.2, 1.5, 2.0, 2.5, 3.0, 4.0 | Continuously |
| 1.5–6 | 2.0–16 | 40–160 | 1.5, 2.0, 2.5, 3.0, 4.0, 5.0, 6.0 | Adjustable |
| 1.5–12 | 4.0–16 | | GYC53, IAC54-80-81, IBC53-54, | 1.5, 2.0, 2.5, 3.0, 4.0, 5.0, 6.0, 7.0, 8.0, 10.0, 12.0 | |
| 2.0–16 | 10–40 | | IBCG53-54, IBCV53-54, JBC53-54, | 2.0, 2.5, 3.0, 4.0, 5.0, 6.0, 7.0, 8.0, 10.0, 12.0, 16.0 | |
| 4.0–16 | 10–80 | | JBCG53-54, JBCV53-54 | 4.0, 5.0, 6.0, 8.0, 10.0, 12.0, 16.0 | |
| | | | | 4.0, 5.0, 6.0, 7.0, 8.0, 10.0, 12.0, 16.0 | |

4-80 (3M)      GENERAL ELECTRIC CO., POWER SYSTEMS MANAGEMENT, PHILADELPHIA, PA. 19142      088880270

**Figure A.4** G.E. IAC 53. dc saturation arising from asymmetrical fault currents and/or a premagnetized CT core may reduce the output of a CT to almost zero for the first few cycles of the fault. Badly saturated CTs (sometimes called "soaked" CTs) will cause timing errors in electromechanical relays. When this happens, the actual operating times indicated in this time-current characteristic will be slower (shifted upward). Refer to manufacturer for complete specifications.

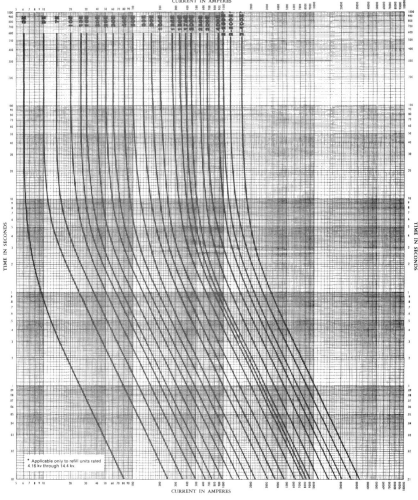

CURRENT IN AMPERES

## MINIMUM MELTING TIME-CURRENT CHARACTERISTIC CURVES

### SM REFILL UNITS—S&C STANDARD SPEED

**BASIS**—These refill units are tested in accordance with the procedures described in ANSI Standard C37.41-1981, and they are rated to comply with ANSI Standard C37.46-1981. As required by these standards, the minimum melting current is not less than 200% of refill-unit ampere rating, and the minimum melting curves are based on tests starting with the refill unit at an ambient temperature of 25°C and no initial load.

**CONSTRUCTION**—Fusible elements for refill units rated 3E through 7E amperes are nickel-chrome, under controlled tension; fusible elements for refill units rated 10E through 400E amperes are silver, helically coiled. All are of solderless construction.

**TOLERANCES**—Curves are plotted to minimum test points. Maximum variations expressed in current values are:
Plus 10% for 10E through 400E ampere ratings.
Plus 15% for 5E and 7E ampere ratings.
Plus 20% for 3E ampere rating.

**APPLICATION**—Like all high-voltage fuses, these refill units are intended to accommodate overloads, not to interrupt them. Accordingly, they feature fusible elements which are designed with a minimum melting current of 200% of the refill-unit ampere rating (for refill units rated 100 amperes or less) or 220% of the refill-unit ampere rating (for refill units rated over 100 amperes). As a result, these refill units have considerable peak-load capabilities; however, they should never be exposed to loading in excess of the peak-load capabilities listed in S&C Data Bulletin 240-190.

Since refill units having nickel-chrome or silver element construction are not subject to damage by aging or transient overcurrents, it is unnecessary to replace unblown refill units of either of these constructions in single-phase or three-phase installations when one or more refill units have blown.

**COORDINATION**—Any preloading reduces melting time. While this phenomenon is especially pronounced in other makes of fuses having minimum melting currents appreciably less than 200% of rating, the effect of preloading must nonetheless be determined for the S&C refill units represented by these curves (see S&C Data Bulletin 240-195) and adjustments to these curves must be made:
1. When close coordination is required;
2. When, regardless of the preciseness of coordination, the refill unit is subjected to temporary overloads.

There are cases where the coordination requirements may be very exacting; for example, in coordinating a transformer-primary fuse with a secondary breaker and a source-side breaker. The time interval between the operating characteristics of the two breakers may be very narrow. Under these circumstances there must be an extremely short time interval between the minimum melting and the total clearing characteristics of the fuse.

The refill units represented by these curves possess this short time-interval feature, since—having a nondamageable fusible element of precise construction—they require:
1. As little as 10% total tolerance in melting current—compared to the 20% tolerance of many fuses (20% and 40% respectively in terms of time).
2. No "safety-zone" or setback allowances.

This narrow time band normally will provide the desired coordination. If the selected S&C Standard Speed refill unit does not meet the coordination requirements, check to see if the same ampere rating in the S&C Slow Speed will satisfy.

Sometimes a selected ampere rating will fail to meet the coordination requirements in any available speed. In this case the selection of another ampere rating for either the protecting or protected fuse usually will satisfy all requirements.

Do not assume that other fuses that do not employ S&C's silver, helically coiled fusible element construction can better resolve a coordination impasse than the use of another ampere rating in one of the S&C speed options. Such other fuses, including "time-lag" speeds, "super-slow" speeds, and "high-surge" speeds, require the use of "safety-zone" or setback allowances and, in addition, they have larger construction tolerances (plus 20% in current; plus 40% in terms of time). The application of these two factors will give a time interval between the adjusted minimum melting curve and the total clearing curve greater than in the case of S&C speed options.

**REFILL UNITS AVAILABLE—**

| Refill Unit | Kv Nom. Ratings | Ampere Ratings |
|---|---|---|
| SM-4 | 7.2 through 34.5 | 3E through 200E |
| SM-5 | 4.16 through 14.4 | 3E through 400E |
| SM-5 | 25 and 34.5 | 3E through 300E |

Supersedes TCC No. 153-4 dated 2-23-76      © 1985

**S&C ELECTRIC COMPANY** · Chicago
**S&C ELECTRIC CANADA LTD.** · Rexdale

**TCC NUMBER 153-4**
Page 1 of 1
March 18, 1985

**Figure A.5**   S&C TCC 153-4. Refer to manufacturer for complete specifications.

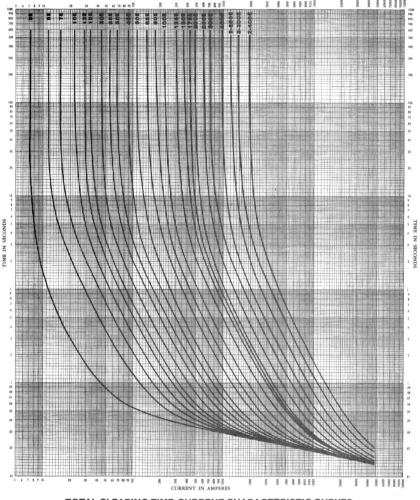

## TOTAL CLEARING TIME-CURRENT CHARACTERISTIC CURVES

### SM REFILL UNITS—S&C STANDARD SPEED

**BASIS**—These refill units are tested in accordance with the procedures described in ANSI Standard C37.41-1981, and they are rated to comply with ANSI Standard C37.46-1981. As required by these standards, the minimum melting current is not less than 200% of refill-unit ampere rating, and the minimum melting and total clearing curves are based on tests starting with the refill unit at an ambient temperature of 25°C and no initial load.

**CONSTRUCTION**—Fusible elements for refill units rated 3E through 7E amperes are nickel-chrome, under controlled tension; fusible elements for refill units rated 10E through 400E amperes are silver, helically coiled. All are of solderless construction.

**TOLERANCES**—Curves are plotted to maximum test points. All variations are minus.

**APPLICATION**—Like all high-voltage fuses, these refill units are intended to accommodate overloads, not to interrupt them. Accordingly, they feature fusible elements which are designed with a minimum melting current of 200% of the refill-unit ampere rating (for refill units rated 100 amperes or less) or 220% of the refill-unit ampere rating (for refill units rated over 100 amperes). As a result, these refill units have considerable peak-load capabilities; however, they should never be exposed to loading in excess of the peak-load capabilities listed in S&C Data Bulletin 240-190.

Since refill units having nickel-chrome or silver element construction are not subject to damage by aging or transient overcurrents, it is unnecessary to replace unblown refill units of either

of these constructions in single-phase or three-phase installations when one or more refill units have blown.

**COORDINATION**—These curves represent the total time required for a refill unit to melt and interrupt a fault current, and should be followed in coordination problems where fuses are applied as "protecting" devices.

Any preloading reduces melting time. With respect to the "protected" fuse, the effect of preloading must be determined and adjustments made to its minimum melting curve:
1. When close coordination is required;
2. When, regardless of the preciseness of coordination, the protected fuse is subjected to temporary overloads.

There are cases where the coordination requirements may be very exacting; for example, in coordinating a transformer-primary fuse with a secondary breaker and a source-side breaker. The time interval between the operating characteristics of the two breakers may be very narrow. Under these circumstances there must be an extremely short time interval between the minimum melting and the total clearing characteristics of the fuse.

The refill units represented by these curves possess this short time interval feature, since—having a nondamageable fusible element of precise construction—they require:
1. As little as 10% *total* tolerance in melting current—compared to the 20% tolerance of many fuses (20% and 40% respectively in terms of time).

2. No "safety-zone" or setback allowances.

This narrow time band normally will provide the desired coordination. If the selected S&C Standard Speed refill unit does not meet the coordination requirements, the selection of another ampere rating for either the protecting or protected fuse usually will satisfy.

Do not assume that other fuses that do not employ S&C's silver, helically coiled fusible element construction can better resolve a coordination impasse than the use of another ampere rating in one of the S&C speed options. Such other fuses, including "time-lag" speeds, "super-slow" speeds, and "high-surge" speeds, require the use of "safety-zone" or setback allowances and, in addition, they have larger construction tolerances (plus 20% in melting current and the total clearing curve greater than in the case of S&C speed options).

**REFILL UNITS AVAILABLE—**

| Refill Unit | Kv Nom. Ratings | Ampere Ratings |
|---|---|---|
| SM-4 | 7.2 and 14.4 | 3E through 200E |
| SM-5 | 4.16 through 14.4 | 3E through 400E |

Supersedes TCC No. 153-4-2 dated 2-23-76       © 1985

**S&C ELECTRIC COMPANY** · Chicago
**S&C ELECTRIC CANADA LTD.** · Rexdale

**TCC NUMBER 153-4-2**
Page 1 of 1
March 18, 1985

**Figure A.6**   S&C TCC 153-4-2. Refer to manufacturer for complete specifications.

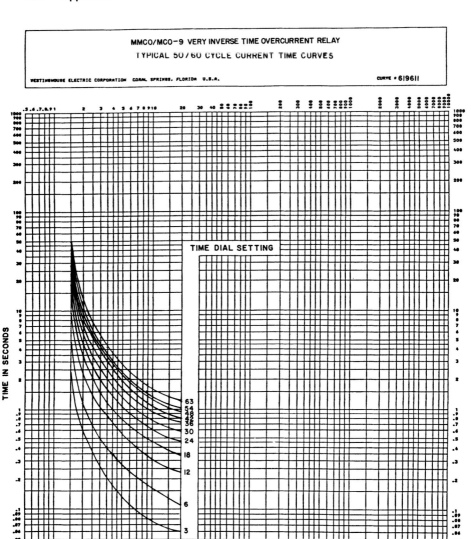

**Figure A.7a**   ABB MMCO. Refer to manufacturer for complete specifications.

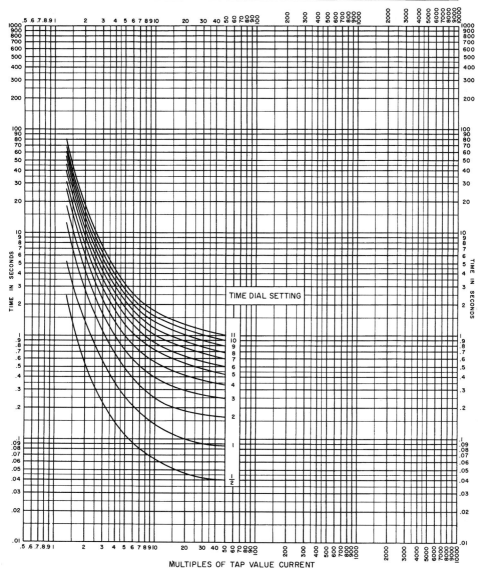

**Figure A.7b**   ABB CO-9. Refer to manufacturer for complete specifications.

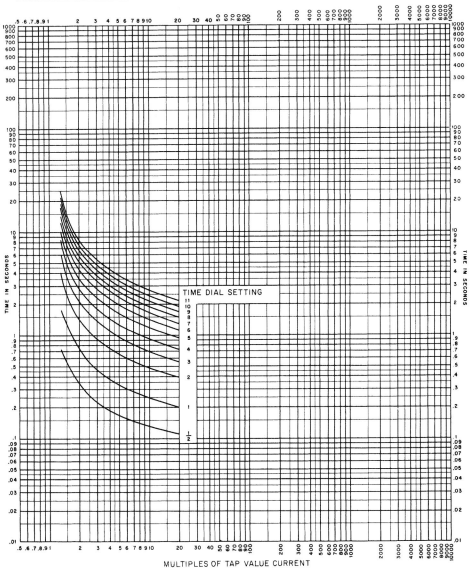

**Figure A.7c**   ABB CO-7. Refer to manufacturer for complete specifications.

Application Data
**32-860A**

## DIGITRIP RMS 500/600/700/800
### Typical Time-Current Characteristic Curve (LS) for Type DS Circuit Breakers

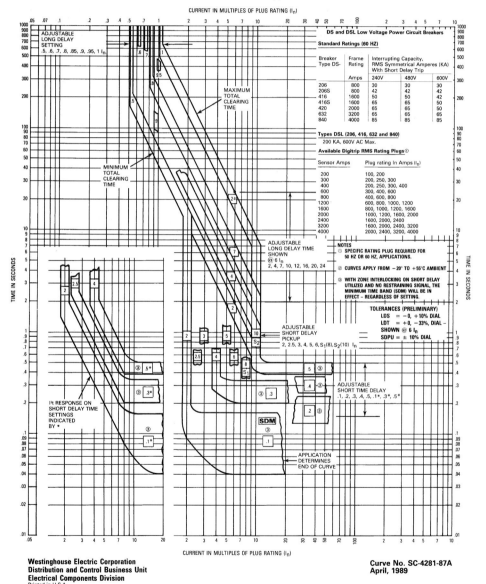

Westinghouse Electric Corporation
Distribution and Control Business Unit
Electrical Components Division
Printed in U.S.A.

Curve No. SC-4281-87A
April, 1989

**Figure A.8**   Westinghouse Digitrip—LS TCC SC4284-87. Refer to manufacturer for complete specifications.

Application Data
**32-860A**

**DIGITRIP RMS 500/600/700/800**

Typical Time-Current Characteristic Curve (G)
for Type DS Circuit Breakers

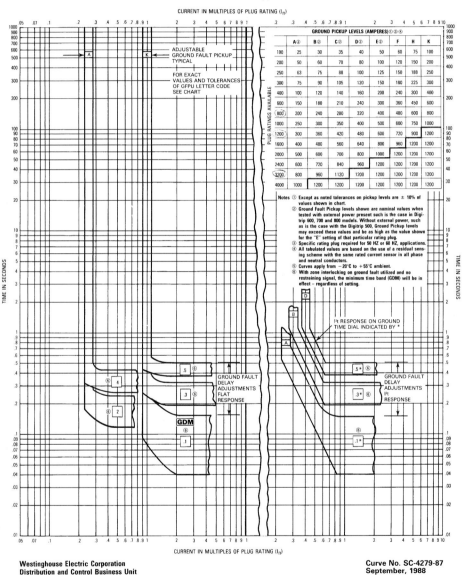

CURRENT IN MULTIPLES OF PLUG RATING ($I_n$)

GROUND PICKUP LEVELS (AMPERES) ① ③ ④

| | A② | B② | C③ | D② | E② | F | H | K |
|---|---|---|---|---|---|---|---|---|
| 100 | 25 | 30 | 35 | 40 | 50 | 60 | 75 | 100 |
| 200 | 50 | 60 | 70 | 80 | 100 | 120 | 150 | 200 |
| 250 | 63 | 75 | 88 | 100 | 125 | 150 | 188 | 250 |
| 300 | 75 | 90 | 105 | 120 | 150 | 180 | 225 | 300 |
| 400 | 100 | 120 | 140 | 160 | 200 | 240 | 300 | 400 |
| 600 | 150 | 180 | 210 | 240 | 300 | 360 | 450 | 600 |
| 800 | 200 | 240 | 280 | 320 | 400 | 480 | 600 | 800 |
| 1000 | 250 | 300 | 350 | 400 | 500 | 600 | 750 | 1000 |
| 1200 | 300 | 360 | 420 | 480 | 600 | 720 | 900 | 1200 |
| 1600 | 400 | 480 | 560 | 640 | 800 | 960 | 1200 | 1200 |
| 2000 | 500 | 600 | 700 | 800 | 1000 | 1200 | 1200 | 1200 |
| 2400 | 600 | 720 | 840 | 960 | 1200 | 1200 | 1200 | 1200 |
| 3200 | 800 | 960 | 1120 | 1200 | 1200 | 1200 | 1200 | 1200 |
| 4000 | 1000 | 1200 | 1200 | 1200 | 1200 | 1200 | 1200 | 1200 |

Notes ① Except as noted tolerances on pickup levels are ± 10% of
values shown in chart.
② Ground Fault Pickup levels shown are nominal values when
tested with external power present such is the case in Digitrip 600, 700 and 800 models. Without external power, such
as is the case with the Digitrip 500, Ground Pickup levels
may exceed these values and be as high as the value shown
for the "E" setting of that particular rating plug.
③ Specific rating plug required for 50 HZ or 60 HZ, applications.
④ All tabulated values are based on the use of a residual sensing scheme with the same rated current sensor in all phase
and neutral conductors.
⑤ Curves apply from − 20°C to + 55°C ambient.
⑥ With zone interlocking on ground fault utilized and no
restraining signal, the minimum time band (GDM) will be in
effect − regardless of setting.

ADJUSTABLE
GROUND FAULT PICKUP
TYPICAL

FOR EXACT
VALUES AND TOLERANCES
OF GFPU LETTER CODE
SEE CHART

I²t RESPONSE ON GROUND
TIME DIAL INDICATED BY *

GROUND FAULT
DELAY
ADJUSTMENTS
FLAT
RESPONSE

GROUND FAULT
DELAY
ADJUSTMENTS
I²t
RESPONSE

GDM

TIME IN SECONDS

CURRENT IN MULTIPLES OF PLUG RATING ($I_n$)

Westinghouse Electric Corporation
Distribution and Control Business Unit
Electrical Components Division
Printed in U.S.A.

Curve No. SC-4279-87
September, 1988

**Figure A.9**   Westinghouse Digitrip—G TCC SC-4282-87. Refer to manufacturer for complete specifications.

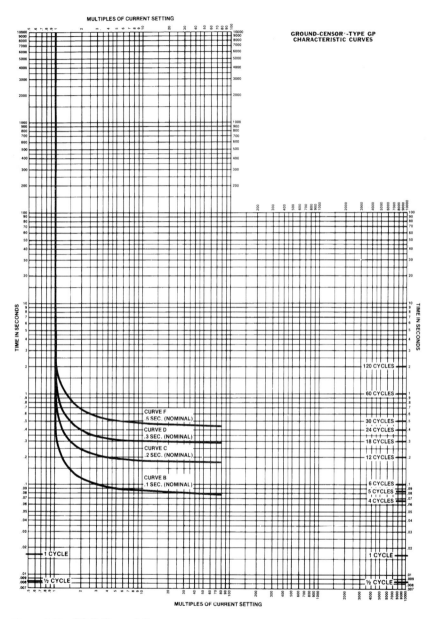

**Figure A.10**    SQ-D Ground Censor.

## A.5    Data for Short-Circuit Calculations

### A.5.1    Per unit formulas

*Utility contribution:*

$$Z_{pu} = \frac{kVA_{base}}{kVA_{source}}$$

*Motor contribution:*

$$Z_{pu} = X_d'' \times \frac{kVA_{base}}{kVA_{motor}}$$

*Feeders:*

$$Z_{pu} = \frac{Z_f \times kVA_{base}}{(KV_{LL})^2 \times 1000}$$

where   $Z_f$ = feeder impedance in ohms
$X_d$ = subtransient reactance

For transformers:

$$Z_{pu} = \frac{(Z_{tr}\% \times kVA_b)}{100 \times kVA_{tr}}$$

$$Z_{tr} = \%Z \text{ of transformer}$$

| *Ohms equal* | *3ϕ* | *1ϕ* |
|---|---|---|
| Using L-N kV | $\dfrac{30(kV_{LN})^2\%Z}{kVA_{3\phi}}$ | $\dfrac{10(kV_{LN})^2\%Z}{kVA_{1\phi}}$ |
| Using L-L kV | $\dfrac{10(kV_{LL})^2\%Z}{kVA_{3\phi}}$ | $\dfrac{10(kV_{LL})^2\%Z}{3kVA_{1\phi}}$ |

## A.5.2   Table of asymmetry factors

TABLE A.2   **Asymmetrical Factors***

| Short-circuit power factor, percent | Short-circuit X/R ratio | Ratio to symmetrical rms amperes | | |
|---|---|---|---|---|
| | | Maximum 1-phase instantaneous peak amperes mp | Maximum 1-phase rms amperes at ½ cycle $M_m$ (asymmetrical factor) | Average 3-phase rms amperes at ½ Cycle $M_a$ |
| 0 | ∞ | 2.828 | 1.732 | 1.394 |
| 1 | 100.00 | 2.785 | 1.696 | 1.374 |
| 2 | 49.993 | 2.743 | 1.665 | 1.355 |
| 3 | 33.322 | 2.702 | 1.630 | 1.336 |
| 4 | 24.979 | 2.663 | 1.598 | 1.318 |
| 5 | 19.974 | 2.625 | 1.568 | 1.301 |
| 6 | 16.623 | 2.589 | 1.540 | 1.285 |
| 7 | 14.251 | 2.554 | 1.511 | 1.270 |
| 8 | 13.460 | 2.520 | 1.485 | 1.256 |
| 9 | 11.066 | 2.487 | 1.460 | 1.241 |
| 10 | 9.9301 | 2.455 | 1.436 | 1.229 |
| 11 | 9.0354 | 2.424 | 1.413 | 1.216 |
| 12 | 8.2733 | 2.394 | 1.391 | 1.204 |
| 13 | 7.6271 | 2.364 | 1.372 | 1.193 |
| 14 | 7.0721 | 2.336 | 1.350 | 1.182 |
| 15 | 6.5912 | 2.309 | 1.330 | 1.171 |
| 16 | 6.1695 | 2.282 | 1.312 | 1.161 |
| 17 | 5.7947 | 2.256 | 1.294 | 1.152 |
| 18 | 5.4649 | 2.231 | 1.277 | 1.143 |
| 19 | 5.1672 | 2.207 | 1.262 | 1.135 |
| 20 | 4.8990 | 2.183 | 1.247 | 1.127 |
| 21 | 4.6557 | 2.160 | 1.232 | 1.119 |
| 22 | 4.4341 | 2.138 | 1.218 | 1.112 |
| 23 | 4.2313 | 2.11 | 1.205 | 1.105 |
| 24 | 4.0450 | 2.095 | 1.192 | 1.099 |
| 25 | 3.8730 | 2.074 | 1.181 | 1.093 |
| 26 | 3.7138 | 2.054 | 1.170 | 1.087 |
| 27 | 3.5661 | 2.034 | 1.159 | 1.081 |
| 28 | 3.4286 | 2.015 | 1.149 | 1.075 |
| 29 | 3.3001 | 1.996 | 1.139 | 1.070 |
| 30 | 3.1798 | 1.978 | 1.130 | 1.066 |
| 31 | 3.0669 | 1.960 | 1.121 | 1.062 |
| 32 | 2.9608 | 1.943 | 1.113 | 1.057 |
| 33 | 2.8606 | 1.926 | 1.105 | 1.053 |
| 34 | 2.7660 | 1.910 | 1.098 | 1.049 |
| 35 | 2.6764 | 1.894 | 1.091 | 1.046 |

**TABLE A.2   Asymmetrical Factors\*** *(Continued)*

| Short-circuit power factor, percent | Short-circuit X/R ratio | Maximum 1-phase instantaneous peak amperes mp | Maximum 1-phase rms amperes at ½ cycle $M_m$ (asymmetrical factor) | Average 3-phase rms amperes at ½ Cycle $M_a$ |
|---|---|---|---|---|
| 36 | 2.5916 | 1.878 | 1.084 | 1.043 |
| 37 | 2.5109 | 1.863 | 1.078 | 1.039 |
| 38 | 2.4341 | 1.848 | 1.073 | 1.036 |
| 39 | 2.3611 | 1.833 | 1.068 | 1.033 |
| 40 | 2.2913 | 1.819 | 1.062 | 1.031 |
| 41 | 2.2246 | 1.805 | 1.057 | 1.028 |
| 42 | 2.1608 | 1.791 | 1.053 | 1.026 |
| 43 | 2.0996 | 1.778 | 1.049 | 1.024 |
| 44 | 2.0409 | 1.765 | 1.045 | 1.022 |
| 45 | 1.9845 | 1.753 | 1.041 | 1.020 |
| 46 | 1.9303 | 1.740 | 1.038 | 1.019 |
| 47 | 1.8780 | 1.728 | 1.034 | 1.017 |
| 48 | 1.8277 | 1.716 | 1.031 | 1.016 |
| 49 | 1.7791 | 1.705 | 1.029 | 1.014 |
| 50 | 1.7321 | 1.694 | 1.026 | 1.013 |
| 55 | 1.5185 | 1.641 | 1.015 | 1.008 |
| 60 | 1.3333 | 1.594 | 1.009 | 1.004 |
| 65 | 1.1691 | 1.553 | 1.004 | 1.002 |
| 70 | 1.0202 | 1.517 | 1.002 | 1.001 |
| 75 | 0.8819 | 1.486 | 1.0008 | 1.0004 |
| 80 | 0.7500 | 1.460 | 1.0002 | 1.00005 |
| 85 | 0.6198 | 1.439 | 1.00004 | 1.00002 |
| 100 | 0.0000 | 1.414 | 1.00000 | 1.00000 |

\* Reprinted with the permission of NEMA, Pub. No. BU 1-1972, Part 3, pg. 12, 13.

## A.5.3   Multipliers for source SC current contributions

**TABLE A.3    Multipliers for Source Short-Circuit Current Contributions**

| Type of Source(s) | First-cycle | | Interrupting | | Medium-voltage circuit breaker close and latch* | |
|---|---|---|---|---|---|---|
| | Multiply SCA or $SCA_M$ by | Multiply $Xd''$ by | Multiply SCA or $SCA_M$ by | Multiply $Xd''$ by | Multiply SCA or $SCA_M$ by | Multiply $Xd''$ by |
| Utility or power company | 1.0 | 1.0 | 1.0 | 1.0 | 1.0 | 1.0 |
| Generators[†] | 1.0 | 1.0 | 1.0 | 1.0 | 1.0 | 1.0 |
| Synchronous motors | 1.0 | 1.0 | 0.667 | 1.5 | 1.0 | 1.0 |
| Induction motors | | | | | | |
| Above 1000 hp at 1800 rpm | 1.0 | 1.0 | 0.667 | 1.5 | 1.0 | 1.0 |
| Above 250 hp at 3600 rpm | 1.0 | 1.0 | 0.667 | 1.5 | 1.0 | 1.0 |
| All others, 50 hp and above | 1.0 | 1.0 | 0.333 | 3.0 | 0.833 | 1.2 |
| All smaller than 50 hp | 1.0 | 1.0 | Neglect | Neglect | Neglect | Neglect |

\* Refers to calculations for medium-voltage circuit breakers as developed in national standards.
[†] Use $0.75Xd'$ for hydrogenerators without amortisseur windings.

## A.5.4  Modification factors

**TABLE A.4    Modification Factors for Momentary and Interrupting Duty Calculations**

| Duty calculation | System component | Impedance value for medium- and high-voltage calculations per ANSI/IEEE C37.010-1979 and ANSI C37.5-1979 | Impedance value for low-voltage calculations ANSI/IEEE C37.13-1980* |
|---|---|---|---|
| First cycle (momentary) calculations | Utility supply | $X_s$ | $X_s$ |
| | Plant generators | $X_d''$ | $X_d''$ |
| | Synchronous motors | $X_d''$ | $X_d''$ |
| | Induction Motors | | |
| | Above 1000 hp > 1200 r/min | $X_d''\ddagger$ | $X_d''\ddagger$ |
| | Above 250 hp > 1800 r/min | $X_d''\ddagger$ | $X_d''\ddagger$ |
| | All other motors | | |
| | 50–1000 hp | $1.2\,X_d''\ddagger$ | $X_d''\ddagger$ |
| | Less than 50 hp | neglect | $X_d''\ddagger$ |
| Interrupting calculations | Utility supply | $X_s$ | † |
| | Plant generators | $X_d''$ | † |
| | Synchronous motors | $1.5\,X_d''$ | † |
| | Induction Motors | | |
| | Above 1000 hp > 1200 r/min | $1.5\,X_d''\ddagger$ | † |
| | Above 250 hp > 1800 r/min | $1.5\,X_d''\ddagger$ | † |
| | All other motors | | |
| | 50–1000 hp | $3\,X_d''\ddagger$ | † |
| | Less than 50 hp | neglect | |

* Impedance ($Z$) values can be used for low-voltage breaker duties.
† Not applicable.
‡ $X_d''$ for induction motors = locked rotor reactance.

There are other sources of data for short-circuit calculations which are not included in this text. The following is a list of data and assorted empirical design factors that come up in practice.

From the *IEEE Buff Book:*

Table 1: Impedance Data For Three-phase Transformer with Primaries of up to 15,000 V and Secondaries of 600 V or Less

Table 2: Data For Three-phase Transformer with Secondaries of 2400 V or More (750–60,000 kVA)

Table 3: Constants of Medium-voltage Copper Conductors for 1 Foot Delta Spacing

Table 4: Constants of Medium-voltage Aluminum Cable Steel Reinforced for 1 Foot Delta Spacing

Table 5: 60 Hz Reactance Spacing Factor Xb in Milliohms per Conductor per 100 Foot

Table 6: 60 Hz Reactance Spacing Factor Xb in Milliohms per Conductor per 100 Foot

Table 7: Typical Conductor Spacings for Overhead Lines

Table 8: Approximate Minimum Conductor Spacings for Medium-voltage Cable (Copper and Aluminum) in Conduit

Table 9: Medium-voltage Cable in Conduit—reactance Factor M for Various Constructions and Installations

Table 10: 60 Hz Low Voltage Cable in Conduit-resistance (R) in Reactance (X) Data For Insulation Types Thw, Rhw, Rhh and Use in Milliohms per Conductor per 100 Foot at 25 Deg C Copper Conductor

Table 11: 60 Hz Low Voltage Cable in Conduit-resistance (R) in Reactance (X) Data for Insulation Types Thwn, Thhn in Milliohms per Conductor per 100 Foot at 25 Deg C Copper Conductor

Table 12: 60 Hz Low Voltage Busway Resistance (R) and Reactance (X) Data in Milliohms per Conductor per 100 Foot at 25 Deg C Copper Conductor

Table 13: Multipliers for Source Short Circuit Contributions

Table 14: Impedance Data for Single Phase Transformers

### A.5.5    Impedances of circuit elements

The *IEEE Red Book* contains "Typical Impedance Data for Short-Circuit Studies List of Data Tables and Figures." These are practical values based upon accumulated experience. When manufacturer information is nonavailable, you can get close. The advantage of a computer model is helpful because it makes it easy to update your system model based upon new information.

Table N1.1: Typical Reactance Values for Induction and Synchronous Machines, in Per-Unit of Machine kVA Ratings

Table N1.2: Representative Conductor Spacings for Overhead Lines

Table N1.3: Constants of Copper Conductors for 1 ft. Symmetrical Spacing

Table N1.4: Constants of Aluminum Cable, Steel Reinforced (ACSR), for 1 ft. Symmetrical Spacing *[There are formulas that can be used to adjust for other spacing.]*

Table N1.5: 60 Hz Reactance Spacing Factor XB, in Ohms per Conductor per 1000 ft.

Table N1.6: 60 Hz Reactance of Typical Three-Phase Cable Circuits, in Ohms per 1000 ft.

Table N1.7: 60 Hz Reactance of Typical Three-Phase Cable Circuits, in Ohms per 1000 ft.

Figure N1.1: X/R Ratio of Transformers (Based on ANSI/IEEE C37.010-1979)

Figure N1.2: X/R Range for Small Generators and Synchronous Motors (Solid Rotor and Salient Pole)

Figure N1.3: X/R Range for Three-Phase Induction Motors (*from ANSI/IEEE C37.010-1979*)

Multiplying Factors for Three-Phase Faults Fed Predominantly from Generators (*from ANSI/IEEE C37.5-1979* [*p306*])

Figures 103 & 104: Multiplying Factors for Line-to-Ground Faults Fed Predominantly from Generators (*from ANSI/IEEE C37.5-1979* [*p307*])

Table 24: Rotating-Machine Reactance (or Impedance) Multipliers

Table 27: Passive Element Reactances in Per Unit, 10 MVA Base

Table 28: Subtransient Reactances of Rotating Machines, Modified for First Cycle (Momentary) Duty Calculations, in Per Unit, 10 MVA Base

Table 29: Reactances, X/R Ratios, and Resistances for AC High Voltage Circuit Breaker Contact Parting Time (Interrupting) Short Circuit Duties

## A.6   Fuse Application Data

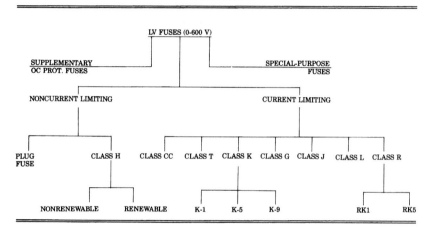

**Figure A.11**   UL classifications for low-voltage fuses.

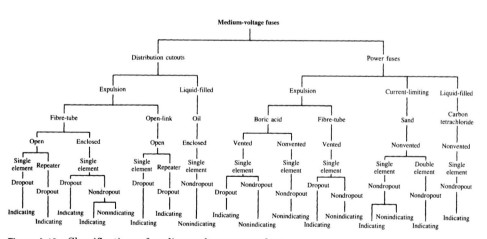

**Figure A.12**   Classifications of medium-voltage power fuses.

## A.7    Circuit-Breaker Application Data

TABLE A.5    Typical Interrupting Current Ratings of Molded-Case Circuit Breakers for Commercial and Industrial Applications*

| Frame size (amperes) | Number of poles | Interrupting rating in rms symmetrical amperes (000s) at ac voltage | | | | |
|---|---|---|---|---|---|---|
| | | 120 | 240 | 277 | 480 | 600 |
| 100 | 1 | 10 | — | — | — | — |
| | 1 | — | — | 14 | — | — |
| | 1 | — | — | 65 | — | — |
| 100, 150 | 2, 3 | — | 18 | — | 14 | 14 |
| | 2, 3 | — | 65 | — | 25 | 18 |
| 225, 250 | 2, 3 | — | 25 | — | 22 | 22 |
| | 2, 3 | — | 65 | — | 25 | 22 |
| 400, 600 | 2, 3 | — | 42 | — | 30 | 22 |
| | 2, 3 | — | 65 | — | 35 | 25 |
| 800, 1000 | 2, 3 | — | 42 | — | 30 | 22 |
| | 2, 3 | — | 65 | — | 50 | 25 |
| 1200 | 2, 3 | — | 42 | — | 30 | 22 |
| | 2, 3 | — | 65 | — | 50 | 25 |
| 1600, 2000 | 2, 3 | — | 65 | — | 50 | 42 |
| | 2, 3 | — | 125 | — | 100 | 65 |
| 3000, 4000 | 2, 3 | — | 100 | — | 100 | 85 |
| | 2, 3 | — | 200 | — | 150 | 100 |

* Does not include molded-case circuit breakers intended primarily for residential applications. Refer to specific manufacturers for information on those constructions.

NOTE:    Ratings shown are typical. Variations among manufacturers or product changes may result in actual ratings that differ from those shown. Consult specific manufacturers' literature for guidance.

**TABLE A.6    Summary of Breaker Ratings (Example ratings of low-voltage power circuit breakers)**

| Rated voltage (Nominal) 60 Hz | Breaker type | Frame size (Amperes) | Short-circuit ratings RMS symmetrical kA | | |
|---|---|---|---|---|---|
| | | | Short-time | With instantaneous trip | Without instantaneous trip |
| 600 | AK-25 | 600 | 22 | 22 | 22 |
| | AKR-30S | 800 | 22 | 22 | 22* |
| | AKR-30 | 800 | 30 | 30 | 30 |
| | AKR-30H | | 42 | 42 | 42 |
| | AKS/AKR-50 | 1600 | 42 | 42 | 42 |
| | AKS/AKR-50H | | 65 | 65 | 65 |
| | AKST/AKRT-50H | 2000 | 65 | 65 | 65 |
| | AKR-75 | 3200 | 65 | 65 | 65 |
| | AKR-100 | 4000 | 85 | 85 | 85 |
| 480 | AK-25 | 600 | 22 | 30 | 22 |
| | AKR-30S | 800 | 22 | 30 | 30* |
| | AKR-30 | 800 | 30 | 30 | 30 |
| | AKR-30H | | 42 | 42 | 42 |
| | AKS/AKR-50 | 1600 | 50 | 50 | 50 |
| | AKS/AKR-50H | | 65 | 65 | 65 |
| | AKST/AKRT-50H | 2000 | 65 | 65 | 65 |
| | AKR-75 | 3200 | 65 | 65 | 65 |
| | AKR-100 | 4000 | 85 | 85 | 85 |
| 240 | AK-25 | 600 | 22 | 42 | 22 |
| | AKR-30S | 800 | 22 | 42 | 42* |
| | AKR-30 | 800 | 30 | 42 | 30 |
| | AKR-30H | | 42 | 50 | 42 |
| | AKS/AKR-50 | 1600 | 50 | 65 | 50 |
| | AKS/AKR-50H | | 65 | 65 | 65 |
| | AKST/AKRT-50H | 2000 | 65 | 65 | 65 |
| | AKR-75 | 3200 | 65 | 85 | 65 |
| | AKR-100 | 4000 | 85 | 130 | 85 |

\*    Triple Selective Trip at 1× short-time rating when standard instantaneous trip is omitted.

1. The maximum fuse rating is the largest fuse which tests show will result in proper performance of the breaker and fuse in combination under short-circuit conditions. Only Gould fuses should be used for proper coordination.

2. Fuses are mounted on separate fuse roll-out element.

3. Refer to time-current curves GES-6000 (for EC-1) and GES-6005 (for EC-1B).

4. Only dual ratio sensors are available on AKR-30S when programmers are furnished with high-range instantaneous or triple selective trip.

(*Table is used courtesy of General Electric.*)

**TABLE A.7  Preferred Ratings ‡ for Medium-Voltage Indoor Oilless Circuit Breakers**

| Rated maximum voltage[1] kV, rms | Rated voltage range factor K[2] | Rated continuous current at 60 Hz[3] amperes, rms | Rated short-circuit current* (at rated maximum kV[4,5,6]) kA, rms | Transient Recovery Voltages[9] | | | Rated interrupting time[7] cycles[8] | Rated maximum voltage divided by K kV, rms[¶] | Maximum symmetrical interrupting capability and rated short-time current[4,5,8] kA, rms | Closing and latching capability 2.7K times rated short-circuit current[4] kA, crest |
| | | | | Rated time to point P T2[†] μ sec | Rated rate R kV/μ sec | Rated delay time T1 μ sec | | | | |
|---|---|---|---|---|---|---|---|---|---|---|
| 4.76 | 1.36 | 1200 | 8.8 | — | — | — | 5 | 3.5 | 12 | 32 |
| 4.76 | 1.24 | 1200, 2000 | 29 | — | — | — | 5 | 3.85 | 36 | 97 |
| 4.76 | 1.19 | 1200, 2000, 3000 | 41 | — | — | — | 5 | 4.0 | 49 | 132 |
| 8.25 | 1.25 | 1200, 2000 | 33 | — | — | — | 5 | 6.6 | 41 | 111 |
| 15.0 | 1.30 | 1200, 2000 | 18 | — | — | — | 5 | 11.5 | 23 | 62 |
| 15.0 | 1.30 | 1200, 2000 | 28 | — | — | — | 5 | 11.5 | 36 | 97 |
| 15.0 | 1.30 | 1200, 2000, 3000 | 37 | — | — | — | 5 | 11.5 | 48 | 130 |
| 38.0 | 1.65 | 1200, 2000, 3000 | 21 | — | — | — | 5 | 23.0 | 35 | 95 |
| 38.0 | 1.0 | 1200, 3000 | 40 | — | — | — | 5 | 38.0 | 40 | 108 |

* For the related required capabilities associated with the rated short-circuit current of the circuit breaker, see Note 4.

† These rated values are not yet standardized. Work is in progress.

‡ For service conditions, definitions, and interpretation of ratings, tests, and qualifying terms, see ANSI/IEEE C37.04-1979, ANSI/IEEE C37.09-1979, and ANSI/IEEE C37.100-1981.

§ The interrupting ratings are for 60-Hz systems. Applications on 25-Hz systems should receive special consideration.

¶ Current values have been rounded off to the nearest kiloampere (kA) except that two significant figures are used for values below 10 kA.

[1] The voltage rating is based on ANSI C84.1-1982, where applicable, and is the maximum voltage for which the breaker is designed and the upper limit for operation.

[2] The rated voltage range factor, K, is the ratio of rated maximum voltage to the lower limit of the range of operating voltage in which the required symmetrical and asymmetrical current interrupting capabilities vary in inverse proportion to the operating voltage.

[3] The 25-Hz continuous current ratings in amperes are given herewith following the respective 60-Hz rating: 600–700; 1200–1400; 2000–2250; 3000–3500.

[4] Related required capabilities. The following related required capabilities are associated with the short-circuit current rating of the circuit breaker. (a) Maximum symmetrical interrupting capability (kA, rms) of the circuit breaker is equal to K times rated short-circuit current. (b) 3-sec short-time current carrying capability (kA, rms) of the circuit breaker is equal to K times rated short-circuit current. (c) Closing and latching capability (kA, rms) of the circuit breaker is equal to 1.6 K times rated short-circuit current. If expressed in peak amperes, the value is equal to 2.7 K times rated short-circuit current. (d) 3-sec short-time current carrying capability and closing and latching capability are independent of operating voltage up to and including rated maximum voltage.

[5] To obtain the required symmetrical current interrupting capability of a circuit breaker at an operating voltage between 1/K times rated maximum voltage and rated maximum voltage, the following formula shall be used:

Required symmetrical current interrupting capability

$$= \text{rated short-circuit current} \times \frac{(\text{rated maximum voltage})}{(\text{operating voltage})}$$

For operating voltages below 1/K times rated maximum voltage, the required symmetrical current interrupting capability of the circuit breaker shall be equal to K times rated short-circuit current.

[6] With the limitation stated in 5.10 of ANSI/IEEE C37.04-1979, all values apply for polyphase and line-to-line faults. For single phase-to-ground faults, the specific conditions stated in 5.10.2.3 of ANSI/IEEE C37.04-1979 apply.

[7] The ratings in this column are on a 60-Hz basis and are the maximum time interval to be expected during a breaker opening operation between the instant of energizing the trip circuit and interruption of the main circuit on the primary arcing contacts under certain specified conditions. The values may be exceeded under certain conditions as specified in 5.7 of ANSI/IEEE C37.04-1979.

[8] Current values in this column are not to be exceeded even for operating voltages below 1/K times rated maximum voltage. For voltages between rated maximum voltage and 1/K times rated maximum voltage, follow (5) above.

## A.8   Transformer Protection Data

Original 11×17 onionskins of these curves are available from the IEEE and ANSI Publications Department.

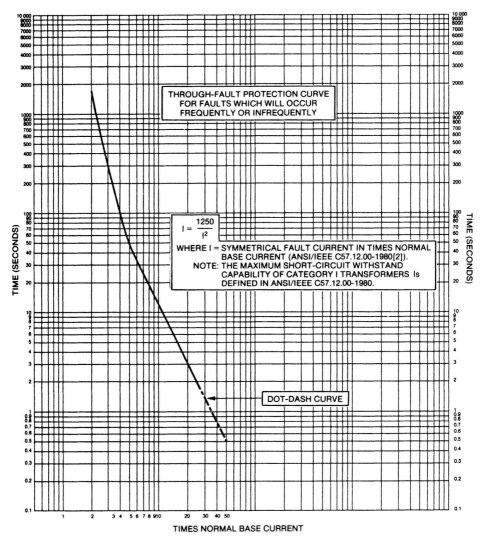

**Figure A.13**   Damage curves for Category I transformers, 5 to 500 kVA single-phase, 15 to 500 kVA three-phase.

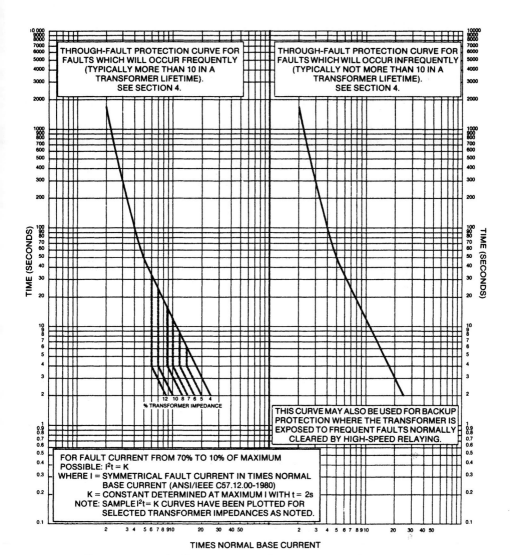

**THROUGH-FAULT PROTECTION CURVE FOR FAULTS WHICH WILL OCCUR FREQUENTLY (TYPICALLY MORE THAN 10 IN A TRANSFORMER LIFETIME). SEE SECTION 4.**

**THROUGH-FAULT PROTECTION CURVE FOR FAULTS WHICH WILL OCCUR INFREQUENTLY (TYPICALLY NOT MORE THAN 10 IN A TRANSFORMER LIFETIME). SEE SECTION 4.**

% TRANSFORMER IMPEDANCE

THIS CURVE MAY ALSO BE USED FOR BACKUP PROTECTION WHERE THE TRANSFORMER IS EXPOSED TO FREQUENT FAULTS NORMALLY CLEARED BY HIGH-SPEED RELAYING.

FOR FAULT CURRENT FROM 70% TO 10% OF MAXIMUM POSSIBLE: $I^2t = K$
WHERE I = SYMMETRICAL FAULT CURRENT IN TIMES NORMAL BASE CURRENT (ANSI/IEEE C57.12.00-1980)
K = CONSTANT DETERMINED AT MAXIMUM I WITH t = 2s
NOTE: SAMPLE $I^2t = K$ CURVES HAVE BEEN PLOTTED FOR SELECTED TRANSFORMER IMPEDANCES AS NOTED.

TIME (SECONDS)

TIMES NORMAL BASE CURRENT

**Figure A.14**  Damage curves for Category II transformers, 501-1667 kVA single-phase, 501-5000 kVA three-phase.

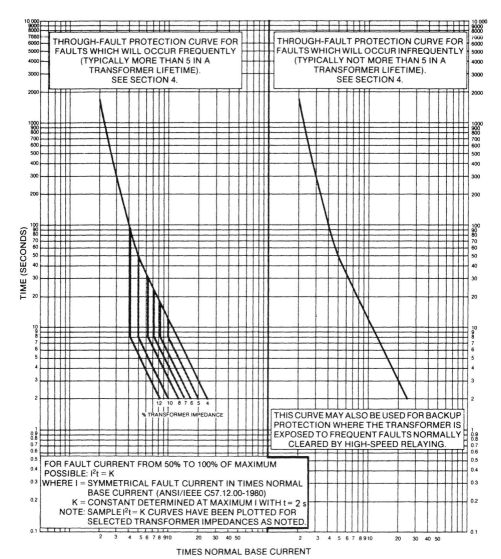

**Figure A.15** Damage curves for Category III transformers, 1668 to 10,000 single-phase, 5001 to 30,000 kVA three-phase.

## A.9   Instrument Transformer Data

**TABLE A.8   Standard Accuracy
Class Ratings\* of Current
Transformers in Metal-
Enclosed Low-Voltage Power
Circuit Breaker Switchgear**

| Ratio | B 0.1 | B 0.2 |
|-------|-------|-------|
| 100/5 | 1.2 | 2.4[†] |
| 150/5 | 1.2 | 2.4[†] |
| 200/5 | 1.2 | 1.2 |
| 300/5 | 0.6 | 0.6 |
| 400/5 | 0.6 | 0.6 |
| 600/5 | 0.6 | 0.6 |
| 800/5 | 0.3 | 0.3 |
| 1200/5 | 0.3 | 0.3 |
| 1500/5 | 0.3 | 0.3 |
| 2000/5 | 0.3 | 0.3 |
| 3000/5 | 0.3 | 0.3 |
| 4000/5 | 0.3 | 0.3 |

\* See ANSI/IEEE C57.13-1978.
[†] Not in ANSI/IEEE C57.13-1978.
From ANSI/IEEE C37.20-1969.

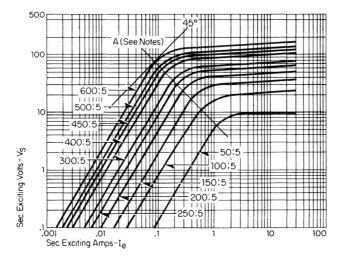

| Current<br>Ratio | Turn<br>Ratio | Sec.<br>Res. 1 |
|---|---|---|
| 50:5 | 10:1 | .061 |
| 100:5 | 20:1 | .082 |
| 150:5 | 30:1 | .104 |
| 200:5 | 40:1 | .125 |
| 250:5 | 50:1 | .146 |
| 300:5 | 60:1 | .168 |
| 400:5 | 80:1 | .211 |
| 450:5 | 90:1 | .230 |
| 500:5 | 100:1 | .242 |
| 600:5 | 120:1 | .296 |

**Notes:**

1) Above The Line, The Voltage for a Given Exciting Current Will Not be Less Than 95% of The Curve Value.

2) Below The Line, The Exciting Current for a Given Voltage Will Not Exceed The Curve Value by More Than 25%.

**Figure A.16** Excitation curves for a multiratio bushing current transformer with an ANSI accuracy classification of C100. Curves like this will differ among manufacturers and will especially differ among construction styles

Because accuracy in relaying CTs is of importance at higher magnitudes or current, the ANSI method for specifying accuracy is described by the secondary voltage the CT can develop at twenty times rated secondary current without exceeding 100 percent ratio error. At the knee point of the secondary excitation curve, the exciting current drawn by the core increases far more rapidly than does the secondary excitation voltage, and thus the ratio error of the current transformer rapidly becomes more severe.

These secondary excitation characteristics are a simplification of the far more involved B-H hysteresis curve of magnetic materials which relates core flux density B and magnetizing force H. Secondary excitation characteristics are often accompanied by phase angle curves which can be used to restore the complex nature of the core impedance by expressing the angular shift between exciting current and excitation voltage. The use of phase angle curve along with complex manipulation of impedances will give greater precision to approximation calculations. (*From* Applied Protective Relaying, *Marcel Dekker, 1994*)

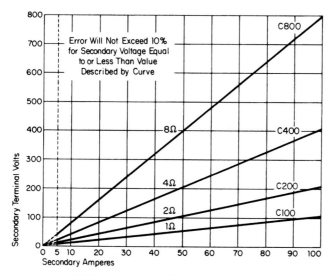

**Figure A.17**  ANSI accuracy standard chart for four (4) Class C current transformers. (*From* Applied Protective Relaying, *Marcel Dekker, 1994*)

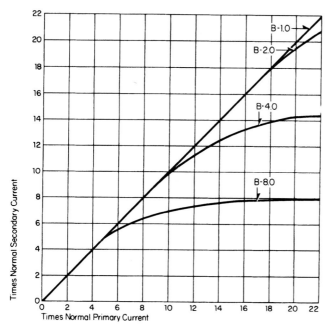

**Figure A.18**  Typical overcurrent ratio curves for a T Class current transformer. (*From* ANSI C57.13 *and* Applied Protective Relaying, *Marcel Dekker, 1994*)

TABLE A.9  Ratings and Characteristics of Voltage Transformers*

| Rated primary voltage for rated voltage line-to-line (V) | Marked ratio | Basic impulse insulation level (kV crest) |
|---|---|---|
| 120 for 120Y | 1:1 | 10 |
| 240 for 240Y | 2:1 | 10 |
| 300 for 300Y | 2.5:1 | 10 |
| 480 for 480Y | 4:1 | 10 |
| 600 for 600Y | 5:1 | 10 |
| 2400 for 2400Y | 20:1 | 45 |
| 4800 for 4800Y | 40:1 | 60 |
| 7200 for 7200Y | 60:1 | 75 |
| 12,000 for 12,000Y | 100:1 | 110 or 95 |
| 14,000 for 14,000Y | 120:1 | 110 or 95 |
| 24,000 for 24,000Y | 200:1 | 150 or 125 |
| 34,500 for 34,500Y | 300:1 | 200 or 150 |

* Voltage transformers primarily for line-to-line service; may be applied line-to-ground or line-to-neutral at a winding voltage equal to the primary voltage rating divided by $\sqrt{3}$.

TABLE A.10  Standard Burdens for Voltage Transformers

| | Characteristics on standard burdens* | | Characteristics on 120-V basis | | |
|---|---|---|---|---|---|
| Designation | Volt-amperes | Power factor | Resistance (ohms) | Inductance (henries) | Impedance (ohms) |
| W | 12.5 | 0.10 | 115.2 | 3.04 | 1152 |
| X | 25 | 0.70 | 403.2 | 1.09 | 576 |
| Y | 75 | 0.85 | 163.2 | 0.268 | 192 |
| Z | 200 | 0.85 | 61.2 | 0.101 | 72 |
| ZZ | 400 | 0.85 | 30.6 | 0.0503 | 36 |
| M | 35 | 0.20 | 82.3 | 1.07 | 411 |

* These burden designations have no significance except at 60 Hz.

## A.10    Guide to ANSI/IEEE Standards

Although the list of ANSI/IEEE standards may seem overwhelming, the material itself is surprisingly readable. The following is a list of the most relevant to the protection specialist.

ANSI/IEEE C37.20.1-1987, *IEEE Standard for Metal-Enclosed Low-Voltage Power Circuit Breaker Switchgear*

ANSI/IEEE C37.16-1980, *American National Standard Related Requirements and Application Recommendations for Low-Voltage Power Circuit Breakers and AC Power Circuit Protectors, Preferred Ratings*

ANSI/IEEE C37.13-1980, *American National Standard for Low-Voltage AC Power Circuit Protectors Used in Enclosures*

ANSI/IEEE C37.14-1980, *American National Standard for Low-Voltage AC Power Circuit Protectors Used in Enclosures*

ANSI/IEEE C37.29-1974, *American National Standard Related Requirements and Application Recommendations for Low-Voltage AC Power Circuit Protectors Used in Enclosures*

ANSI/IEEE C37.16-1980, *American National Standard Related Requirements and Application Recommendations for Low-Voltage Power Circuit Breakers and AC Power Circuit Protectors, Preferred Ratings*

ANSI/IEEE C37.16-1980, *American National Standard Related Requirements and Application Recommendations for Low-Voltage Power Circuit Breakers and AC Power Circuit Protectors, Preferred Ratings*

ANSI/IEEE Std 142-1991, *IEEE Recommended Practice for Grounding of Industrial and Commercial Power Systems*

ANSI/IEEE Std 241-1990, *IEEE Recommended Practice for Electric Power Systems in Commercial Buildings*

ANSI/IEEE Std 446-1980, *IEEE Recommended Practice for Emergency and Standby Power Systems for Industrial and Commercial Applications*

ANSI/IEEE Std 242-1986, *IEEE Recommended Practice for Protection and Coordination of Industrial and Commercial Power Systems*

ANSI/IEEE Std 399-1990, *IEEE Recommended Practice for Power Systems Analysis*

ANSI/IEEE Std 602-1986, *IEEE Recommended Practice for Electric Systems in Health Care Facilities*

ANSI/NFPA 70-1993, *National Electric Code*

ANSI/IEEE C37.35-1976, *Guide for Application, Installation, Operation, and Maintenance of High-Voltage Air Disconnecting and Load Interrupter Switches*

ANSI/IEEE C37.32-1972, *Schedules of Preferred Ratings, Manufacturing Specifications, and Application Guide for High-Voltage Air Switches, Bus Supports, and Switch Accessories*

ANSI/IEEE C97.1-1972, *American National Standard for Low-Voltage Cartridge Fuses, 600 Volts or Less*

ANSI/IEEE C57.13-1978, *Requirements for Instrument Transformers*

ANSI/IEEE 57.12.01-1979, *IEEE Standard General Requirements for Dry-Type Distribution and Power Transformers*

# Index

Alias effect in microprocessor-based relays, 289
American National Standards Institute (ANSI):
  C37.010, 65
  C37.101, 268
  C37.13, 181, 65
  C37.20, 383
  C37.5, 65
  C37.61, 343
  C37.90, 290
  C37.91, 197, 321
  C57.12, 249
  C57.13, 101, 108, 383
  C57.13, 98
  C57.92, 108
Amp frame/sensor/trip notation, 246
Analog-to-digital converter in microprocessor-based relays, 288–290
Anderson, P. M., 47, 48
*ANSI/IEEE Standards*, guide to, 387
Arcing faults, 12, 63, 137–139, 353
  in induction motors, 216
  table of minimum per-unit values, 138
Asea-Brown-Boveri (ABB), 34, 166, 249, 281, 362–364
Asymmetry factors, 86–87, 352, 369–370
Automatic transfer switches, 165

Basic impulse ratings, 3
Basler Electric Co., 289
Beeman, D. L., 48, 69
Bergen, A., 53
Blackburn, J. L., 16, 43, 48, 52, 108, 155, 203, 238, 274, 290
Bolted pressure switches, 206
Boundary conditions, 48–49

Branch circuit:
  protection requirements, 173
  receptacles, 150
  taps, 174–175
Breaker-fuse coordination, 241
Breaker short-time ratings, 23
Bulk distribution switching stations, 267–312
Burden, in current transformers, 99, 103
Bus:
  differential protection, 153, 301–302
  overcurrent protection, 158, 301
  tie-line protection examples, 281, 332
Bussman (Cooper Industries), 27, 200

Cable:
  coordination study, 194
  faulted medium voltage, 141
  protection, 246
  shielding considerations at medium voltage, 141, 157
Category I transformer protection, 106–107, 197
Category II transformer damage curve, 262
Category III transformer protection example, 321
Category IV transformers, 321
Checklist for coordinating overcurrent devices, 350
Circuit breaker
  application of low voltage, 180–189
  application principles, 95–98
  frame ratings, 24
  trip curves, 24
Close-and-latch ratings in medium-voltage breakers, 84, 268
Cold load pickup, 8–9

Combination motor starter, 206
Combination starters, fused for motors, 214
Computer software, 67–69
Computerized graphic databases, 24
Conductor(s):
  protection at low voltage, 189
  short-circuit protection, 190–194
*Consulting/Specifying Engineer* magazine, 179, 182, 198
Cooper-Bussman, 177, 356–357
Coordination of primary fuses with main breakers, 241
Coordination study, double-ended substation, 260–265
Coordination time intervals, 113–122
  across a delta-wye transformer, 121–122
  delays, 20
  fuses over fuses, 116
  fuses over relays, 116
  instantaneous device over instantaneous device, 120
  relay over relay, 115
  relay over trip devices or fuses, 116
  time-delay relay over time-delay relay, 121
  trip device over trip device, 119
  trip devices over fuses, 119
Core balance current transformers, 156
Crnko, Timothy, 92
Current transformer(s):
  application data, 383–385
  application example, 98–105
  calculations, 103–104
  connections for transformer differential protection example, 304–306
  core balance, 156–158
  ratio, selection procedure for medium-voltage radial feeder, 295–300
  saturation, 114
  window type, 158
Current-limiting fuses, 12, 88, 92, 234–238, 351

Dc transients, 66
Dedad, John A., 292
Definition of overcurrent, 23
Delayed trip, 85
Delta-wye transformers, 351
Differential principle, 4
Differential principle, application in ground-fault protection, 158

Differential relays, 125
  application principles for medium-voltage switchgear, 303–306
  protection, 17
  ways to assure improper operation, 306
Direct-acting trip units, 114–115
Direct-axis transient reactance, 14
Directional ground overcurrent relays, 317–319
Directional phase overcurrent relays, 280–285
Directional power relay, 319
Distance protection, 17
Distance relays, 125
Double-ended substation, 246
Double-line-to-ground fault(s), 47
  calculation example, 61–62
Dual feed service, 325–337
Dunki-Jacobs, 63, 135, 139
Duty, definition, 83

Edison, Thomas, 81
Edison Electric Institute (EEI), 94
EDSA Micro Corporation, 70–71, 108, 123, 257
Effectively grounded system, 129, 150
*Electrical Construction & Maintenance* magazine (*EC&M*), 198, 201
Elmore, Walter, 285, 288, 306
Emergency generation, overcurrent protection for, 330
Equipment ground, 130–133
Estimated clearing times of protective devices, 355
Expulsion fuses, 93, 233

Farrell, George, 64
Fault current:
  asymmetry, 41
  dynamics, 64
  low levels of, 63
  maximums, 66–67
  medium-voltage cable, 141
  minimums, 63, 66–67
  waveforms, 48, 56
Fault impedance, 41
Fault real time frame, 12
Fault-clearing period, 13
Faults, origins of, 10–12
Ferroresonance, 154, 197
Fire pump protection, 198
Flowchart for selection of substation breaker trip functions, 264–265

Four pole transfer switches, 165
Free neutral, grounding system, 129, 140
Full-voltage starting, in motors, 209
Fuse(s), 81
  arcing time, 91
  cartridge, 177
  classes, 89
  common plug, 176
  current-limiting, 92, 234–238
  dual-element, 90, 176
  expulsion, 93, 233
  family trees, 375
  $I^2t$ considerations, 89–90
  let-through considerations, 89
  low-voltage current-limiting, 176
  low-voltage non-current-limiting, 176
  medium voltage, 93–95, 231
  melting time, 91
  minimum melt curve, 93
  selectivity ratios, 177–178
  series ratings, 90
  short-time rating, 89
  single-element low voltage, 90
  speed ratio, 94
  total clearing curve, 93
  total clearing time, 91
  voltage considerations, 88

General Electric, 29, 259, 285, 359
Generalized overcurrent relays, 275–277
Generator(s):
  fault contribution, 52
  field excitation, 52
  reactances, 52
Giengar, J. A., 160
Ground fault(s):
  coordination in unit substations,
    256–259
  current, 61
  detector relay, 317
  example in double-ended substation, 263
  impedance, total, 47
  in double-ended unit substations,
    252–253, 256–259
  overcurrent relays, 316
  pick-up, 189
  protection, 129–169
  protection, modified differential
    scheme, 258
  protection, where not required, 164
  protection, where required, 164
  protection in critical applications, 166
  protection schemes, 159–166

Ground fault(s) (Cont.):
  relay sensitivity, 285
  sensing sensitivity, 159
  trip curves, 24
  using fuses only, 160–164
  with low-voltage relays, 162–164
Ground, equipment and system, 130–133
Grounding:
  high impedance, 143–146
  high-speed switch, 313
  low impedance, 146
  low-voltage distribution systems,
    151–153
  medium-voltage distribution systems,
    154
  solid, 147–150
  system classification summary, 150
Ground relays, directional overcurrent,
  284–285, 317
Ground return impedance, 43
Ground return sensing, 158

Hamer, Paul S., 293
Handy numbers, 351
Harmonic restraint, in transformer differ-
  ential relays, 303
Harmonics, effect on microprocessor
  relays, 288
Heaters, for motors, 206
Henville, C. F., 280
High-impedance grounding, 143
High-resistance grounding, 150
High-speed grounding switches, 313
Hot load pickup, 9–10

$I^2t$:
  curves, 321
  fault energy, 21
  IN/OUT, 185
  tripping characteristic, 189
IEC Type 1 and Type 2 Coordination,
  222
International Electrotechnical
  Commission (IEC), 70, 82, 222, 288
Impedances of circuit elements, data
  references, 373
Induction motor(s), 40, 53–56
  equivalent circuit, 203–205
  rotor, 54
  stator, 54
  wound rotor, 54
Infinite bus short-circuit calculation, 41,
  42, 53

Instantaneous:
  elements, 278–279
  override, 25
  pick-up, 189
  ratings, in power circuit breakers,
    180–181
  relay setpoint calculation, 240
  trips, 85
Instrument transformer(s), 98–105
  data, 383–386
  solved application problems, 269–275
Insulated case breakers, 180
Internal faults, in transformers, 319
Interrupting ratings, 84–86, 96
  for motor control centers, 217–219
  for unit substation secondary breakers,
    245
Inverse overcurrent relay, overview,
    276–277
Isolation transformers, 146, 165

$K_0$ and $K_1$ factor for low-voltage cables,
    190
K multiplier, 138
K-factor, 83
Kaufman, R. H., 160
Kerite, 282
Keuffel & Esser log-log paper, 26
Kresser, J. V., 16

Light box, 29
Lighting:
  circuit protection, 179
  panels, 39, 174
Line pilot relays, 316–317, 346
Line-to-line fault, 47
Locked rotor amperes, 6–7, 199, 215, 217
  asymmetrical in motor starting, 223
Long delay pickup, 186–187
Long delay time, 186–187
Love, Daniel J., 85, 139
Low voltage:
  circuit breaker application data,
    376–377
  circuit breaker sensors, 24
  circuit breaker trip units, 24
  fuse applications, 88, 176
Low-impedance grounding, 146

Main breaker-primary fuse coordination,
    241
Main-tie-main phase protection, 255–256

Margins, time between tripping charac-
    teristics, 113–122
Maximum asymmetry, 42
McPartland, Joseph, 221
Medium voltage
  breaker, ANSI preferred ratings,
    378–379
  breaker switchgear specification calcu-
    lations, 306–309
  breakers, 268–269
  cable shields, 292–294
  circuit breaker, MVA Class, 98
  feeder overcurrent protection, 291–301
  feeder protection, 272–275
  transformer protection, 230–242
Microprocessor-based relays, 122
Mining system grounding, 147
Models of faulted circuits, 135
Modification factors for momentary and
    interrupting capacity calculations,
    372
Molded case breakers, 24, 150, 180
  interchangeability in, 24
Momentary fault current, 14
Momentary ratings, 85
Motor(s), 5
  branch circuit protection, 207–210
  branch circuit taps, 175
  circuit protector, 221, 250
  combination starters, 217
  control center interrupting ratings,
    217–219
  control center withstand ratings,
    217–219
  control centers, 203–228
  energy efficient, 7
  fault-current contribution, 53
  feeder protection, 247–249
  full-load amperes, 7
  group branch circuit design example,
    223–227
  group protection, 216–221
  inrush amperes and asymmetry, 7
  low full-load currents, 212
  major causes of malfunctions, 205
  protection design, groups of motors,
    223
  protection rules, 207–208
  starting current, 6, 205
  Type 1 and Type 2 coordination in, 222
  variable frequency drives, 221
  various starting characteristics, 215

Motor control, 223–225
    power requirements, 286–287
    relay application considerations,
        286–291
    reset, 287
Multipliers for source short-circuit contri-
    butions, 371

Nash, Hugh O., 139, 153, 165
National Electric Code (NEC):
    NEC Art. 100, 23, 83, 84, 132
    NEC Art. 110, 179, 353
    NEC Art. 110-9, 84
    NEC Art. 210, 171
    NEC Art. 215, 171
    NEC Art. 220, 171
    NEC Art. 220-10(b), 83
    NEC Art. 225, 171
    NEC Art. 230, 229, 246, 353
    NEC Art. 230-95, 135, 152
    NEC Art. 240, 171, 172, 179, 230, 246,
        353
    NEC Art. 240-3, 248
    NEC Art. 240-6, 187, 195–196
    NEC Art. 240-21, 174
    NEC Art. 250, 132
    NEC Art. 250-5, 148
    NEC Art. 310, 189, 223, 230, 291
    NEC Art. 384, 216
    NEC Art. 410-73, 179
    NEC Art. 430, 174, 177, 207, 210,
        216–217, 225–227, 353
    NEC Art. 430-7(b), 7
    NEC Art. 430-52, 90
    NEC Art. 430-62, 220, 247
    NEC Art. 430-150, 7, 221, 223
    NEC Art. 430-152, 90, 221
    NEC Art. 450, 195, 230, 247, 351
    NEC Art. 450-3, 242
    NEC Art. 517, 151
    NEC Art. 710, 353
    NEC Chapter 9, 172
    NEC, core requirements for overcurrent
        protection, 21–22
National Electric Code Handbook, 22,
    173, 198
National Electrical Manufacturers
    Association (NEMA), 7, 43, 65, 94, 95,
    222
Negative sequence impedance, 43
Neher-McGrath, 292
NEMA Starters, 5

Neutral:
    current, 134
    current transformers, 154–155
    grounding, 166
    inversion, 155
    relaying, in ground-fault protection,
        159
    sensors, 246
Neutral-to-ground, multiple connections,
    134
Nochumson, Charles J., 248, 346
Northeast power blackout, 286

Ohm's Law, 43, 46, 48
Okonite Cable Company, 192
Onan Electric Company, 146
Overcurrent:
    application principles, 172
    devices, definition of, 4
    protection in multiple-source circuits,
        300–301
Overload protection, for unit substation
    transformers, 241
Overload relays in motors, 205, 211
Overrides in trip functions, 188
Overtravel, in electromechanical relays,
    114, 276

Paape, Kenneth L., 89, 212
Parallel operation, overcurrent protection
    for, 334–337
Password entry to microprocessor-based
    relays, 286
Peak-let-through current, 200
Per-unit formulas, 368
Percentage differential relay, 111–113
Phadke, Arun, 291
Phase protection, main-tie-main in dou-
    ble-ended substations, 255–256
Phase-fault trip curves, 24
Pilot wire protection, 21
Pilot-line relays, 125, 316–317
Positive sequence impedance, 43
Positive sequence network, 41
Powell, Louis, 285
Power angle, 12
Power distribution panels, 150, 170–202
Power factor, 12
Power panels, 171–202
Power sources, ground-fault protection in
    alternate, 164
Prefault load current, 40

Pressure relays, 318
Primary and backup protection, 18
Primary fuse-circuit breaker coordination, 241
Principal applications for relays, 122–124
Protected and protecting, 16
Protective device specification flowchart, 264–265
Protective zone boundaries, 16–20

Radial circuit definition, 300
Rating plugs, for secondary breakers, 243
Ratio correction factor, 102
Reactance grounded, 150
Reclosers, 313–314, 342–346
Residual connection, grounding, 155–156
Resistance grounded, 150
Restraining windings in differential relays, 111–113
Rotating machine reactance, 53

Safety factor(s):
    in coordination time intervals, 114
    in current transformer ratio sizing, 282
Saturation, in current transformers, 102–103, 359
Schwartzburg, William E., 248
Schweitzer, Edmund O., 291
Secondary breaker(s), 245
    features of microprocessor-based, 244–245
    in unit substations, 242
    main breakers, 166–168
    trip unit test equipment, 244
Sectionalizers, 314
Sensors (98):
    coordination with trip units, 24
    for secondary breakers, 246
Separately derived service/system, 132, 165, 256
Service factor, 209, 211
Service factor, applied motor circuit design, 223
Short delay pick-up, 186–187
Short delay time, 186–187
Short-circuit calculations, 39–80
    fault power method, 56–63
    single-phase, 64
Short-circuit performance of transformers, 106
Short-time ratings, 87, 96
Short-time ratings, in power circuit breakers, 180–181

Shunt faults, 48
Siemens-ITE, 27, 358
Single-feed service, 319–325
Single-line-to-ground fault(s), 50, 137–139
    calculations, 43–46, 59, 64
    in transformers, 235–240
Single-point grounding, 164
SKM Analysis, 74–78, 185, 235, 249
Smeaton, 325, 332
Smith, Robert L., 63, 139
Software, computer, 67–68
Software for microprocessor-based relays, 286
Solid grounding, 147–150
Solid-state relays, 104
Solid-state trip units, 183, 186–189
Solid-state variable percentage differential relay, 112–113
Source plot, 26
Square D (SQ-D) Ground Censor, 367
Squirrel-cage induction motors, 209
Standby generators, protection for, 333
Steel frame breakers, 180
Stevenson, William D., 52, 306
Stray neutral current, 132
Substation coordination study example, 249–250
Subtransient reactance interval, 12, 14, 54, 66
Sudden pressure relay, 333
Symmetrical components, 40, 42
Synchronizing relays, 340–342
Synchronous machine reactance, 66
Synchronous motors, 53–54
System ground, 130–133

Tap changing, effect of differential protection, 303–304
Target plot, 26
Thermal overload(s), 205
    protection for motors, 214–215
Thermal-magnetic breakers, 182–186
    applied to motors, 213
Thevenin impedance, 48
Thevenin voltage, 40
    calculation, 40
    three-phase bolted faults, 43, 50
Tie circuit protection, 259
Time required to solve coordination problems, 4
Time-current scaling arithmetic, 25–35
Time-delay bands, 24

Tolerance zones, in medium-voltage relay time-current characteristics, 114–115
Tone telemetry, 346
Transfer considerations in standby generators, 248
Transfer switches, automatic, 165
Transformation ratio, 29, 32
Transformer connection phase shift, 240
Transformer(s):
  Category I, 106–107
  Category II, 107
  Category III, 107–108
  Category IV, 108
  damage curve shifting, 8
  damage curves, 23
  damage curves, Category II, 235–240
  damage protection, Category I, 197
  differential protection, 109, 302–303
  differential relays, 317, 333
  fault-current reflection through, 108–110
  impedance, 52
  inrush current, 8, 197
  isolation, 146, 165
  leakage impedance, 52
  low voltage, 195–200
  nameplate data, 42
  neutral relays, 318
  primary circuit breakers, 238–240
  primary fuse application example, 321–322
  protection data, 380–382
  protection for small, 247
  protection rules, per NEC, 108, 230–242
  self-cooled ratings, 40
  temperature relays, 318
  through-fault protection, 105–108
Traveling wave relaying, 291
Triggered current limiters, 95
Trip unit:
  coordination with sensors, 24
  dials, 25
  interrupting rating, 25

Unbalanced fault conditions, 47
Underwriter's Laboratories (UL), 83, 86, 95, 177, 243, 352
  Recognized Component Directory, 178
  Standard 489, 178
  Standard 508, 222
  Standard 1503, 246
Ungrounded systems, 140–143

Uninterruptible power systems, 92
Unit substation(s), 40
  feeder breakers, 151
  overcurrent protection in, 229–266
Unlatching time, in low-voltage breakers, 183
Up-over-and-down method, 178, 200
Utility:
  interconnect, overcurrent protection at, 313–347
  impedance, 50
  short-circuit current availability information, 51
  system stiffness, 48

Valvoda, Frank, 64
Variable frequency drives, for motors, 221
Voltage, nominal ratings, 82–83
Voltage detection, 154
Voltage drop, 277–278
Voltage transformers, 99–100
  application data, 386
  ground detection with, 154–155

Wafer, 183
Wagner and Evans, 43, 46, 48
Watchdog circuit, 275
Westinghouse Electric Corp., 10, 259
Westinghouse-Cutler-Hammer, 98, 309, 365–366
Withstand ratings, 84
  in motor control centers, 217–219
Wood, Barry M., 293

X/R ratio(s), 181, 40, 42, 48, 51, 86
  equal to 15 or less, 86
  equal to 6.6, 87
X/R ratio, relevance in application of medium-voltage breakers, 268–269

Yuen, Moon, 62

Zero sequence:
  impedance, 43, 59
  impedance network, 137
  relays, 158
Zone selective:
  ground-fault protection system, 165
  interlocking (ZSI), 20, 152, 244, 253–256
Zones of protection, 17

## ABOUT THE AUTHOR

Michael Anthony is an electrical power engineer for the
University of Michigan Plant Operations.